To live well and stay young
till the end of your days

PHILOSOPHY OF LIFE

Anna Ciesielska

Publisher: CENTRUM ANNA UK Ltd
Suite U505A Threshold and Union House
65-69 Shepherds Bush Green
London W12 8TX

Centrum Anna UK Ltd website address is:
www.centrumanna.co.uk

First Published by Centrum Anna, 2001

English edition published by Centrum Anna UK Ltd, 2014

A catalogue record for this book
is available from the British Library

Paperback ISBN	978-0-9926519-3-0
.epub ISBN	978-0-9926519-4-7
.mobi ISBN	978-0-9926519-5-4

Printed in Great Britain

Although every effort has been made to ensure the contents of this book are accurate, it must not be treated as a substitute for qualified medical advice. Always consult a medical practitioner. Neither the author nor the publisher can be held responsible for any loss or claim arising out of the use, or misuse, of the information and suggestions contained in this book, or the failure to take medical advice.

CONTENTS

INTRODUCTION TO THE ENGLISH VERSION 9

GATEWAY TO LIFE 10

A PINCH OF PHILOSOPHY 12

The Philosopher's Stone 13

FROM POTATO SOUP TO SPIRITUALITY 14

THE ORDER APPLIES TO EVERYONE AND EVERYTHING 18

WHAT COMES NEXT? 19

TURN NEGATIVES INTO POSITIVES 21

LOVE AND FEAR 23

BECOME AN ANGEL 29

PUPPY POSTURE 30

IS SUFFERING UNNECESSARY? 31

IS FREEDOM A NECESSARY ILLUSION? 33

TWO WORLDS 39

10 Pearls of Wisdom 40

ENERGETIC SEE-SAW 41

Energies 42

THE TREE OF LIFE 56

EXCESSES AND DEFICIENCIES 59

ECOLOGY 63

PHYSIOLOGY 65

Homeostasis and the Yin–Yang balance 66

Thermoregulation within the body 68

Immunity 71

Acid-base homeostasis 73

Metabolism 77

Contraction and expansion 84

Blood types 88

Why do we age? 91

Sport 93

ILLNESSES 98
- Treatment 99
- Infections 101
- Spring fatigue 102
- The liver and lungs in spring 105
- Allergies 108
- Diabetes 117
- Shingles, chickenpox, herpes 130
- Psoriasis 132
- Coeliac disease 134
- Fungal infections (mycosis) 135
- Circulatory problems 136
- Heart attack 142
- Venous thromboembolism 143
- Hyperacidity and heartburn 145
- Rheumatism 149
- Rheumatoid arthritis 151
- Nipple cancer and other cancer-related diseases 152
- Multiple sclerosis 160
- Osteoporosis 162
- Headaches 164
- Urinary incontinence and overactive bladder 169
- Dislocation of bodily organs 173
- Depression 174
- Fear 177
- Spine 180
- Cellulite 183
- Constipation 185

PORTION OF REASON 192
- Diets 193
- Cooking means creating 202
- Nutrition for pregnant women, babies and small children 204
- Nutrition of the elderly 220
- Healthy vs. unhealthy 224
- Mediterranean cuisine 248

COOKING 252
- Such will be our nation as our nutrition 253

RECIPES.......258
SOUPS.......258
Rice Soup.......258
Lentil Soup.......258
Lentil and Chickpea Soup.......259
Mediterranean Bean Soup.......260
Lemon Soup.......261
The Autumn Blues Broth.......261
Good-for-all Carrots.......262
Clear Tomato Soup.......262
Mushroom Soup II.......262
Pumpkin Soup.......263
Garlic Soup – great in autumn and winter.......264
Sorrel Soup.......264

SECOND COURSES.......265
Traditional Meat Marinade.......265
Beef Goulash for Russian Dumplings.......265
Russian Dumplings.......266
Sweet White Runner Beans with Beef.......267
Veal Cutlets with Fried Eggs.......268
Beef Cutlets with Garlic.......269
Beef Cutlets with Greens.......270
Beef Stew with White Wine.......270
Beef Tenderloin in a Hot Tomato Sauce.......271
Beef Schnitzels.......272
Beef Rolls.......272
Beef Rolls II.......273
Veal Goulash with Button Mushrooms.......274
Veal and Pork Goulash with White Wine.......275
Cabbage Parcels.......275
Roast Pork with Garlic.......276
Pork Goulash.......277
Meat à la Paul.......277
Spicy Pork Chops.......278
Sweet Ribs with Turmeric and Wine.......278
Lamb Goulash.......279
Chicken in a Vegetable Sauce.......280
Chicken with Garlic and Lemon.......280
Chicken Livers.......281
Turkey Livers.......281
Turkey Stomachs.......282
Turkey with Vegetables.......282
Turkey Legs with Vegetables.......283

Turkey Goulash....283
Spicy Duck with Oranges....284
Different Style Risotto....285
Pasta with Meat....285
Noodles with Sauerkraut....286
Dumplings....287
Potato Casserole (Tortilla)....287
Cheese Sauce....288
Potato Cutlets....288
Potatoes with Eggs....289
Potato Blinis....289
Raw Potato Dumplings....289
Country Delight....290
Pilaf....290
Couscous with Vegetables....291
French Dumplings....292
Meat, Gherkin and Tomato Sauce....292

CAKES AND DESSERTS....294
Cherry (or Apricot) Cake....294
French Pastries....295
Poached Pears in White Wine....295
Fruit Tart....296
Cupcakes....296
Poppy Seed Cake I....297
Poppy Seed Cake II....298
Cold Cheesecake....299
Croissants....300
Angel Wings....301
Mountain Cake....301
Sour Cream Cupcakes....302
Cocoa Cake....302
Orange Cake....303
Redcurrant Cake....304
Cheesecake I....304
Cheesecake II....305
Poppy Seed Roulade....306
Yeast Cake....307

BREAKFAST AND SUPPER DISHES....309
Breakfast Cottage Cheese....309
Vegetable Jelly....309
Meat Jelly....310
Polenta Casserole....311

Lentils with Rice....312
Fried Sausages....312
Hummus....313
Croutons....313

SALADS....314
Kidney Bean Salad....314
French Bean and Sweet Corn Salad....314
Apple and Onion Salad....314
Tuna Salad....315
Broccoli Salad....315
Spinach....316
Sauerkraut with Carrot....316
Cucumbers in Sour Cream....317
Cucumbers in Natural Yogurt....317
Canned Sweet Corn....317

SIDE DISHES....318
Young Fried Potatoes....318
Fried Potatoes....318
Baby Potatoes....318
Potatoes à la Figaro....319
Potato Croquettes....319
Rice for the Turkey Stew....320
Rice with Turmeric....320
Buckwheat....321
Buckwheat with Rice....321
Rice....321
Pearl Barley....321
Polenta....322
Steamed Dumplings....322

SAUCES....324
Garlic Yogurt....324
Yogurt Sauce (for beef tenderloin)....324
Garlic Sauce with Greens....324
Garlic Sauce with Saffron....325
Plum Sauce....325
Typical Tomato Sauce....326
Horseradish Sauce....326
Vinaigrette Sauce....326

SPECIAL RECIPES....327
- Refinement of Ham and Sausages....327
- Herbal Mix by Paprzecki....327
- Meat Essence for Convalescents....327
- Buckwheat Remedy....328

MEALS FOR SPECIAL OCCASIONS....329
- Christmas Sauerkraut....329
- Split Pea (to mix with the Christmas sauerkraut)....329
- Christmas Tortellini....329
- Carp in Jelly....330

BABY FOOD....332
- Carrot Soup....332
- Porridge for breastfed babies....332
- Soup I....333
- Soup II....334
- Soup III....334
- Soup IV (for 7–8-month-old babies)....336
- Soup V....336
- Baby Goulash (for at least 1-year-old baby)....338

TEAS....339
- Tea for indigestion, colic and high temperature....339
- Refreshing Tea....339

Table: Harmful Excesses....340

SOMETHING TO THINK ABOUT....342

INTRODUCTION TO THE ENGLISH VERSION

Dear Reader,

It is very beneficial for you that both books, "Philosophy of Health" and "Philosophy of Life", are published simultaneously. Between them, you will be able to find answers to many doubts and questions that come up in your mind while reading.

The second part is, in fact, a necessary complement to the first. I suggest you read these books many times, for a better understanding and acceptance of the Order which they describe.

My purpose is to help you, because I know that with this knowledge you can completely re-evaluate your current outlook on life and health.

It is important that you fully understand and accept the knowledge in these two books and do not implement my recommendations in a partial manner, picking and choosing only what suits you.

Do not panic if you find that your current way of life radically differs from the one that I recommend. Nature is patient and will support you in setting your life. Just trust it.

Anna Ciesielska

GATEWAY TO LIFE

By losing Paradise, we subsequently lost a certain kind of balance. That was our own decision, though. We lost Paradise and, in consequence, we turned ourselves into “Creators”. Since then, we have become able to make our own choices and “create” our life and the surrounding reality. From that particular moment, our life started running according to our own will.

We rejected the idea of Divine happiness and started going our own way. And we have been doing so, in suffering and toil, for hundreds of generations. We have been searching for love, acceptance and tenderness, always doubting God’s existence. Does God really exist? And if so, does He or She represent Love? We have always been very proud and stubborn, convinced of our own hegemony on Earth. We have believed that we are allowed to live by our own rules, one of which is the rule of patriarchy, and the other – the rule of disrespect towards Nature.

But the fact is that here on Earth we have everything we need in order to make the right choices and live in balance, happiness and health. There is a vast abundance of God’s creations, pulsating in their eternal rhythms of Yin and Yang, of breathing in and breathing out, of contraction and expansion, of night and day – it is called the Order, Tao.

Like a wise parent, God let us go our own way. And like a parent would do, He (She) is watching over us, loving us and knowing that there will come a time when we will finally stand on our own feet and start walking full of inner strength, faith in our own abilities and trust in the Order. God knows that our bruises are an inevitable life experience. According to one parable, those who are not afraid of the new, who reject old models, who follow their own way and who have the courage to confront their own parents or the ruling majority are especially appreciated by God. Therefore do not fear the new, do not be afraid of using your own willpower in order to make choices and decisions. You should multiply your own experiences and talents.

Our human rebellion against the Order is repeated over and over through the conflict between generations, which, in all honesty, is simply a process of freeing young people from old models and allowing them to follow the path of self-definition. We must let this happen! It is, in fact, a chance for our own catharsis. Those who never experience such a thing go through life bitter, frustrated, unable to understand the laws of life and other people as well.

Like a child who goes away and eventually comes back richer in its own experiences, we – adults – have to free ourselves from stereotypes, reject the models of our great-grandparents, grandparents and parents and enter the path of balance. We cannot approach the new without rejecting the old, just as we cannot reach balance without losing it in the first place.

A pinch of philosophy

The Philosopher's Stone

"Alchemy is a toilsome work; one must not skip a step in the process (...)". Alchemy is usually associated with the quest for the Philosopher's Stone or the Elixir of Life and the ability to transform base metals into gold. However, from the intuitive point of view, alchemy stands for the process of our inner transformation.

I do mention alchemy in my other book, *Philosophy of Health*; the Centre of our inner selves resembles an alchemical cauldron inside of which the energy is being transformed into matter and matter into energy, producing the essence of life. Such essence could be turned into the Elixir of Life. But in order for this to happen, people would need to find their own "inner" Philosopher's Stone. They could achieve this by purification – that is, by abandoning the pride that prevents them from acknowledging and respecting the Order.

Do not purify your body but rather your consciousness. Do not display your suffering. If you suffer, it means that you do not respect the Order. I want you to understand this correctly. What I am trying to say is that our suffering should always lead to revealing and understanding its causes and its meaning, and should enrich us with a new kind of wisdom. Suffering should help to purify our inner selves from pride, teach us humility and not strengthen our Ego.

FROM POTATO SOUP TO SPIRITUALITY

Why is taking care of and energizing our body so important? The answer is simple! Stronger vibrations within our body will influence the quality of our relationships. We will begin to understand and accept each other. And this is how we will experience the Love that we are constantly looking for. This kind of Love can only be created in our consciousness, and consciousness depends on appropriate vibrations. Love, in the form of Greater Energy, will come to us once we are ready to accept it.

You will not find Love in the outer world; you can only find it within yourself once you allow your inner transformation to happen. Start with yourself. Start exploring the process of cooking and the energy of flavours.

I dedicate this part of the book to all mothers, wives and lovers, for they are the ones who give life and birth, who feed, cherish and bring happiness to everyone. Being a woman entails certain responsibilities. Remember that you have decided to take up this role and that being a woman is not a punishment. Do not abnegate your femininity and do not abnegate your duties. It is not allowed! Certain fashions come and go, and the same happens with various trends, but you should always try to stick to common sense and your female intuition. Nobody has gained anything by going against Nature.

Ladies, do you actually realize that life on Earth depends on us? It does not depend on politicians, their disputes and armament plans, but on us – women – and our attitude.

If a woman does not put enough energy into creating this so much recently ridiculed family home, if she will not caress, take care of, cuddle and feed those who live in it, then one day they will leave this home full of fears, stresses, complexes and the feeling of rejection and guilt. They will become dependent on their psycho-sexual energy, which revolves merely around Ego and leads to fear, aggression, struggle and sexual dependency. It is a closed circuit of a very low vibration. For generations, it has affected the people we love, the people who are close to our heart but live on the other side of an invisible wall that has been created by the different vibrations of our and their consciousness.

Women need to understand that, as those who give and protect life, they perceive reality with a different kind of consciousness. They need to allow themselves to be more open; only then will they be able to transform the existing model of reality and bring better times. Especially nowadays, there should be no room for emancipation and feminism but rather for giving oneself to others, with a simultaneous protection of one's own identity, individuality, distinctiveness and self-respect.

Is it possible to communicate with a person of a different vibration and energy, with a person of a different consciousness (our neighbour, friend, husband or child)? Yes, it is possible. We need only to discipline ourselves in creating a deeper understanding of somebody else's distinctiveness. We might, however, experience difficulties when it comes to communication on the spiritual level, as that is a very subtle and personal matter. Nevertheless, we should do anything to make communication with those close to our hearts possible.

Some of us will ask: how can I give more than I have already given? The answer is: give in a different way and give something else. Give it with your full acceptance. And never expect gratitude. Give a good word, a smile, but do not expect a sudden transformation of those you love. Do whatever you want to do but without any expectations. Do anything, but simply for the joy of doing and creating, and everything will start changing. Do only things you want to do, and if you are not entirely comfortable with something – do not do it. You have every right to decide.

You may wonder, what is the key to communicating with your loved ones? It all comes down to vibrations and the energy of Love, which with time will be returned to us. Only through preparing well-balanced food on a "real" fire can we provide our body with the energy that will raise the level of our vibrations and lead to many positive changes within the spheres of our health, emotions and consciousness. Only then will such characteristics as acceptance, openness, love and responsibility run through us involuntarily. We will not need to worry about anything.

You will not solve your problems and worries by being overly active on the outside. It is merely an illusion that you are totally free, whilst in reality you experience a feeling of inner emptiness. Do you not sometimes feel like a hollow trunk? At the same time, you often experience the need to fill this void with tenderness, harmony, understanding, acceptance, closeness and giving. It is a strange contradictory feeling indeed. I am sure, however, that there are many feelings inside of you to share with the whole world. I am also sure that by doing so you do not want to place yourself in the position of victim. How to reconcile all these contradictions?

First of all, you need to understand that the pain and suffering that you carry inside has been caused by a stereotype according to which women are reduced to the position of victims. And it has been like this for many generations because we have not been strong enough to fight it. However, present times make it finally possible, as we are stronger and we also possess the Secret of the Universe. Cook well-balanced food, strengthen your inner vibrations, transform your present energy into the energy of feelings and observe what happens. It will be like a miracle: you will become a free and happy woman! You will be creating and protecting life; you will start giving, and your inner strength will fill you and never leave you again. You have to understand all of it! Do not be afraid, your spirituality is secured by the fact that you are a woman. You will not be deprived of anything just because you make some soup for your loved ones; you will not miss anything; you have it all inside of you.

The most important people in your life are usually your family members. They sometimes inspire you, sometimes irritate or annoy you, but they also love you and stimulate you to change. Think of your parents and what kind of role they have or have had in your life. Remember, no matter who they are and how they act towards you, they are absolutely indispensable! Their only, maybe not even fully conscious role, is to guide and inspire you, so in the future you can discover for yourself who you want to be as a person and what you want to change within yourself. It is not the outer world that enslaves you, but the model in which you and your Ego are stuck.

If you are about to make a decision, look deep inside yourself and try to find your initial intention. Was this intention dictated by your fear or guilt? I must, I should, I ought to, I have to – our intrusive Ego confuses us all the time. Try to choose, to like, to be in the mood for, to enjoy and to be convinced that you deserve it all. But most of all, have the courage to say what you do not want.

So, what shall we cook today? Believe me, potato soup and spirituality are only one step apart.

THE ORDER APPLIES TO EVERYONE AND EVERYTHING

The Order exists within Nature and within us, too. It has been applied from above. Mankind does not possess the power to change it and it is impossible to find a place on Earth to which the Order does not apply.

The Order exists whether we are conscious or unconscious of it; whether we accept and follow it or whether we claim that we do not believe in such heresy or have no time, are too old or ill for it. The fact is that the Order is present in every moment of our life.

In order to gain strength or be able to withstand the impact of the elements and the harshness of fate, people should learn how to use the Order in their favour. But it is a choice only brave, wise, good-hearted and strong people can make. You need to contemplate your own limitations and accumulate enough energy and willpower to become a doer (think: "I want").

This kind of attitude will lead you to constant self-development and change. It will lift you above all of the high and low tides, above all of the victories and defeats, enabling a broader outlook on life. Your reality will become parallel to your inner emotions and needs. The problems that you have to go through in order to learn a valuable life lesson will start having a lesser effect on you and will disappear much more quickly because your consciousness will be able to distance itself from them and your emotions (Ego) will become less dominant.

WHAT COMES NEXT?

When you feel lost or are suffering, when you find yourself in a closed circuit of hopelessness and you do not know where to start, simply – make some potato soup and eat it together with your loved ones. Then cook something else and share it with them again. Soon after, your energy and consciousness will start changing. The reality will remain the same, only you will see it differently. Trust me!

Do not vegetate. Try to lead an active life; do something better each day; reflect on things around you and try to improve them; learn something new; strengthen your body and take good care of yourself. Every night think of what you have done during the day – what new has happened? what did you talk about with your friend, son or husband? what did they teach you then? Whilst eating your dinner, try to appreciate every mouthful of it and be proud of your cooking skills. Watching a film, think of how it can enrich your consciousness. Make your own decisions. You have every right to choose the people you want to be with, the situations you want to experience, the books you want to read and the films you want to see. You need to know what strengthens and motivates you, what brings you joy and relaxation.

Try to observe and analyse surrounding reality. Reflect on your life and make sure you really want to live this way. You need to concentrate, as this is a very important decision. Do not allow yourself to be slapdash. We choose the reality we live in; therefore think whether you are happy with where you are at the moment. Maybe you would actually prefer to change it? You have every right to do so.

Think of what you want to change. You have to be very precise about this. Say it out loud many times. Write it down on a piece of paper so you will not forget it and to start off the machine of your intentions. Remember, though, that from this moment, all your choices need to be consistent and not contradictory to the route you have taken. Also remember that, even if in half a year you are still not living in the house of your dreams, it does not mean that nothing has changed at all. Surely your consciousness will have changed by then and many things around you. Try to notice it! Everything happens in its own time and there are many things to learn on the way. Each moment brings something new and this leads to a transformation within us and within the environment we live in. We need to know who we want to become. And we will achieve it when the time is right; we will get whatever we need but we must have enough willpower.

TURN NEGATIVES INTO POSITIVES

Some people claim that suffering and illnesses are engraved in our subconscious to the point that only changing our perception (turning negatives into positives) can bring ultimate healing. It seems so obvious, yet for the majority of people it is difficult to understand and seems to be a rather ineffective method. And the reasons for this mode of thinking are rather prosaic. Simply, many of us overlook this very important detail that our thoughts and actions are the major driving force in our life.

We all know the proverb: “fine feathers make fine birds”. Its message is very clear. Yet many of us, set in our convenient way of thinking, claim that what is important is not how we look but what we do and what kind of people we are. My Dear Readers, I have to tell you that in saying so we are fooling ourselves. What we do is not as important as the kind of intentions that lead us to do things. And remember that we are always perceived as a single whole. Therefore we are often judged on our outer appearance, neatness, stature, behaviour, mode of speaking, and also on our facial expressions and eyes. Our face and eyes can either radiate our inner beauty or the contrary – expose the dark abyss of our inner vibrations, which cannot be disguised with make-up, an extravagant piece of clothing or sackcloth. Very often those who like judging others (they should not be doing so at all) are unable to see them as a whole.

It is obvious that the inner matrix of our subconscious (soul) has a direct influence on the state of our body. Our body responds to these set models of our subconscious. But the truth is that we are here on Earth to disentangle ourselves from these models and to enhance our inner vibrations. Can we do this by changing the way we think? Isn’t it that our thoughts reflect our consciousness, and our consciousness is directly influenced by the vibrations and the state of our bodily organs? And so the circuit closes. Can we actually change anything by the way we think if our outer-selves (our bodies) have very low vibrations, which are notoriously sustained by a bad diet (sour, raw and cold food)? Can we turn a leaky mug into a china cup only by filling it with elixir?

It is important to realize at this stage that only by improving our bodies can we improve our consciousness, which should then enable us to free ourselves from the rigid models of our subconscious. By applying a healthy diet and a healthy lifestyle, we will improve the vibrations of our body. Only then can we start turning our negative pattern of thinking into a positive one.

LOVE AND FEAR

Love and fear are the two energies that rule over the whole world and consequently over human life. They are like Light and Darkness, Heaven and Hell. Can we say that one of these energies is more important than the other? No. Similarly, we cannot say that Yin is more important than Yang, or Yang more important than Yin. Love would not exist without the energy of fear. And Yang would not exist without the energy of Yin. The energy of Yin binds the energy of Yang to the Earth.

Love Light Spirit Heaven Me	Earth	Fear Darkness Body Hell Ego
Yang	☯	Yin

The most destructive things for us are all kinds of excesses. And for centuries the most dominating (excessive) energy on Earth has been the energy of fear and suffering. It seems that we exist within this irrational reality without having a chance for its unbiased assessment. Therefore we cannot become a unity.

We all know how difficult it is to distinguish between evil, love, hatred, Yang and Yin. Our assessments of reality always bear a certain level of subjectivity as each one of us perceives and analyses the world differently. However, all the energies of the world create and inspire each other and merge into one Divine energy. Tao is the path between these contradictory forces. One must remember that the loss of balance leads to all kinds of disturbances, cataclysms and suffering.

It is also very difficult to distinguish between "I" and Ego. Therefore, in order to discover our inner-selves, to understand and distinguish between our overweening emotions of Ego and noble emotions of "I", we need to go through many internal breakdowns, downfalls and struggles.

We often lose ourselves to "giving" and simultaneously neglect our own life and health. What is more, we are convinced that this is the right thing to do. I mean the total sacrifice and giving every inch of oneself to others. There are people who think this way, who believe that this is the best they can do. But we have to understand that most of these kinds of attitudes derive from a feeling of guilt, fear of rejection, lack of self-acceptance or low self-esteem. We have to understand that sometimes our "giving-attitude" is dictated by our selfish longing to be accepted, liked or even loved. We are convinced of our own benevolence and this helps us to feel self-assured. But the fact is that we are doing this in our own interest, for we expect some kind of prize for it! One of the prizes is acceptance.

It is not important what you do but what kind of intentions and motives inspire you.

Explore your inner-Self, and do not panic if you find something not to be proud of. You must not feel guilty. Whatever you did in the past, you did the best you could in accordance with your level of consciousness. In life, everything happens according to your will and your initial intentions. If you feel that you are on a different level of consciousness right now – try to change yourself.

Everything in our life forms an absolute unity. The balance between Yin and Yang is present in Cosmos, in Nature, in our body and even in our daily problems (as mentioned before). Our emotional struggles signify an imbalance between Yin and Yang, between Ego (Yin) and "I" (Yang). The major cause of this imbalance is fear.

For generations, right up to the present day, we have lived under the domination of Ego, with all the consequences, such as suffering, solitude, fear, aggression, alienation, depression, overwhelming hopelessness, insecurity. But recently something has started to change. Just wait and see!

Is it possible to eliminate Ego? Absolutely not. Ego is our root, our bond with the Earth; it is our physicality and our animalistic nature (psycho-sexual energy). Ego protects us from danger. But should it rule over our life? We know that all kinds of excess are destructive; sometimes they can even kill. Can someone go through life carrying this constant fear, worry, and mistrust towards everyone and everything? This would simply be a sad life, which would eventually end with madness.

Ego is always in hiding; it takes different shapes; it is like a chameleon changing its colours according to a situation or its own needs. One time it behaves like a child needy for cuddles and tenderness; another time it becomes a hysterical woman or a bossy and cruel macho man. But regardless of its chosen character, Ego always worries, speculates, seeks attention and fears many things. We must not let any of these characters dominate our consciousness, e.g. if we choose to behave like a child we might eventually become infantile. We are mature and conscious people and it is about time we started controlling our emotions and fears.

But how can those stuck in the density of their Ego (fear) help themselves to get out of it? It is very difficult to do indeed. It does happen, though, that people open up to the change and start feeling it inside. Can we use only the power of our consciousness to reach emotional balance within our body? Absolutely not. Firstly, our body needs to raise its vibrations. How do we achieve this, though? There is no other way but to supply the right amount of energy to each organ and cell within our body. And this particular kind of energy can come only from a well-balanced diet of warming properties.

And how can we define the other (opposite) kind of energy, the energy of our proud "I" (Yang)? "I" is simply the ubiquitous light, the sparkle in our eyes, our openness, trust, joy, peace, acceptance of everything and everyone, of all

God's creations. "I" never fears anything; it is always trustful and conscious of its own importance, no matter what. "I" does accept the rules of the Order.

If we want to create a state of balance between these two powerful energies in our life and our consciousness, then we need to remember that Ego stands for condensation, contraction (fear), whilst "I" stands for dispersion and expansion (acceptance). Therefore we need to try at all costs to understand the source of our fears. Only then will we be able to rid ourselves of this paralysing contraction.

Is our fear justified? Or is it something engraved in our consciousness during our childhood? Are we able to change things when we are full of fear? Has our fear ever helped us in anything? You can help yourself by turning this fear into courage and accepting all that you fear. If you are afraid of driving cars – just stop thinking about your fear, get inside a car and simply start driving. If you are afraid of your boss – say a word to them and your fear will disappear. In order to be rid of your fears you have to do all that you are afraid of.

Remember, Ego is always full of fear, pride, pretensions, abuses and aggression; it is always tearful, seeking attention and never has enough. Would you really let it dominate your life? You need to be in control over your own emotions; they should not rule over you but you and your "I" over them. Keep your Ego in order, talk to it, explaining things and accept your outer-Self. Your outer-Self is always good. But if you feel that you want and you can improve it, then do so and stop complaining.

Get to know your emotions and accept their causes. In order to tame your emotions (Ego) you must try to understand them rather than shutting them in the box of your subconscious. Tell your own Ego that you are a mature, intelligent, calm and level-headed person full of love and acceptance towards everything and everyone. If your Ego cries out for tenderness, you need to convince yourself that this tenderness is within you; you only need to find it. Start giving when you think you have nothing. This does not mean, however, that you should lose yourself to it. Most important are your intentions – warm gaze, nice gesture, a phone call, anything. Do not focus on what you do not have but on the process of creation. Exchange the "wanting" of Ego for the generosity of "I".

Why is fear so dominant? Why does it take over our consciousness? Remember that fear is a powerful tool in the hands of manipulators, who use it to influence other people's lives.

The concept of fear has been present since the beginning of the world and is mostly connected to religious beliefs. The fear of gods' or God's anger stands behind many of our decisions and choices. There is also the fear of law; however, the fear dictated by religious motives is much stronger. Therefore we must not be surprised that it has had such a great impact on our inner-selves.

Fear is a nucleus of all wars and tragedies caused by violence. It can turn a man into a monster. Evil has fearful eyes. The paradox of fear is that both oppressors and victims are full of fears – oppressors kill because of their fear, and victims are killed because they fear being killed. Fear generates more fear. Fear attracts fear.

Our fear gets greater if we become weaker. How can we help ourselves and our loved ones in those moments of fear? Simply, show them some affection, make them some soup, talk to them. Look into their eyes with love and acceptance. And do not reprimand them.

At this point, I need to mention something very important – forgiveness. My Dear Reader, forgiveness is a trap set by your Ego. Who do you think should forgive? The wiser and better one? Absolutely not. It is just a trick of your Ego. You are not supposed to forgive but understand the one who caused you pain. Why did it happen? What have you learnt from this experience? You do not have to forgive but merely accept! You actually must not forgive if you do not understand why you are suffering. By forgiving you only make others feel guilty, and you must not do this! You should know that nobody consciously aims to cause suffering.

Also, you must not judge others. It is not our job to judge anyone, because we never know what is inside a person or what the real causes of someone's behaviour are; we also do not know what kind of life mission they are on. Maybe someone's strange or annoying behaviour is something they (or you) need at a certain moment of their life; maybe it gives them inspiration to awaken or free themselves? We can only analyse but never judge their behaviour, because no matter who they are, they behave in a certain way for a reason.

BECOME AN ANGEL

Did you know that the secret behind an Angel's ability to fly is that they treat themselves "lightly"? You can fly, too. Do not let your Ego pull you down and make you hit the ground. Ego is a low and condensed vibration of your emotions, fears, anxieties and mistrust.

An ability to treat oneself with a bit of humour is a Divine skill indeed. Try to be this way! Laugh at your own reactions; laugh at your own Ego. Try to neutralize your emotions through laughter, "lightness" of being and ease of manner. Believe me, it will make things easier.

You are the Creator here; create yourself as a joyful person. It is an important skill that can be acquired only when you start treating your life consciously. Do not let guilt manipulate the way you feel. You have the power to "move mountains" and create your own reality.

Become an Angel! I wish you this from all of my heart.

PUPPY POSTURE

Stand sideways in front of a large mirror and examine your posture. Is your back slightly hunched? Does your head lean forward? Are your buttocks tucked under?

If so, then try standing straight and relax your buttocks, and your whole body posture will change immediately. Your back will align and your head will go up. It may be difficult at first, as your muscles will not be used to this new position. When you relax your buttocks, your whole posture gains in stability and the centre of gravity shifts back to its correct position.

Once you get used to this, it will not be so easy to go back to the bad habits and the sad face that came with it. Your gait will become lighter and more relaxed; your legs will carry you everywhere. You will stop walking with your upper body leaning forward, dragging your buttocks somewhere behind you. This time you will walk as one whole. It is a great pleasure, indeed. Try it.

To become aware of this, perhaps trifling, matter is inevitably more important for women. Which one of you ladies would not want to walk with elegance and grace?

Tucking your bum (your tailbone) under is typical of the so-called puppy posture. It not only looks bad but, more importantly, sends out a message about your fear of the surrounding reality, of your sadness and sorrow; it says that you are scared of facing reality and that you would rather hide in a kennel.

Change your posture! Be a braver and more joyful person, full of virtues, perfection and divinity. Trust the world!

IS SUFFERING UNNECESSARY?

When I was writing *Philosophy of Health* I came to understand that suffering is an indispensable element of our evolution and transformation process. However, I also realized that there is all too much suffering around us and it is often completely unnecessary.

But now I see it slightly differently. Over the last few years I have experienced and observed a lot of human suffering and I know now that it has the power to shake and awaken us; that it has the power to steer us off the "wrong path". It is like an electric fence reminding us to stay in order, when, attracted by dense vibrations of pride, emotions and flavours in the surrounding environment, we become trapped in a circle of suffering, aggression, intolerance and hopelessness.

Each kind of suffering has its cause; it gives us a lesson on the order of the Universe; it also signals our dietary mistakes and encourages us to free ourselves from emotional patterns that we have got used to living in. Discovering new layers of consciousness, entering a world of new vibrations, "giving birth to a new self" – all of these things derive from physical pain and a psychological "low". All new things are usually created in pain, darkness and solitude (maximal Yin). Do not reject it; do not panic, as all of it happens for a reason. Try to accept and seek the new. Have the will to understand the cause of your pain; have the will to find that pearl of wisdom lying somewhere at the bottom of your suffering.

The process of fighting the pain is not the only condition for the transformation and maturation of wisdom. Only by accepting the Order and switching to a well-balanced diet will we rid ourselves of our physical suffering, transform our consciousness and gain understanding and wisdom. It is a fantastic process!

There are many miraculous situations in our life which turn it into a never-ending process of transformation and accumulation of wisdom. We eventually start feeling satisfied with the condition of our health, amazed at the wisdom we have gained and think to ourselves that all is going well. And it is usually then that we start making silly mistakes (a coincidence?), for example: we stop eating properly, we do not get enough sleep, we forget to relax, we do not exercise, we eat too many sweets or too much fruit, or we lose control over our emotions. This triggers a chain reaction which takes us by surprise. All of a sudden, we are "sucked" into this incapacitating black hole. This is how the suffering begins; we become trapped by it and the only thing we can rely on is the sparkle of our consciousness. We either seek help from the outside (and that is how we incapacitate our transformation; we stop trusting ourselves) or sit quietly in a corner suffering and trying to comprehend the situation. If we are patient enough, the understanding will come to us in its own time and it will be an exciting moment indeed.

Remember: your suffering is not a form of punishment. In order to stop your suffering, you have to try to see its second "bottom". Do not alienate yourself from everyone around you; do not feel offended by their presence. Once you let the Order into your life, it will become easier to free and regenerate yourself; it will fill you with joy and gratefulness for being able to do all of this consciously.

Do not compare yourself to anyone else; you risk losing your internal peace. Other people have to go through exactly the same thing. If you think that they do not have to understand anything or they do not suffer and always get what they want, well this is merely your own point of view. Maybe they have already gone through that process… or maybe they have not even started yet?

I am sure you will now ask: what about children? How can we explain their suffering? Thankfully, in most cases we are able to deal with our children's suffering. But we certainly still need to respect the Order. Only then will we be able to benefit from it in our everyday life. I am talking here about a well-balanced diet. Remember, though, that we are here on Earth in order to give our children a chance of transformation and freedom. Therefore, whatever may happen to them, even if it happens against your hopes and expectations, you should try to understand the true causes behind every situation. Let's not forget that our children's suffering can teach us a lot and change and improve us, too.

IS FREEDOM A NECESSARY ILLUSION?

In order to reach the state of true freedom and be able to use free will, one must realize that there is an alternative to the enslavement and pressure of modern times.

What is freedom? Freedom, in its broader sense, means freedom of choice, freedom of thought and free will; it is an internal kind of freedom which leads to self-creation. I am not referring here to the notion of freedom in a political or social sense. Freedom is simply an ability to make decisions about the quality of one's own life, of one's own health and happiness. The freedom of choice, however, must always lead to responsibility, empathy and love. Otherwise, spiritual growth will not be possible.

Freedom is the foundation of human existence and human evolution. What sort of value would human life and evolution have if people were to be constantly surrounded by external and internal factors whose meaning they were not able to understand? It would lead them to pain, fear, joy and sadness, without even the chance of making a conscious decision about any of these feelings. Should the archetypal figure of Job become our role model? What kind of value would our relationship with God have if we were constantly restricted by our law and its orders, which would decide upon the quality of our own life? Where would there be a place for our exploration of life? How could we become responsible and empathetic without experiencing spontaneity and being in charge of our own decisions? What kind of value is present in an act dictated by fear?

We all know that not everyone feels the need to be free. There are people who escape responsibility and prefer all decisions to be made by others: doctors, employers, government or clergy. Fear, fanaticism or stupidity do not sit well with the idea of freedom. The need for freedom derives from our consciousness; we should not blindly accept all of the rules and laws inflicted upon us; we should also not accept all of the suffering. There are many people out there who really want to change their life. They try many things, hoping for a better quality of life or an improvement in their health. But the results are not satisfying. They know they are doing something wrong, but do not know what it actually is.

My books will help only the conscious and responsible ones. Within them I try to explain the determinants of life, health and emotions, all of which refer to the process of self-creation that can only happen under certain conditions. Determinism as a method of analysis and evaluation of human life is a concept that has been present in the sciences and philosophy since antiquity. However, whilst the ancient idea of determinism was mostly linked to the perception of God as the First Cause, since Newtonian times it has been replaced by the idea of materialistic determinism.

Science has been diverted towards the analysis of the materialistic side of the world, and not the principles of its existence and functionality. As a consequence, the human context seems to have been omitted in theories relating to the functioning of the world, yet science does not realize how close the solutions are.

In order to make the simple interdependences between the material world and the unseen one possible, one must stop being presumptuous about science. We have to acknowledge that in order to perceive reality and the processes and phenomena within it as one whole, we have to use our logic and senses as well as our feeling and intuition. We need to accept the physical (material) world experienced by our senses and the world of energy and vibrations, which relies on our intuition. The existence of these two worlds is supported by the general rule on the functioning of the physical world, which argues about the state of balance between matter and energy. This rule applies equally to human life; it leads us towards the balance between the body (matter) and Spirit (energy). So, it is out of place to speculate here with a dose of irony whether Spirit is also susceptible to the neurological processes of the brain, even though such nonsensical speculations would probably satisfy scientists.

Yes, our body is a true humdinger and a puzzle for our brain. But should we really focus merely on solving the mystery behind its anatomy and keep analysing over and over again the molecular processes within it? Should we not really acknowledge the tools that have been given to us, the tools that could help our body to reach its optimal condition, which would benefit us all?

Science, and especially molecular medicine, has lost touch with reality recently. On one hand, scientists seem to be satisfied with the results of their research, which testify that our life is a result of genetic evolution and multiplication (which they perceive as the original cause of life, not taking into consideration that it could also be just the result of a simple coincidence or perhaps even Divine intervention), and our thoughts merely an effect of the neurological functions of our brain. On the other hand, there is this confusion; if we really are controlled by our genes (or Divine intervention), what then of the notion of freedom and free will? The idea of a total loss of freedom and free will seems to be a heavy burden for scientists, as it would simply signify the nonsensicality of human existence. It would mean that people are merely material machines, steered perhaps by some Higher Intelligence. Scientists realize that it is impossible to live like this. Therefore, in order to comfort us all, they claim that freedom and free will are necessary illusions. They try to convince us about the absurdity of our existence, saying that the differences between people and their talents create the illusion of freedom. But true freedom can only happen through perfecting the gifts that have been given to us.

Scientists claim that a human being is determined merely by physical and neurological processes. But they simply ignore that our present consciousness enables us to understand things that were originally beyond our comprehension. Thanks to our physical and genetic evolution, but also thanks to the ability to regulate our own energetic levels, we are finally able to do this. **Human beings are the only living creatures who can regulate their energy not only by choosing their external energetic factors (colours, tastes, temperature), but also by a conscious selection of thoughts and emotions.** We differ from animals not only through our genetic code or our brain capacity but also by the energetic field of our body. Every object, plant and animal has a different energetic vibe. We also produce a subtle energy which is a derivative of our thoughts and the condition of our body. There is a difference between the vibration of fear and love, or between the vibration of illness and health.

Science, with its belief in materialist determinism as the factor regulating creation, prioritizes the sensual perception of the world. This automatically leads to an imbalance in the process of our evolution. Analysing the hierarchy within the Universe, science should acknowledge the existing rules. Otherwise it will go against us and Nature.

Absolute determinism is the First Cause of everything in this world; it is our *perpetuum mobile*. It puts the creation and Universe in order.

The rule that keeps the physical world in order is based on the theory of contradictions or bipolarization (Yin–Yang). On the other hand, the order in Nature and life is regulated by the Five Elements Theory. Each theory should complement the other. Therefore we have to thoroughly analyse the multiplicity of factors determining life on Earth. And in order to do this we have to take into consideration both the Yin–Yang and the Five Elements Theory. We also have to keep the balance of our perception, which translates as the balance between the right and left hemispheres of the brain, between our rational thinking and our intuition, between what is visible and what is invisible. If we are to stick to the rules of determinism, then we should do it properly. If there is this scientifically proven connection between physico-chemical factors (such as temperature, environment, food) and the biological processes within the body (including changes in the genetic code), then it is understandable that such illnesses as psoriasis, arthritis, asthma, allergies and diabetes will all depend on the same factors. The fact that the temperature and the chemical composition of food have a significant impact on the body should not be just a matter of scientific reasoning. In direct contact with a patient, scientists should not ignore this fact and claim that they are not able to find the true cause of an illness. Where would the illnesses have come from otherwise? One should not, and must not, keep the knowledge about these kinds of interdependences to oneself or merely use it as a tool of pressure to fulfil one's private ambitions to make oneself feel more important and respectable than others.

The most straightforward explanations for the causes of illnesses are: a lack of vitamins, alcohol abuse, smoking, promiscuity, gluttony, infections or stress. But one must understand that these are actually the results of the imbalance and not its causes! The true causes of all these states should rather be explained by the excesses and deficiencies of certain physico-chemical and energetic factors. And science knows about these factors and their impact on the human body. These factors are similar to those which influence natural selection and genetic changes – the processes which affect many generations.

Science (which aims at revealing the secrets behind human physiology) should look more into the nature (energy) of the stimuli that have been affecting the human body throughout many generations (up to now). These stimuli are: the nature of climates, flavours, emotions and colours. Such an approach would bring the beginning of an effective preventive treatment against illnesses and suffering. It would stop being just a matter of dabbling with molecular medicine by a group of passionate scientists. Only then would we be able to freely and consciously choose the factors that are of benefit to our health. Only then would people feel free and responsible for their own choices. And this would lead them to an authentic spiritual freedom.

The world of science should finally admit that we must respect all aspects of life, all energetic levels and all factors that shape our being. Determinism should not be selective. The acceptance of certain factors must not rely on a schematic scientific perception.

What is fanaticism, then? Should we associate it merely with religion? Is there such a thing as scientific fanaticism? In both cases, one does not allow other ways of thinking, feeling and seeing things.

We should become more conscious of the times we live in and be more responsible for what we leave behind and the lives we create. Can you really not see from your own experience that our quality of life depends on how we think and imagine things? Is it true that free will and an ability to choose, which make it easier to navigate our life and be responsible for it, are merely necessary illusions? Did mankind create free will just to feel closer to God? Or is it rather that our existence on Earth is a constant process of unconditional and unrestricted self-creation and freeing; in other words, individual determinism?

The freedom and the choices which can improve our quality of life are not an illusion. They do exist. It is only a question of being willing to see them, accept them, understand them and use them.

TWO WORLDS

Does what I have written so far negate the world of science and the world of conventional medicine? Absolutely not, even though some of you may see it this way. My intention is to make you aware that the core of all we do is the Order, or, in other words, the balance between two energies: Yin and Yang, Nature and science, woman and man, unperceivable and perceivable.

I am just trying to explain here in the most approachable way that medicine can only be efficient once it starts accepting the role of our right hemisphere and the energy of Nature together with our sensitivity and intuition.

Science has lost the connection with the unperceivable and immeasurable. In its attempts to find a cure for illnesses it always misses the crucial element. What use is it to know that an illness X is caused by a genetic error Y? It is certainly not the true cause of an illness but the result of an imbalance that eventually led to this genetic error. In order to find the true cause of this imbalance we have to use our right hemisphere; that is, our intuition, imagination, openness to many aspects of life, to be able to reason, make comparisons and calm ourselves. Once we introduce the full perception of the world (by using both hemispheres) we will be able to understand that the mutation of genes happens under the influence of external factors (e.g. a low temperature, stress, inappropriate diet). Is then the fascination with genetic medicine the way we should follow? We have to be aware of the fact that all of these scientific discoveries are usually biased and that they can lead to risky outcomes.

It would be ideal to merge the world of science and the world of Nature and its energies together, so they could complement and inspire each other. This could lead to a world of order, understanding and tolerance, one in which solutions could be found to many problems. Right now, these two worlds exist somewhere next to each other, full of mutual mistrust, fear, struggle, rejection, the feeling of guilt, uncertainty and suffering.

Should medicine follow its present path without taking into consideration the laws of Nature and the Order? Or should it rather stop ignoring and rejecting it after all?

10 Pearls of Wisdom

1. Cook and taste your own food.
2. Become an Angel and treat yourself lightly.
3. Be conscious of your own Divine power.
4. Think continuously who you want to become.
5. Reject the old and accept the new.
6. Love and accept yourself.
7. Your intentions are more important than the things you actually do.
8. Do not forgive – you are supposed to understand and accept, but do not forgive.
9. Do not judge.
10. Find time for work, relaxation and creativity.

Energetic see-saw

Energies

In order to benefit from the knowledge I am sharing with you here, your belief in its goodness and in the Order of this world is not enough.

Your belief must turn into knowledge. I know that it works, therefore I am not afraid and I no longer have any doubts. I accepted the knowledge and that is how I gained peace of mind. But in order to know it well and stop doubting things, you also have to understand it all. I did.

The following analysis on the subject of energy should make things easier to grasp. However, there is one thing to remember: you have to want to understand it. We are a microcosm and subject to the same laws that rule over our bodies, lives, Nature and the Universe.

Nature has enormous power and we are directly connected to it; we are a part of Nature. Therefore, it is entirely up to us whether we choose to disregard the mightiness and laws of Nature and are eventually destroyed by its elements or choose to tune into Nature's rhythms – the rhythm of breathing in and breathing out – and gain Divine power that would help us survive… *In going against Nature we lose the gift of imagination.*

When an adult person diverts away from Nature, it can be compared to a child losing its mother. In this sort of situation, a child panics and loses its mind. A similar thing happens to an adult when they lose contact with Nature. From wise, Divine beings they turn into greedy little people men, who are eventually slapped harder and harder by Nature. We cannot cheat Nature in the same way we cannot cheat our mothers. Nature rejects all that disturbs its rhythms.

What is the rhythm of Nature? What sort of energy does it consist of? It consists of the contradictory but complementary energies of Yin and Yang, which balance on the pivot (axis) called the Earth. They interact with the energies of the seasons constituting the Five Elements Theory.

Let's imagine a see-saw with the Earth as its pivot; on one side there is Yin and on the other side Yang.

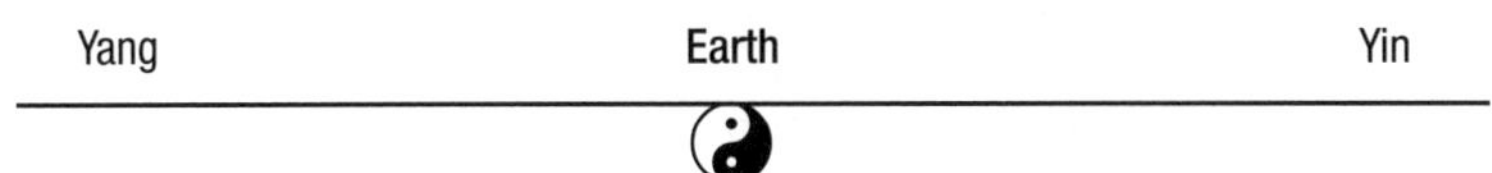

Older people usually say that when there is a severe winter (strong Yin) then the summer will be beautiful (strong Yang) and when there is a mild winter (weak Yin) then the summer will be cold (weak Yang).

Let's incorporate the seasons into our see-saw, then.

Do you recall from my other book, *Philosophy of Health*, that between each of the seasons there is a short period called "dojo"? This period acquires the energy of a late summer, or in other words, the Centre (stomach, spleen, and pancreas). The energy of late summer not only relates to an intensive production of the essence and fluids, but also signifies stalling, silence and a time needed to balance out other energies – it is simply the earthly pivot. The pictures below will help you to understand the placement of the dojo period in relation to the other seasons.

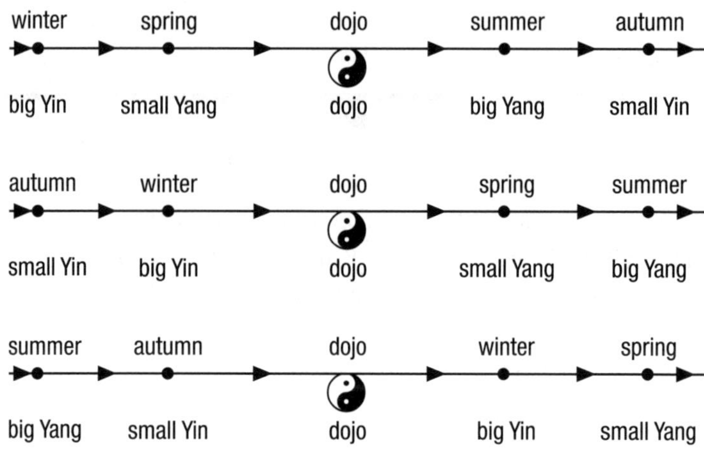

The balancing and rhythmical pulsation of energy, including the rhythm of breathing in and breathing out, is best pictured as a sinusoid. This helps us to understand that the time of birth and the time of death have the same energy (vibration). Within the sinusoid we can place all the processes that simultaneously happen in the life of a human, Nature and the Cosmos.

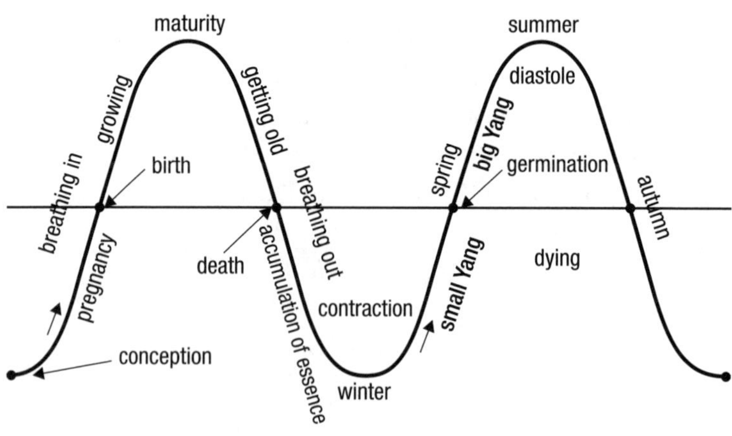

The next picture represents a typical nutrient and control cycle that relates to the seasonal changes and the energy of particular organs of the body.

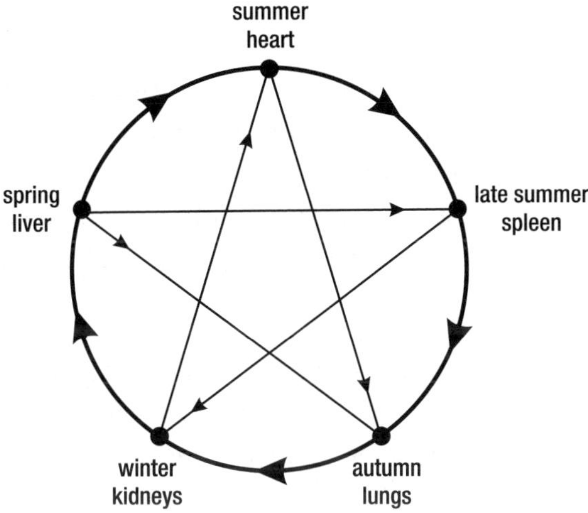

The energy of every single season is constant and has a specific function. Below you can see the different natures of these energies.

spring

Spring – Small Yang – this is a very powerful energy; it is directed towards the Sky; it is the time of waking back to life, of pregnancy and seed bursting; plants start drinking the juices and growing upwards towards the Sky, towards the world.

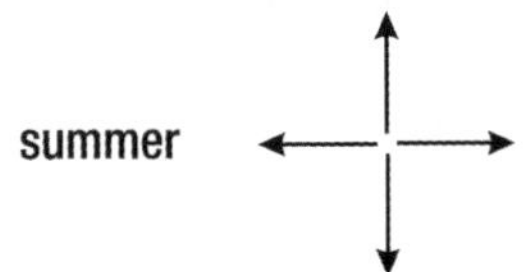

Summer – Big Yang – this is the energy of spreading, building, becoming bigger; it is the time of growth and maturation.

late summer 

Late Summer – Dojo – this is the time of energetic equilibrium and stalling, the time of maturity and expulsion of juices.

autumn

Autumn – Small Yin – this is the energy directed downwards towards the Earth, the energy of dying and drying out; it is the time of accumulation of essence somewhere deep down within the soil, the essence that will be much needed to survive the difficult time ahead.

winter

Winter – Big Yin – this is the energy of total concentration and contraction; the energy concentrates at one point in order to eventually turn into a new life.

All these energies are connected to specific organs of the body; all human bodily organs depend on the energies of the seasons. Their functioning beautifully reflects the functioning of these energies within Nature:

spring

liver – is supposed to move all stalls upwards (the essence from the spleen)

summer

heart – has the energy of spreading; it helps in blood and energy circulation

late summer  **spleen** – represents stalling; it is only responsible for the production of essence

lungs –direct the energy towards the kidneys and Earth

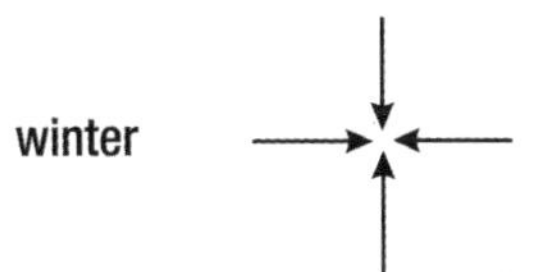

kidneys –concentrate and accumulate the energy in one place; this energy protects the essence.

According to the order of energies within Nature, summer is opposite to winter, and spring opposite to autumn. So, for example, if summer reaches its maximum then winter should reach its minimum; and if spring reaches its maximum, then autumn should reach its minimum and vice versa.

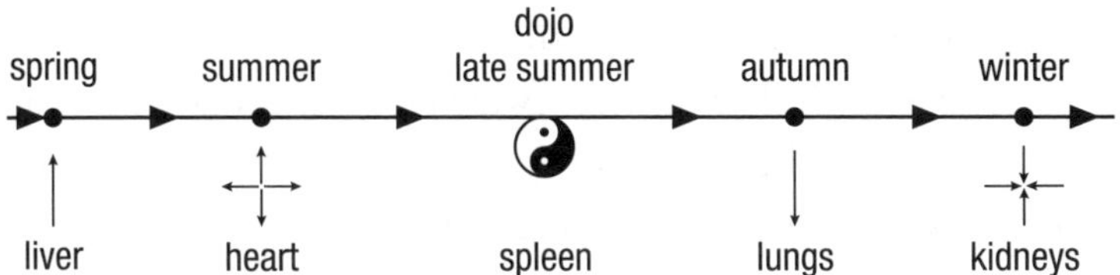

Similar dependences happen within our body. If during autumn and winter we accumulate enough essence and energy, then during spring our liver will become very active. Therefore we should avoid all kinds of starvation diets during the time of spring. There are two major reasons for this:

- During spring, the liver reaches its peak (maximum) and the lungs their trough (minimum). If we start a starvation diet during this period, the energy of our liver will not be strong enough to lift the necessary portion of essence and energy towards the lungs (and by the way – there may not be anything to lift at all). This way we put our lungs at risk of all kinds of allergies, catarrhs, and asthma. All of these ailments are caused by weak lungs and not by an accumulation of toxins. Toxins are a different issue. All spring illnesses are caused by weak lungs which simply contain too much cold moisture. A starvation diet will not get rid of this moisture; it can only increase the problem.

- Analogically, Nature "takes care" of all trees in spring, like a gardener who will do what they can during that time to improve the growth of their trees. Not everyone is aware that when you pick ripe fruit the branches of those fruit trees are already covered in buds. These buds will contribute to next year's harvest. Therefore the quantity of fruit the following year depends on how we take care of the fruit trees during spring and summer.

A similar kind of thing happens with our liver in autumn when it reaches its trough (minimum). Autumn is a very bad time for eating fruit and fresh salads. If we do, we not only weaken the liver (which is at its energetic low anyway) and lungs (which should be strong by then), but we also restrict the production of essence that is necessary for surviving winter. The autumn energetic levels within our body drop because of our thoughtless weakening of the liver (sour food, tiredness, stress) and can lead to all kinds of cold and flu symptoms.

In analysing the interdependences between summer and winter, we must remember that summer is the time for charging one's batteries rather than draining them. We should do anything we can to make our body accumulate the maximum of Yang energy (lots of sunlight plus cooked meals) and the maximum of good quality essence. If we do not do that, then our batteries will go flat at some point and we will stop somewhere in the middle of the road. What should we eat during summer, then? Everything! Just remember not to overcool your body. Is there then a good time for refreshing and cooling? No, there is not! In winter we should eat warm, rich, and fatty food, for two main reasons:

- The energy loss during that time is enormous (the energy is used up to warm your body);
- The Yang energy of summer (blood circulation, heart) reaches its low (minimum) and we should replenish this energetic gap with the warming type of food and dress in appropriate clothing.

We should also remember that the Earth is dependent on the cyclic changes of Yin and Yang and the energies of the different seasons to give it life. But in order to do so, it needs to be supported and regulated by the energies of the different climates: wind, high temperature, moisture, dryness and low temperature. Only when these energies harmonize and mutually complement each other will the Earth be able to give life. The energies of flavours work in the same way; they create a certain energetic value in food, stimulating the production of essence.

The energies of the climates determine the characteristics of the energies of the elements:

- **Wind** determines the characteristics of the element of **Wood**,
- **High temperature** determines the characteristics of the element of **Fire**,
- **Moisture** determines the characteristics of the element of **Earth**,
- **Dryness** determines the characteristics of the element of **Metal**,
- **Low temperature** determines the characteristics of the element of **Water**.

Let's allocate all of these characteristics within our see-saw chart.

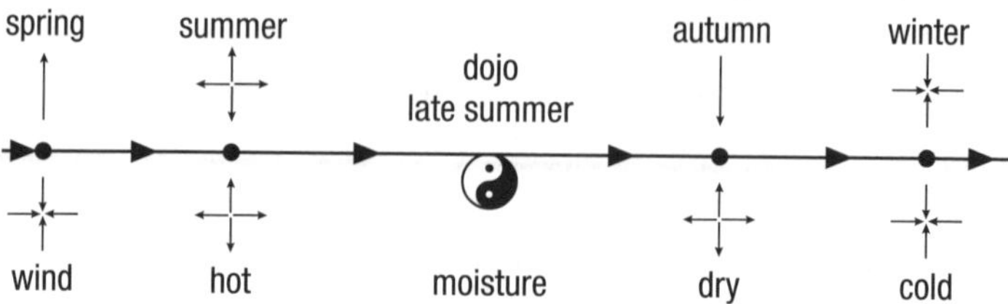

Climates are to Nature like flavours are to our body and bodily organs. By creating the right compositions of flavours in our meals, we can strengthen the Yang (Fire) energy. This helps the spleen (Centre/Earth) with the production of the essence and enables renewal and birth. In a similar way, climates – mutually complementing and determining each other – enriched with the Yang energy of the sun, ensure that the Earth has the right conditions to give and support life.

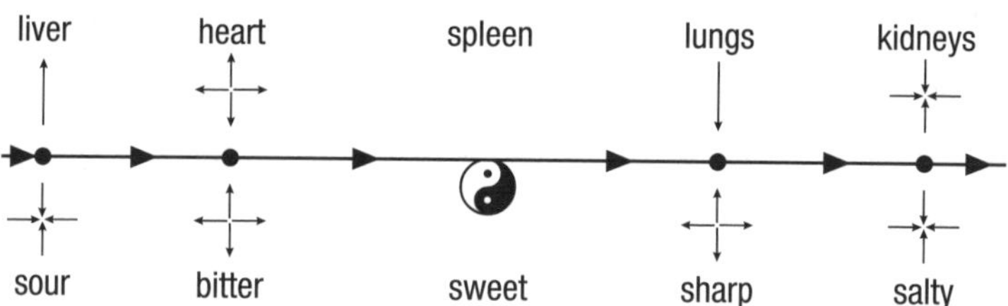

At this point, we should give shouts of joy over the precision of the Creation. One cannot invalidate its powers or statistically prove its wrongdoings. This precision is a fact and it is working just fine. Everything in this world has been created for our benefit, to enrich and spiritually elevate us. We can consciously decide and choose from the palette of colours, flavours and emotions.

Let's have a closer look at the energies of flavours.

- **Sour flavour:** the energy of the liver is directed upwards, and the sour flavour, which is ascribed to this particular bodily organ, is supposed to tame its over-activeness and expansiveness. This flavour has shrinking and contracting properties. Therefore it is indispensable in every single meal; its energy balances and creates the appropriate energetic composition that then enables the proper functioning of the liver. What happens, then, to our liver if the sour flavour is the dominant flavour in our diet? One of the doctors of the East stated that, in this situation, the liver looks more or less like a half-baked cake. How can a liver in such a state lift the energy during the winter/spring solstice? How can the essence and the energy of the spleen reach the lungs when the liver has practically contracted? Will it be possible for the liver to fulfil its physiological function of detoxifying and being the central location of protein, carbohydrate and fat metabolism? Can such a liver contribute to the good quality of nervous and connective tissue? Can it assure the good functioning of the intestines and the work of the smooth and skeletal muscles, etc.?

If you still want to continue eating fruit, fresh salads, ice cream, fruit yogurts and sweets, and keep drinking beer and water, then – it is your own choice.

It is important to notice here that nowhere else except in civilized Europe and America do people eat so much raw, sour and cold food.

- **Bitter flavour**: it contains the dispersing and drying kind of energy, supporting the functioning of the heart and blood circulation. It is indispensable in preventing the accumulation of toxic mucus and moisture. The bitter flavour inherently weakens the properties of the sour flavour. If there is not enough of it in our diet then the body becomes paler, greyish and all sorts of pathological metabolites (toxins, mucus) start to accumulate, weakening the functioning of the liver, heart, spleen and lungs. Look around your kitchen and find all of the bitter-flavoured spices. When was the last time you actually added them to your food? The bitter flavour is absolutely indispensable when you want to lift your mood and rid yourself of depression.

- **Sweet flavour**: the energy of this flavour does not produce any movement. As long as it is not the energy of sugar, the sweet flavour stimulates production of moisture (essence), which is beneficial to our body only when our diet is well complemented energetically with all the other flavours. The essence produced then acquires the sweet flavour and contributes to the building and regeneration of our body. Similarly, the Earth is not capable of giving birth to a new life if one of the climates is missing. For the sake of continuation of life, all of the climates must be in constant motion, interacting with each other. Mono-flavoured types of diet or diets composed of only cold, sour or raw products are entirely human inventions, testing the patience of God.

- **Spicy flavour:** my fascination with arranging the appropriate "platform for a healthy life" is especially strong when it comes to the energies of the sour and spicy flavours. They are incredible indeed. The liver, which is stimulated by the energy of spring (the energy that is always directed towards the Sky), can be tempered by the contracting energy of the sour flavour. On the other hand, the lungs, which are stimulated by the energy of autumn (the energy of dying directed towards the Earth), can be controlled by the dispersing energy of the spicy flavour.

- Do you know why we sometimes crave alcohol (spicy flavour)? Well, we cannot lead a balanced life constantly eating sausages, meat, sauerkraut, pickles, herrings, tomato soup, gherkins, and so on. Energy of this kind of food has shrinking and contracting properties, constantly "dragging" us downwards. We become sad, depressed and apathetic. In order to "straighten up", catch a deep breath, become more trustful towards life, we need to have a shot of alcohol. And those who drink from time to time know it well. Then we can go back to eating the usual: herrings, gherkins, fresh salads, meat, and so on.

The spicy flavour has opening properties. But instead of drinking vodka we can add some hot spices to our appropriately energetically balanced food. The spicy flavour can unblock and move stalled energy and create motion. If there is not enough of it in our diet then our energy becomes more condensed and our consciousness "heavier". Can an excess of the spicy flavour have a bad effect on us? Yes, but only when we eat too much sour, raw and cold food, and when the spicy flavour is mainly ingested by drinking too much alcohol.

- **Salty flavour**: similar to the energy of the kidneys (winter), the energy of this flavour has concentrating properties; therefore it supports their functioning. The most typical salty food product is salt. We must not avoid adding it to our food; it is absolutely essential in a well-balanced diet. However, if we eat too much salty food products (pork, ham and sausages, salt, fish, soya) then our body becomes stiff and numb and our energy more condensed, dragging us towards the Earth (death). Be careful, because it is very dangerous.

A person consists of two integral parts: psyche and soma. The emotions that appear within us are directly affected by the Yin–Yang balance or imbalance and the functioning of our bodily organs. It is a physiological interdependence. If we want to be healthy and improve the functioning of our organs then we have to be conscious of the emotions within us and the way we react in everyday life. This will make things much clearer to see, as, for example, negative emotions (fear, sorrow, apathy, aggression, the blues) occur when certain bodily organs are in a state of imbalance.

If our inner selves, as well as our bodily organs, are in a state of balance then the positive emotions will show without us even realizing it. This kind of state is called emotional balance. Once we reach this balance, we will be able to react to the outside world with a certain distance and become more conscious of it, too.

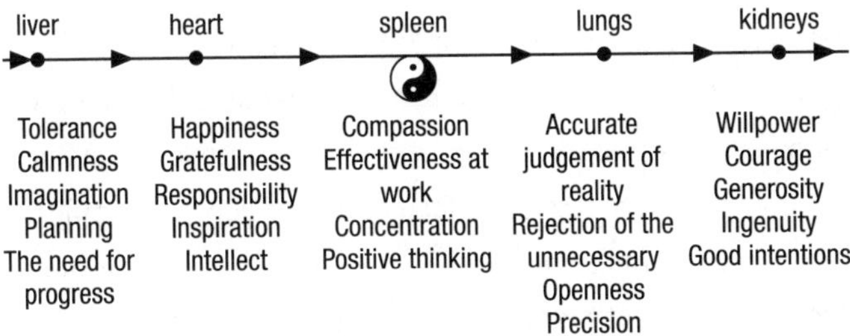

However, we must not expect to feel inner peace all the time; life is a process of filling oneself with all kinds of energies. Therefore, we should be prepared for the negative emotions, too, but we should always try to recognize the true cause of this state. This way we can be certain that our subconscious will not let in any “unprocessed” emotional codes. Do not judge these kinds of situations, though, and, especially, do not blame yourself if they occur. This will give you a guarantee that you are in control of the dark side of your life, your Giants, your Ego.

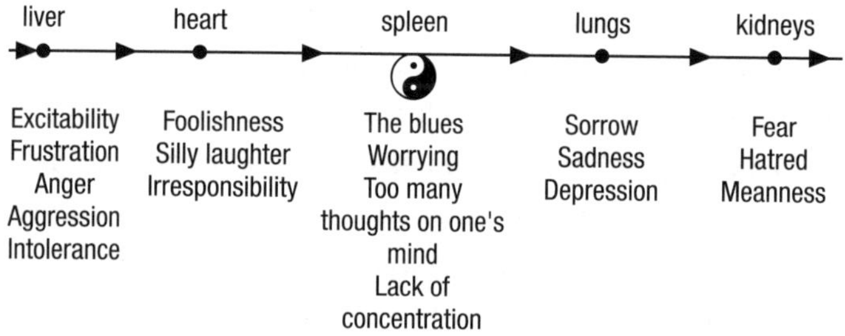

It should be quite obvious that all negative emotions never accumulate in one person, even if they feel very low. Although, maybe…? But the most important thing is to remember that all these emotions will not appear because somebody wants to be this way, or because they are lazy, greedy, aggressive or sad, but because their inner energetic system creates such emotional states. It is very hard not to be aggressive when there is not enough moisture in the liver (blood), or sad when lungs are deprived of Yang energy and start showing symptoms of dying; it is hard not to experience fear when your kidneys are neutral (“on zero”); it is because you eat too many yogurts and drink too much water. It is very hard to concentrate when you “feed” your spleen with apples and sweets and it is hard to be tolerant when you “feed” your liver with too much cheese, etc. It is hard not to react aggressively towards other people when your diet consists only of pizzas, crisps, chocolate bars, bread rolls, apples, beer or cold drinks.

We can try using the systems of positive thinking, but it will only mean treating our problems at their surface and generating new bad habits, patterns and codes. We have to ask ourselves whether we want to react merely like Pavlov's dogs or be more conscious of our choices. Should we employ positive thinking? Yes, why not? But, firstly we should try to understand our emotional state and only then turn negatives into positives.

THE TREE OF LIFE

In order to clearly visualize the influence of energy on our life, I will use the very well-known symbol of the Tree of Life. The Tree of Life is deeply rooted in the Earth. It grows out of the Earth strong and stable with its branches directed towards the Sky.

It derives its vitality from the essence of Earth, which gives it enough strength to stand up to the elements. At the same time, it is nourished by the energy of the sun. Its majesty and strength are commonly admired. The Tree of Life gives shelter to birds, animals and humans. It is a symbol of peace, trust and strength.

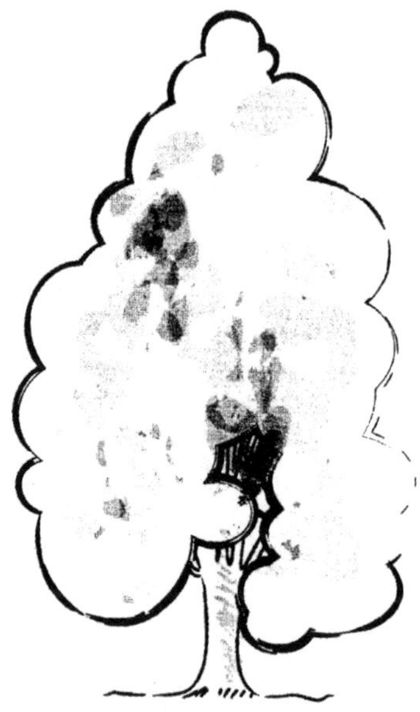

Let's have a look at this picture. The Tree is a reflection of our own life. How can we reach the Sky? Simply, by following the example of the Tree and letting our "roots" unify with the Earth. How should we interpret this? To root means to respect our physicality, our body and its physiological needs, as well as the Earth and Nature. It means union and continuous contact with one's own body, an understanding of its needs and the signals it sends out; it means continuous contact with Nature, recognition and understanding of the cycles of Nature and respect of its rules and Order. It also means eating proper food which enables the Earth (spleen) to produce valuable essence, support the kidneys and "root" us properly, so we can grow towards the Sky.

Only respect towards every aspect of our physicality and good "rooting" can make it possible to reach the depths of our subconscious and our dormant true intentions. It enables us to enter the "Route of Our Own Legend". When we "root", we involuntarily wake up our consciousness, open up to the new, free ourselves from old models and get in touch with the Sky and the Overmind.

Let's think what can happen to the Tree when the Earth is dry and lacks the necessary essence. It simply withers. And when it is too close to the sun it can even burn. This fire, however, is not our spirituality. Is there a tree that can grow and develop peacefully among raging elements – continuous winds (sour flavour), low temperature (salty flavour), an excess of moisture (sweet flavour) or dryness…? Do not surrender to various temptations; rather be conscious of the surrounding energies and the energies you "put into your mouth". The fact that they look nice, that they have been created by God, does not mean anything. We are supposed to decide and choose what is good for us; that is why we have been given free will. Do not be tempted by the idea of reaching the Sky too fast as you can burn on the way up. This is why the words of the prayer say: "and lead us not into temptation…"

Our body and physicality, when deeply rooted, will give us as much spirituality as we can take in at a particular moment of our life. They will give us a chance to experience all that we originally intended to experience. If we carry on like this, only those things that were meant to happen will happen to us. Do let yourself "give birth" to your own essence of life, to your true Self. Let yourself be and experience your own physicality; do not kill it instead. We live for the purpose of experiencing our own physicality. Only in this way can we elevate our spirituality. Do not rush anywhere. You have all you need here at this moment. Simply, be thankful for all you have got.

The role of the Tree of Life in our body is ascribed to the liver. Our inner balance of Yin–Yang is dependent on its strength and wellbeing, even though the true foundation, or Mother Earth, which feeds and protects us, is our spleen. The liver roots in the essence of the kidneys and reaches up to the energy of the lungs. This way it secures our inner balance and peace of mind, and also provides us with imagination that reaches the Sky. Do then what you need to do: strengthen your vibrations, do not exploit your own body, do not let the low energies make you crash to the Earth.

EXCESSES AND DEFICIENCIES

Everybody will find in this book something for themselves. Perhaps this chapter will bring more answers on the causes of suffering. However, even though I will try to present clearly here all the dependences between the nature of food and certain health problems, I advise you to read the whole book first and only then come back to the table below and start marking what seems important to you. Maybe the number of markings will make you realize that it is high time to start cooking and eating proper food.

An excess of a particular flavour in our diet can result in certain consequences. The effects of our fancies, tendencies and habits can be either very severe or stay dormant for some time. Have you been suffering for years from various diseases? Do they tend to appear practically out of nowhere? This is all to do with the fact that you have never tried to fix the true cause of it (a wrong diet), but merely dealt with the consequences.

How strong must the stereotypes be, then, of fate and suffering, if we constantly ignore the signals our body sends out to us? These signals are the effect of our dietary mistakes and bad emotions within us. We have ignored them, saying that it is all normal and just a matter of bad luck, fate, getting old, carrying "one's own cross". We even try to see the diseases in our children as something normal, something that every child must simply go through. But now, once we understand the dependences between food that is consumed and diseases, we can see how much we have disregarded our own body.

We finally have to acknowledge that everything that surrounds us either strengthens or weakens our vibrations and that it also has an immense impact on our body, emotions and consciousness. It is absolutely the truth that what we eat has the power to shape and transform us. I am talking here, of course, about changes throughout many generations. Food gives us the energy we need. Once we implement a well-balanced diet, we will be more resistant to the negative influences of the surrounding environment. This is especially important in terms of preventing social pathologies, such as poverty or crime, that tend to increase social disorganization and hinder personal adjustment.

In the tables below and in the appendix, I list the ailments and diseases caused by excesses of flavours and emotions. An excess of certain flavours, as well as emotions, can lead to a deficiency of other flavours or emotions. This affects children especially and every new generation gradually becomes weaker and weaker.

A constant penetration of the same outer factors leads to the weakening of our immune system, changes in the functioning of particular bodily organs, and, most of all, genetic mutations.

<table>
<tr><td rowspan="2">WOOD</td><td>Aggression
Anger</td><td>Frustration</td><td rowspan="2">Stalling, venous thrombosis, hormonal disorders, high blood pressure, gynaecological diseases, deficiency of moisture and blood, breast cancer (other cancers too), strokes, embolism, obesity, liver diseases, gallbladder stones, headaches, rheumatism</td></tr>
<tr><td></td><td></td></tr>
<tr><td rowspan="2">FIRE</td><td>Sadness</td><td>Over-
joyfulness</td><td rowspan="2">Cardiovascular diseases, heart attacks, obesity, pale and grey skin, accelerated ageing, intestinal problems</td></tr>
<tr><td></td><td></td></tr>
<tr><td rowspan="2">EARTH</td><td>Worries</td><td>Intellectual
work</td><td rowspan="2">Liver and stomach diseases, spleen failure, cardiovascular diseases, stalling, tumours, cancers, gynaecological diseases, headaches, fatigue, feeling of heaviness, sleepiness, flatulence, problems with concentration, gall bladder stones</td></tr>
<tr><td></td><td></td></tr>
<tr><td rowspan="2">METAL</td><td>Sadness</td><td>Sorrow</td><td rowspan="2">Large intestine diseases, psoriasis and other skin problems, allergies, lung diseases (tuberculosis, asthma), weak immune system, cancer of the large intestine</td></tr>
<tr><td></td><td></td></tr>
<tr><td rowspan="2">WATER</td><td>Stress</td><td>Fear</td><td rowspan="2">Feeling of coldness, heart attacks, cancers, intestinal problems, diarrhoea, cardiovascular diseases, overactive bladder, headaches, hot flushes, insufficiency of the central heater, kidney diseases</td></tr>
<tr><td></td><td></td></tr>
</table>

Destructive excesses

- **Sour flavour:** allergies, asthma, cough, tonsillitis, catarrhs, colds, low temperature of the body, coeliac disease, diarrhoea, constipation, problems with blood circulation, osteoporosis, acidification of the body, ulcers, diabetes, problems with cholesterol levels, high blood pressure, tumours, headaches, hyper-acidity, cerebral palsy, epilepsy, autism and other mental disorders, emotional oversensitivity, hyperthyroidism, hormonal imbalance, anaemia, rheumatism, cellulite, bleeding of the large intestine, teeth problems, periodontal disease, eye problems, lung diseases, alcoholism, sweet craving, acne, flatulence, indigestion, psoriasis and other skin problems, eczema, cancers, heart attacks, strokes, embolism, venous thrombosis, calculi (stones), cirrhosis, kidney stones, problems with the spinal column, cystic fibrosis, mental deficiency and physical underdevelopment in children, Alzheimer's Disease.

- **Bitter flavour**: skin dryness, moisture deficiency, body stiffness, insomnia, mental disorders, susceptibility to fears, emotional excitability, heart problems, liver diseases, joint problems.

- **Sweet flavour**: diabetes, excess of cholesterol, cardiovascular problems, lung diseases, asthma, anaemia, allergies, acne, obesity, jaundice, heart attacks, headaches, leg pains, fatty liver disease, low body temperature, feeling of heaviness, constipation, rheumatism, dislocations of bodily organs, weak ligaments and joints, dementia, diarrhoea, high blood pressure, Alzheimer's Disease, rheumatism.

- **Spicy flavour**: alcoholism – destruction of the whole body (physical and mental); peppermint – eye problems, muscle problems; cabbage – thyroid diseases.

- **Salty flavour**: cardiovascular problems, low body temperature, heart attacks, cancers, diabetes, allergies, asthma, rheumatism, arthritis, diarrhoea, constipation, obesity, headaches, colds, kidney diseases, problems with the spinal column, kidney stones, liver diseases, heart diseases, sclerosis.

- **Cold food:** stalling of blood circulation, deficiency of Yang energy, the feeling of cold, heart attacks, cancers, diabetes, allergies, asthma, constipations, obesity, headaches, colds, metabolic disorders.

Destructive deficiencies

- **Sour flavour**: stalling, nausea, headaches, high blood pressure, loose teeth and bleeding gums, anaemia, haemorrhages, problems with digestion and absorption, flatulence, diarrhoea, flabby muscles, dislocations of bodily organs, leg pains, feeling of heaviness.

- **Bitter flavour:** spleen hyper-activity, accumulation of moisture in the lungs, head and blood vessels, sclerosis, cirrhosis, jaundice, intestinal problems, cardiovascular problems, stomach problems, flatulence, lung diseases, tuberculosis, asthma.

- **Sweet flavour** (but not sugar): irregular psycho-physical development in babies and children, blood diseases, infections, joint, muscle and bone diseases, kidney diseases, hormonal imbalance, dryness of the body, mucus deficiency, hyper-acidity, heartburn, intestinal problems, fast ageing, dry skin, psoriasis, atopic eczema, grey hair, tooth decay, dry liver (fire), diabetes, lung and liver diseases, cancers.

- **Spicy flavour**: indigestion, stalling of blood and energy, tumours, cysts, cancers, fibroids, genital problems, breast problems, headaches, high blood pressure, nausea, flatulence, constipation, lung diseases, asthma, ulcers.

- **Salty flavour**: stomach hypoacidity, anaemia, problems with digestion and absorption, metabolic disorders, problems with regeneration of the epidermis, mucous membrane and bodily organs in general, kidney and liver diseases.

ECOLOGY

When people live in harmony with the elements and the Earth, they are on the way to Tao. But once they attempt to go against the elements, they are in a losing position. The elements can be tamed but not destroyed, calmed but not eliminated. They can bring terrible devastation. Therefore, do not fight against them once they are active, otherwise you must be aware of the consequences. And in order to avoid these consequences you have to activate your imagination, intuition, logic, wisdom. You have to think and become responsible for your choices.

Can we endlessly play with Nature and tease the elements without suffering any consequences? I do not think so. For example, the destruction of wild forests and a total disrespect towards the element of Wood leads to an imbalance within Nature and a disturbance of changes. The creative cycle gets blocked and the destructive cycle activated. Using up oil reserves and forests, chaotic and excessive exploitation of raw materials, excessive exploitation of rural areas (without giving the soil the time to rest), application of all kinds of chemical substances in agriculture, absolutely reprehensible treatment of farm animals, pollution of the environment, inappropriate usage of water resources, nuclear experimentation, using chemical and biological weapons – are all of these things the ideas of a conscious and responsible people? I do not think that we are fully aware that the Earth is a living and feeling creature.

We are trying to trick our conscience by saying that this devastation of Nature is a necessary sacrifice for the sake of technological progress. On the other hand, we join all kinds of pro-ecological organizations. But we do so merely to deafen our compunction. What use is it to parade with this very fashionable slogan of "ecology" if we do not respect the Order? Do we actually understand what "ecology" means? In the dictionary, "ecology" is described as a field of science concerned with research on the interdependences between living organisms and the environment. And this interdependence is very obvious here

– we use our power and intellect to ruthlessly destroy Nature, which in fact is the source of our existence. So, how can we talk here about wisdom and a self-preservation instinct?

Why is it so hard to understand that we should respect the piece of land we live on? Nobody will really understand the need for taking care of the environment, Nature and Earth if they do not respect their own body and the processes within it.

And here we come across the main priority: **to raise our children and youth with a new kind of consciousness. Make them understand the true wisdom of life and not only what is written in books. If we do not teach our children about the relationship between the cycles and changes within our body and the cycles and changes within Nature, if they do not understand that they can decide on the way they look and feel, on their inner peace and harmony, then they will never reach maturity and will not be able to be fully satisfied in life. Their respect and understanding of Nature will not go beyond the frames of the word "ecology".**

Physiology

Homeostasis and the Yin–Yang balance

You do not have to be an expert in dietetics according to the rules of Chinese medicine or understand and know the properties and energies of flavours or the seasons in order to realize that illnesses are caused by the so-called outer excesses of flavours, climates and emotions. Such conclusions can be reached by an analysis of human physiology and its homeostasis. Homeostasis can be interpreted as the Yin–Yang balance.

I would like to remind you here that homeostasis means a stable internal environment achieved through the co-functioning of separate systems, such as: the nervous system, endocrine system, digestive system, respiratory system, cardiovascular system, excretory system, thermoregulatory system and musculoskeletal system. Together they create various systems of regulation and control. The most important of them all is the system of physiological functions (regulatory functions) which, despite constant changes of outer stimuli and factors, enables our body to keep the physico-chemical properties at the same level.

As long as all of these complex and sensitive systems work properly, our inner environment is strong enough to secure balanced cellular development within our body. However, this can change very easily. If exposed to long-lasting negative and unmanageable outer stimuli, these systems can get deregulated and eventually destroyed. Our cells begin to change their functions, begin to degenerate or even die. This leads to deregulation of our homeostasis and creates a chain reaction, or so-called positive feedback, when the result of one thing becomes the cause of the next one.

The loss of homeostasis (Yin–Yang balance) is usually caused by destructive outer stimuli, such as sour, raw and cold food, as well as stress and coldness.

The only difference between homeostasis and the Yin–Yang balance is the energy Chi. In the case of homeostasis there is no mention of Chi, whilst in the case of the Yin–Yang balance, Chi is treated very seriously and with proper respect. The notions of energy, vibrations and matter are very well known among physicists and cyber scientists. However, they seem to be kept away from people responsible for dealing with human health.

All of the systems securing our homeostasis simply collapse because notions such as energy or vibration do not exist in the dictionary of conventional medicine. In this case, it is more convenient to use terms such as "illness unknown" or "genetically determined illness" or "illness caused by viruses or bacteria".

The system securing homeostasis within our body is based on the net of sensors, receptors, detectors and thermoregulators, which, through various stimuli, receive important information. All of these sensors are sensitive to information of all kinds: energetic, hormonal, neuro-hormonal. They are very sensitive to these kinds of stimuli; they are so precise that they are even able to distinguish between information sent by stimuli from the sour, raw and cold kind of food and the warm kind of food, cooked on a "real" fire and balanced with all of the flavours and all kinds of spices. But this is obvious. Our body will react differently to sour food (e.g. sauerkraut) and to sweet food (e.g. egg).

Why, then, do we not try to compare the statistical results based on the very interesting phenomena which take place within the human body after eating a single-flavoured type of food to those phenomena after eating a well-balanced diet? It is so simple! I recommend it to all sceptics.

Thermoregulation within the body

In order to maintain the Yin–Yang balance or homeostasis, the mechanism of control (sensors), which reacts to every change within the environment (outer factors: diet, emotions, stress and temperature), must be super-precise.

One of the basic functions of the control system is to maintain a stable temperature within the whole body. It is very important indeed, as the process of metabolism and all that is related to it (durability of chemical compounds, activeness of enzymes, speed of chemical reactions, absorption of nutrients, energetic charge and others) depends on the temperature of the body.

The normal body temperature in humans (measured under the armpit) is 36.6 °C. Only then can we experience the so-called thermo-comfort. And it is thanks to blood circulation that we achieve the same temperature in all parts of the body. It gets a bit more complicated, though, when we have problems with poor blood circulation caused, for example, by drinking large quantities of cold water and eating raw fruit.

Within our body there are receptors generating impulses; their frequency (vibration) depends on temperature. The central part of our biological thermostat is the thermoregulatory mechanism located in the brainstem and spinal cord. It consists of two mechanisms: the mechanism responsible for lowering temperature and the mechanism responsible for maintaining temperature. One can distinguish here serotonergic neurons responsible for detecting and signalling low temperature and adrenergic neurons responsible for detecting and signalling a high temperature.

Within the thermostatic system there is also a regulatory mechanism, which regulates the right level of temperature according to individual needs. The regulatory mechanism is supported by prostaglandins produced through stimulation of the low temperature detectors. Prostaglandins stimulate higher body temperature by increasing sodium (Na) levels. Blocking synthesis of these chemical compounds or increasing the level of calcium has an antipyretic (fever-reducing) effect. If the body temperature drops below the norm then the thermoregulatory mechanism gets activated and works towards increasing the body temperature and simultaneously preventing any heat loss. If the body temperature rises above the norm, then the cooling mechanism gets activated and works towards a drop in temperature (sweating).

All the impulses from the centre of the thermoregulatory mechanism are transferred to the bodily organs and endocrine glands (pituitary gland, thyroid, adrenal gland and pancreas), which are then responsible for execution of the orders received. The glands start producing more hormones and stimulate the process of metabolism within the liver and adipose tissue. This automatically increases body temperature.

This process is followed by various reactions: vasodilation, relaxing of the skin, lungs and muscles, increased production of sweat, decreased sugar level in the blood, a weaker metabolism within the whole body. The level of endo-energetic anabolic reactions increases and, as a result, the whole body loosens up and relaxes.

But when the body temperature drops, all blood vessels start contracting, the production of sweat decreases, the level of sugar in blood increases (very important for diabetics), the metabolism increases, too, and all skeletal muscles contract.

Thus, knowing that a high temperature is just an alert from the control system about a certain Yin–Yang imbalance (loss of homeostasis), is it wise then to disturb this by application of antipyretic and anti-inflammatory medication? Should we not rather focus on removing the factor responsible for the imbalance and the alerting signal? Otherwise, it would be like getting rid of an indicator light that has just alerted us about a low oil level in our car.

The whole defence system within the body relies on contractions caused by neural, chemical and hormonal stimuli. The defence system is responsible for smooth and skeletal muscles, connective tissue, blood vessels and internal bodily organs. On the other hand, dilation of blood vessels or skeletal muscles or various organs is caused by deactivation of the factor responsible for contraction (low temperature, stress, sour, raw and cold food, calcium).

There is no situation in which the "pressing" factor A (contraction) and "depressing" factor B (expansion) could appear at the same time. Factor A must be deactivated, but only through the correct diagnosis and elimination of the stimuli that led to its activation. If we do not eliminate the stimuli that activated factor A and rather focus on neutralization of this factor (various medications) or elimination of that factor (operations) or neutralization of factor A by introducing factor B (with expansive properties), then we can cause devastation of the whole defence system. Our body enters a never-ending closed circuit of illnesses, as the true cause of an illness is only augmented.

This situation is characteristic of any ailment within our body, but especially so of a state of high temperature. Just think how easily we take and also give to our children all kinds of antipyretic and anti-inflammatory medications, including steroids, calcium, antibiotics, salicylates or food and drinks of sour flavour (juices, lemon tea). Of particular danger are excesses of calcium in our diet (cheeses, yogurts, calcium products), as they prevent activation of the system of thermoregulation. All calcium products create an effect similar to "getting rid of that light bulb"; they neutralize the factor which could warn us about any abnormalities within our body. In this way, we do not eliminate the cause of the "flashing light bulb".

As soon as we detect some negative changes within our body we should immediately focus on finding the original cause of this state and getting rid of it straight away. It is only possible to do this by applying the knowledge of the Five Elements and the Yin–Yang theories.

Immunity

According to the Universal Rules, immunity exists only when there is a state of balance between Yin and Yang within the body – that is between the substances, their appropriate quantities and quality (muscles, bones, blood, bodily fluids, nutritious fluids, lymph, mucus and digestive juices) and the energy Chi and warmth, which both stimulate circulation of blood and energy and activate all physiological processes leading to transformation of matter into energy and vice versa. In a state of balance, all of the bodily organs function properly and the body becomes shielded by a protective kind of energy, the so-called Wei-Chi. The internal strength and energy within the body enable the body to face all kinds of harmful circumstances, such as infections or temporary fatigue.

Using academic terms, we can describe immunity as a process of production of antibodies by lymphocytes and their bonding with both exogenous (external) and endogenous (internal) antigens. This way our body is continuously protected against outer harmful substances and infections as well as against its own faulty or cancerous cells. Immunity relates to the whole body, with special emphasis on blood and the blood-forming organs, such as bone marrow, the spleen, lymph nodes and thymus. All of these bodily organs are involved in the production of lymphocytes.

Bone marrow produces 4.5 million white and red blood cells every second. The production of blood depends on the appropriate quantity of building, energetic and regulating materials. This process is especially sensitive to the composition and properties of the blood, the quality of breathing as well as excretion, and to all kinds of inflammatory conditions within the body. Thus, our immune system is directly dependent on the appropriate quantity and quality of blood, blood circulation and the efficiency and "vigilance" of lymphocytes. In other words, our immunity depends on the production of blood by bodily organs such as the spleen, bone marrow, lymph nodes and kidneys. Therefore, the conclusion is very straightforward: this specific relationship, between human physiology understood from the point of view of modern medicine and human physiology understood from the point of view of Chinese medicine, does exist; this means that the quality of our inner substance is responsible for our immunity.

If our immunity depends on the multiplication of lymphocytes activated by antigen stimuli (which are then fought against and neutralized), then why in a situation of even minor infection do our doctors, instead of stimulating the process of blood production and lymphopoiesis, treat us with antibiotics, vitamin C and all kinds of calcium supplements, which actually block the whole process? Why do they feel outraged each time we mention the spleen and tell us that it is insignificant in this case? After all, we have evidential proof that it is the other way round.

The fact that immunity in children and adults is rapidly going down is becoming a big worry. People “catch” all kinds of diseases. And scientists continuously reject the importance of the spleen, saying that the increasing number of diseases is caused by a degradation of the immune system. It is time to think: **low immunity should be treated as an effect of certain factors and not as a cause of all these diseases**! The true cause of low immunity is the destruction of the stomach, spleen and pancreas and their general dysfunction. All these organs create our Centre and they become our central problem! How can we prevent this? We should eliminate all sour, raw and cold food. And faced with infection, we should not take antibiotics, vitamin C and calcium or drink juices; rather we should eat broths and soups, which would stimulate the functioning of our spleen, pancreas, liver, kidneys and the whole blood-forming process. This way our body will be strong enough to defend itself.

Our immunity can also be improved by exercise, as it stimulates blood circulation and the functioning of the lungs.

How important, then, are all the different types of vaccines? Do they really improve our immunity? Well, it is certain that they cannot protect us against all “environmental evil”.

Vaccines only cover up different kinds of symptoms, e.g. flu symptoms, such as temperature, headaches, catarrh, coughs or muscle aches, or allergic symptoms, such as itchy eyes, hay fever and cough, or jaundice symptoms. But can a vaccine really eliminate the true cause of these diseases? And are they really caused by viruses and bacteria? The occurrence of any of these diseases is merely an effect and not a cause. The true cause of these health conditions is a deregulated body which allows all kinds of microorganisms to multiply. What happens then within our body when we eliminate the effects of those diseases, which are simply viruses, bacteria and other symptoms, but we neglect their true cause – the imbalance of the body? It is simple! A few years down the line, we end up with allergies, asthma, diabetes, cirrhosis, a heart attack, kidney disease and circulatory problems.

Vaccines only block the natural activation and self-defence of our body. I will remind you here that vaccines stimulate production of antigens, which cannot protect us against such external factors as bad diet, cold or stress. Instead, they eliminate the most important alarm signals which could inform us about the imbalance within our body. An active virus is such a signal and it tells us that we are destroying our body and we should instead look for the true cause of this state. By injecting vaccines into our body we simply allow an unrestricted and very damaging penetration by such external factors as the energy of flavours, cold and emotional problems.

Acid-base homeostasis

I often use this sentence: "the proper quality and quantity of blood is indispensable". In terms of what we are talking about here, it is indeed of great importance. From years of observation and experience I have learnt that recommendations from dieticians relating to the acid-forming and/or alkaline-forming impact of particular food products on the body are often not true. Perhaps in laboratory test tubes these dependences represent a constant feature. However, in relation to the human body, all of these suggestions are simply irrelevant.

You only need basic medical knowledge: blood pH (its acid-alkaline impact) is usually quite high. Despite continuous production of acids and bases within the body and their infiltration from the outer environment, the blood is always more alkaline and its pH is normally 7.4 (between 7.3 and 7.5). If the pH is more than 7.8 or below 6.5 then it becomes very dangerous; it leads to deactivation of enzymes (denaturalization of proteins) and the gas exchange during breathing becomes impossible. A stable rate of blood pH is maintained by the constantly functioning buffer system and protective activities primarily of the lungs, liver, kidneys and heart. The buffer system works within blood cells and the plasma.

If the buffer of blood and other bodily fluids is strong enough then one's blood pH usually remains constant, but only under the condition that the respiratory system, nervous system, liver, kidneys and even bones are all functioning properly.

Acidification of the body can happen when there is too much CO_2 within the blood and is usually caused by a low intensity of breathing (a malfunction of the respiratory system) and accumulation of acids (which are a by-product of faulty metabolism) within the blood. In the first as well as the latter case, a stabilizing and cleansing effect can be achieved through intensified breathing (elimination of CO_2) and the kidneys' metabolization and excretion of the acids in urine.

It is possible that a sample of blackcurrant juice (with or without sugar?...) mixed in a test tube with some acid will cause its neutralization. However, this does not mean that it will happen within the human body.

How can we protect our body against acidification? We can only do so when our metabolism is working properly and when the quality of blood and other bodily fluids is good enough.

The spleen and the left kidney are responsible for the blood formation process. All the other organs, the proper quality of the blood (Yin) and good blood circulation (Yang) are responsible for the process of metabolism.

These two deciding factors, as well as emotional balance, are directly related to the quality of our food. Every single meal that weakens the spleen and the stomach has acidifying properties. It is because the food we eat is the true cause and the engine of all processes and interdependences within our body. I have reiterated many times the food products that have a destructive effect on our Centre (stomach, spleen, pancreas). These are mostly mono-flavoured food based on a single food product, cooked with no spices, cold, low calorific or excessively calorific, very fatty or fat free. We tend to go for just chicken, or just pork, or just grains, or just fruit, and we drink large quantities of water and juices. Now think – is it really possible to avoid acidification of your body when you decide to eat grains for some time then switch to eating only vegetables, at the same time drinking large quantities of water? Is it possible to have a well-functioning and non-acidified body when you only eat raw fruit and vegetables and keep sipping cold water?

My observations confirm all I have written earlier. Everything that has a destructive effect on the spleen leads to acidification of the body. This is because the spleen produces fluids of a base (alkaline) nature and simultaneously stimulates all biochemical reactions.

The problem of acidification of the body is quite common among those people who are convinced of their healthy eating habits, and who follow all kinds of diets and eliminate all kinds of food products from their menu. In most cases, this state is caused by raw food; however, this is not always so. It can equally be caused by a vegetarian, macrobiotic or fatty-meat diet. These problems can also cause concern to those who do not follow any particular diet at all, but totally unconsciously eat the wrong kind of food, like, for example, too much ham and sausages, chicken and fish or simply overindulging in eating large quantities of sweets and unhealthy nibbles (crisps).

When the natural balance of flavours and emotions within the body is destroyed, then any kind of diet can cause effects opposite to those we would expect. Within Nature, all things co-exist and co-create with one another; therefore, eliminating even one link from that chain of interdependences destroys the whole system. So…?

As mentioned earlier, every second we produce 4.5 million red and white blood cells. This means that every second, by our own choice, we influence the quality and quantity of blood and all regulating (buffer), building and energetic factors that are contained in the blood.

And one more digression: please, try to remember that an acidified body produces a specific (acidic) odour. Even the best perfumes will not help to cover it up. By eating only fruit or cereal, we will not smell like flowers, hay or summer meadow.

Acidification of the body happens when:

- there is a deficiency of building, energetic or regulating components, such as proteins (including animal proteins), fats (including unsaturated fats), carbohydrates, B vitamins and vitamin A, E and D, mineral salts (magnesium, zinc, chromium and iron);
- we follow various diets based on one flavour or one food product, as they lack the indispensable energetic composition;
- the food lacks Yang energy (energy of fire), that is when it is cooked in microwaves, on an electric cooker or simply when it is served raw and cold;
- we are under the influence of long-lasting stress, which destroys our Centre (stomach, spleen and pancreas).

Metabolism

Metabolism, generally speaking, is simply the process of alchemic transformation of matter into energy and energy into matter. This process depends on the energy of the external factors affecting the body as well as on individual predispositions. In *Philosophy of Health* I have described the process of metabolism according to the philosophy of Tao.

In every person, metabolism runs on a different energetic level, for it depends on our personal choices. Thanks to this, our life is rich in all kinds of experiences on the physical and emotional level.

So what is metabolism in scientific terms? The whole process starts with digestion of food (matter). The food is chewed on and mixed with saliva in our mouth. The longer we chew on it, the better it will be for the digestive process in our stomach where the food becomes mechanically and chemically transformed into a thick liquid. This liquid (half-digested food) is then, portion by portion, transported to the intestines.

The stomach protects the intestines from any extreme or damaging properties of the food, such as solid consistency, coldness, excessive heat, chemical or bacteriological impurities. Pure stomach juice has a pH of 1; when mixed with ingested food, its pH rises to approximately 2.3. It creates a very acidic environment indeed. The concentration of hydrochloric acid is high enough to kill even very dangerous germs. When experiencing certain health problems or undergoing an illness, the stomach juice is affected, too; there is either too much or not enough of it and its chemical composition diverges from the norm; this always leads to digestive problems and infections.

The hydrochloric acid is an important factor of digestive, defensive and metabolic processes. It macerates proteins, accelerates the digestion of meat, coagulates milk, kills germs and prevents their multiplication, protects the intestines from infections, fermentation and rotting; it is also indispensable in the process of absorption of the outer factors enabling blood formation, such as vitamin B12. The stimulator activating the production of the appropriate amount of hydrochloric acid is salt/sodium chloride (NaCl, which can be found in our food).

The stomach juices contain enzymes such as pepsin, cathepsin, rennet and lipase. Pepsin is responsible for the initial digestion of larger molecules of proteins, breaking them up into smaller particles. Rennet can be found in a baby's stomach and is responsible for coagulation of milk. Lipase, on the other hand, is responsible for the initial decomposition of fat into glycerol and fatty acids; this process stimulates production of bile as well as pancreatic and intestinal lipase. All of these processes happen simultaneously; also at the same time, impulses are sent stimulating the pancreas and the small intestine to produce digestive enzymes.

Mucus is also a very important component of the stomach juices. It plays a digestive and protective role. Its digestive function relates mostly to the process of coagulation of milk, and especially casein, into a thicker matter (when there are problems with the spleen and the production of mucus, then problems with digestion of milk normally occur). The protective function of mucus relates mostly to preventing the lining of the stomach from being digested.

The production of stomach juices is a very complex process and depends mostly on what we eat and how we feel (psychological stimulation). This process also depends on the balance within the body and its general condition.

The thick liquid and acid ingest is moved in small portions from the stomach to the intestines, where all of the food components are digested at the same time. The quickest to digest are carbohydrates, followed by fats and, lastly, proteins. Within the intestines, the food is ultimately decomposed into amino acids, monosaccharides, glycerol, fatty acids, mineral salts and vitamins, and entirely absorbed into the system.

The digestive process within the small intestine happens in an (alkaline) environment in the presence of bile and pancreatic and intestinal juices. The pancreatic juice contains trypsin and chymotrypsin, both responsible for digestion of protein, and lipase, phospholipase and esterase, which take part in the digestion of fats, but only in the presence of bile, which plays the role of fat emulsifier.

Summarizing, we can see that ultimate digestion happens within the small intestine. In the stomach, the food is merely macerated with hydrochloric acid and only partially digested (proteins).

The process of digestion is completed in the large intestine – what has not been digested in the small intestine is finally digested here. Within the large intestine, re-absorption of water and the formation of faeces takes place, followed by excretion. Therefore, in order to function properly, the large intestine needs mucus, which enables all of these processes to function more easily. The gut flora does not participate in the process of digestion. They only accelerate the fermentation and rotting of undigested remains of food. If excretion happens regularly, then the final products of rotting and fermentation become neutralized in the liver. But if we do not evacuate our bowels for a few days, then there is a risk of poisoning within the body.

The process of absorption of some nutrients begins in the mouth, but most of it happens in the stomach and the small intestine. It takes place simultaneously with digestion and lasts for a few hours. The length of this process depends on the nature of the food and the way it was prepared; for example, an unbalanced meal composed of meat is digested for up to 6 hours, whilst a well-balanced one takes 3 to 4 hours to digest.

The final products of the digestive process, such as amino acids, fatty acids and monosaccharides, become an important building and energetic material within the body. On the other hand, mineral salts, vitamins and water belong to the group of very ductile and catalytic factors, which co-create an appropriate environment for metabolism.

Amino acids, created during the process of digestion, take part in the synthesis of cellular proteins (cellular rejuvenation), production of enzymes, hormones and other active bodies. They also provide energy or simply transform into lipids.

Monosaccharides (glucose) are "burnt" in the presence of oxygen from blood. They give us the energy required for further metabolism and functioning of the body. Any excess of monosaccharides is stored in the liver and muscles (glycogen) or simply transformed into fat. For this transformation to take place requires not only insulin but also hormones produced in the core and cortex of the adrenal gland, the frontal lobe of the pituitary gland and the thyroid.

Fatty acids and glycerol break down and join in the process of metabolism of sugars, producing energy in effect. The storing of fat is usually caused by malfunctioning of many bodily organs, such as the pancreas, thyroid, liver, stomach, spleen, or by a hormonal imbalance.

Our diet should always include a combination of proteins, carbohydrates and fats. Vitamins and mineral salts are natural components of all these compounds. The process of metabolism is very complex and depends on all kinds of factors, such as the energy and temperature of the body, the quality of food, emotional states, etc. Therefore, one should be very careful before making any final assumptions on the interdependences between different food products and their ultimate exclusion from our diet.

None of the nutrients (proteins, fats, carbohydrates, mineral salts, vitamins) exist in Nature in a separate state; therefore they should not be consumed separately either. They form plant and animal tissues and are digested all at the same time by the enzymes and digestive juices, which are also being produced at the same time. All this happens involuntarily and beyond our control.

Who, then, came up with a theory that the duration of digestion of particular nutrients varies and that they are digested in different parts of the body? Where and when, then? It is an unquestionable fact that the more varied the diet, the better is the process of digestion. Additional spices, the temperature of the food, proper chewing, balanced flavours and our emotional state; all of these factors have a positive impact on the quality of our digestion. And mono-flavoured diets or diets based on one food product only mess up the functioning of the bodily organs and consequently the whole body. In the long run, they lead to serious health dysfunctions.

Our body functions continuously without a break. Therefore each meal should contain all the necessary nutrients, which are then able to maintain a good quality of metabolism and the proper functioning of the bodily organs. And do not forget about cellular rejuvenation, which can only happen with the presence of amino acids. Protein is therefore an indispensable component of every single meal. Unfortunately, some specialists claim that some food products are more beneficial to our health than others; that some of them are "healthy" and others are not. For example, there is a certain preference for products containing lots of vitamins (juices, fruit, yogurts or fresh salads) over products containing fats, carbohydrates or meat.

However, all of these nutrients, supplied simultaneously and accompanied by the appropriate spices, can create a system of mutual support and stimulation and improve the process of digestion, absorption and further metabolism. All diets composed according to certain temporary trends are very dangerous for our health. Here are a few examples. A diet based merely on fats and proteins without any carbohydrates has a poisonous effect on the body in the long run. A similar effect will be seen from a diet based solely on carbohydrates and fats. Combinations such as fruit and dairy products only or fruit and carbohydrates only are very dangerous for the body. Also very dangerous is combining meat with raw vegetables or raw fruit. An indispensable component of a well-balanced meal are spices. Another very important factor in improving metabolism is the Yang energy obtained during the process of cooking.

According to the principles of conventional medicine, we should only pay attention to the calorific value of our food and make sure we also supply our body with appropriate levels of vitamins and mineral salts. Apparently, this should make us stronger. But if that was really the case, most of us should be healthy now. It is quite easy indeed to eat a large portion of meat accompanied by a fresh salad, some juice and a bowl of fruit for dessert. But we now know that it has the opposite effect to the one claimed by conventional medicine. We could say that somebody is trying to play unfairly with us.

Unfortunately, the biggest problem is the ignorance of science, which pretends that if something cannot be seen then it simply does not exist. And thus the effects are obvious. We think that we are eating healthily but in reality we end up being ill more often. The dependence between our diet and the condition of our health is clearly visible. Therefore, I am surprised that, even though students of medicine are being taught about all these dependences, in reality, doctors simply ignore them. In their diagnosis of certain illnesses, this factor is simply blanked out. Yet, all of the laboratories of the world are looking for efficient cures.

Do all these specialists who recommend eating large quantities of fruit and fresh salads and drinking many litres of water or fruit juices know that all the processes and reactions happening within our body rely on a large supply of energy? Even though there is enough glucose, which produces energy when metabolized, there is still a requirement for that initial spark that starts the whole process. Yes, I know that we are born with a certain supply of energy. But we should continuously protect and refill it. Otherwise it will quickly run out and our energetic deficiency will cause us problems and we will have a miserable life.

If the food lacks Yang energy, is cold and with no spices, based on only a few flavours (sour, salty or sweet) then our body loses the Yin–Yang balance, our bodily organs are destroyed and start to malfunction (they are simply too cold). Our physical and emotional suffering simply starts to overwhelm us.

After eating an imbalanced meal with not enough energy in it we still feel hungry. As a consequence of this we reach for something else: fruit compote, some juice, a biscuit, a fruit. This only makes us weaker and more sleepy. For many hours we either have the feeling of a full stomach or feel hungry again very quickly, even though we have eaten not that long ago. We lose concentration, so we start eating more fruit, drinking another cup of tea. We feel a constant craving for something. But the truth is that our body is simply calling for Yang energy! If it does not get it then the bodily organs cannot fulfil their functions properly.

Yang energy, which stimulates the vibrations within our body, can be supplied to our body in the form of a well-balanced meal. The problem of overcooling of the body (deficiency of Yang), which I mention so often, is directly connected to our metabolism. Maintaining the appropriate body temperature (not letting it overcool) is the first condition of good health. A permanently overcooled body often (not always) activates thermoregulation on a level much higher than the required norm and eventually manifests itself as fevers. In this case, the fever is actually needed, as it destroys all dangerous viruses and bacteria and enables the bodily organs to reach the appropriate energetic level. But it is also important to mention here that a fever is not always good. It sometimes happens that it is actually a symptom of a very serious condition within the body; the so-called body fire (deficiency of Yin).

We can openly say that all the illnesses we experience in our life are the direct effect of bad metabolism. An exception here are all mechanical injuries, which, however, can lead to all kinds of complications due to a deficiency of energy and problems with metabolism. Even genetic illnesses are caused by a continuous repetition of the same mistakes throughout generations, which affect metabolism and consequently lead to changes within the genetic code. Every single infection is also caused by bad metabolism which manifests itself in a weakened immune system.

So, how can we claim that psoriasis, heart attacks or asthmas have nothing to do with the dietary mistakes we continuously make? We must remember that they are in fact the core factor of many illnesses.

Contraction and expansion

Contractile tissue consists of smooth and striated muscles, which can further be divided into skeletal and cardiac muscles. Also categorized as skeletal muscles are the diaphragm, the upper part of the oesophagus, the external anal sphincter, the external urethral sphincter, some of the muscles of the head and the external eye muscles. The smooth muscles do not form separate bodily organs; they are merely entwined with other tissues and play a contractile function. They can be found in the walls of blood and lymphatic vessels, in the skin and eyes, the gastrointestinal tract, respiratory system and genito-urinary system.

When not connected to the nervous system, the skeletal muscles become soft and lose their tonic tension. Problems with muscle tone can be observed in people who do not eat healthily (eat too much sugar, dairy or sour, raw and cold food) and whose diet does not contain all the necessary nutrients, such as amino acids, B vitamins and vitamins A, D and E, iron, zinc, magnesium and chromium. The quality of the nervous tissue and the flow of nervous impulses then become badly affected. Also, due to improper metabolism, the liver stops fulfilling its normal function; it stops building, protecting and nourishing the nervous tissue sufficiently.

The whole mechanics of contraction of the skeletal muscles depends on the chemical composition of these muscles. That is why what we eat is very important. An indispensable factor in the process of muscular contraction is also oxygen, which, as we know, is supplied by the blood. Therefore a well-functioning spleen and lungs are very important here, too.

Muscular contraction causes an extensive release of heat. This process will last for only a short time in the absence of oxygen; in this case, the heat will simply have a relaxing effect on the muscle. However, the next stage of this process requires oxygen. The absence of oxygen causes anaerobic glycolysis, which leads to the breakdown of glycogen and a release of lactic acid. This is a direct way towards acidification of the body. On the other hand, if we provide enough oxygen (through proper breathing and a sufficient quantity of good quality blood) then we gain more energy and the breakdown of glycogen ends with production of carbon dioxide. The lactic acid is simply burnt in the presence of oxygen.

According to the Yin–Yang theory, contraction stands for Yin and expansion for Yang. Maximal Yin (contraction) turns into Yang (expansion). Under the influence of negative external stimuli, as a form of self-defence, the contraction of our outer sheathing (skin, skeletal muscles, muscles of the head, kidneys, bladder and spleen) always results in expansion and "freezing" of the function of the spleen; this consequently affects the production of new essence. At the same time, the metabolism of internal bodily organs is activated. As a consequence of this process, more energy is released at the cost of burning the essence of the bodily organs (Yin). This mostly affects the liver, pancreas and heart. I would like to remind you here that such a reaction from our body is something normal and can be expected in situations of exposure to stress, cold or a bad diet.

The behaviour of young people nowadays and the fashion for sour, raw and cold food, vegetarianism or starvation and detox diets very often leads to extremities. Due to a low temperature, inappropriate diet and emotional exhaustion, we often suffer from contraction of our outer sheathing, which in effect leads to inner exploitation and self-burning of the essence (or simply a drying-out of the body). It gives us an illusion of vitality and lightness. But in reality it causes enormous "jamming", both within the body and our consciousness. The consequences can be compared to a tree with its roots cut – it simply wilts.

Some specialists in Chinese medicine refer to this problem as the state of inner fire (liver or heart fire) and advise "cooling it down" by consuming refreshing kinds of food. But, in my opinion, this is a very risky thing to do as this kind of food will simply not activate the spleen and thus will not reconstruct our inner Yin. It will merely cause a temporary effect of "calming" the fire; in other words, it will work in exactly the same way as a pill or tablet. Some people simply do not understand that in our climatic conditions, and with our diet, it is technically impossible to overheat our body. The states of body fire are simply caused by false excesses, which, in turn are caused by continuous contractions stimulated by negative external factors.

If a factor A (e.g. stress or cold) leads to an excess of energy within the body, it does not mean that we should instantly try to cool our body by drinking cold drinks (water, beer). This will only bring temporary relief and intensify the whole problem, causing a deficiency of moisture (blocked spleen), imbalance between Yin and Yang and, of course, an increased susceptibility to the factor A. We should instead protect our body from the external factors which stimulate outer contractions and inner activity.

Our body is ruled by a strand of continuous contractions and expansions, breathing in and breathing out. The blood and energy circulate throughout our body, warming and nourishing it from within and connecting it to the Sky. **The whole philosophy of life is simple – the body should not be kept for too long in the state of contraction**, except for the heart, responsible for the rhythmical pumping of the blood. The rest of our body should be relaxed and in a state of Taoist emptiness, enabling a free flow of energy and blood. Contractions are characteristic of a body which is tired, acidified and malnourished.

Let's have a closer look at the phenomenon of muscle contraction or its permanent contracture. Muscular contraction is the visible effect of irritation of the receptors. The irritation of the receptors initially stimulates chemical, electrical and thermal changes, as well as changes in flexibility followed by contraction. Therefore, an irritating factor (temperature, stress, flavour) leads to stimulation (a chemical change). This, on the other hand, deactivates the "alert system", such as contracture or pain. Then it all depends on our imagination and whether we go for elimination of the true cause of this state, that is the irritating factors, such as an excess of calcium or the sour flavour in our diet or stress, or we decide to "fiddle" with the "alert system", that is the mechanism of contraction.

Acetylcholine is a chemical compound participating in the process of contracting. It is normally released under the influence of nervous impulses activated by the irritating factors. Is it then appropriate in children with cerebral palsy, whose immune system is too weak to withstand the irritating factors (due to an excess of calcium, sour flavour, cold and stress), to eliminate the alert system (contracture) by application of a factor blocking the production of acetylcholine? Rather, shouldn't we make sure that the levels of magnesium and calcium are well balanced within the body? Of course we should. But it is very difficult to achieve, especially in a situation when children with cerebral palsy are being fed cheeses, yogurts, fruit and fruit juices. We should always remember that the calcium ions release mediators (acetylcholine) and that the magnesium ions prevent this process. Therefore, taking into consideration all you have read so far, isn't it a bit terrifying when you hear that contractures in children are being treated with botulinum toxin?

Smooth muscles can be stimulated not only by temperature, stretching, and chemical substances but also through vegetative nerves, whose mediators are noradrenaline and acetylcholine. A mediator is, in other words, a stimulatory substance. The mediators of stimulatory synapses include acetylcholine, dopamine, noradrenaline, histamine and serotonin. Mediators of the inhibitory synapses are still not known. And most probably they never will be, as they simply do not exist due to the fact that inhibition and relaxation happen through elimination of the contracting factor.

Unfortunately, Nature has not secured us in such inhibitory substances. Therefore we should "switch on" our conscious thinking and use our free will and simply eliminate the irritating (destructive) factors.

Blood types

The knowledge of the relationship between diet and blood type came from America with the publication of the book *Eat Right For Your Blood Type*. This book explains a lot about our taste preferences.

Some time ago, I argued with my family, trying to convince them to eat more fruit and fresh salads. They usually opposed this by stating that they are not rabbits. There was always someone sneakily stealing a slice of ham or sausage from the fridge. I felt devastated because of it. But now I know that I was trying to adjust their eating habits to my own needs. It turned out in the end that I have blood type A, which means that I can eat meat, but not too often and not too much. My children's blood type, on the other hand, turned out to be O and their preference for meat is very natural in this case. Ever since I learnt this I have been more tolerant in this matter. It does not mean, however, that my family are allowed to eat whatever they want. I do realize that meat, like any other food product of a specific energy, has to be balanced by other indispensable flavours (energies).

My reflections after reading "*Eat Right For Your Blood Type*":

- We should always remember that we do not live in America and that the climate and culture of our country is very different from those in America.
- Our dietary habits are characteristic of the country we live in and different from those presented in the book.
- Our culinary habits and climatic factors, but also our national mentality and, connected with this, our feelings and emotions, are responsible for the kind of health problems we suffer; they are characteristic of the country we live in and different from those in America.
- People with blood type O and B have a stronger preference towards meat; however, it does not mean that by eating just meat and fatty meals they will

secure good health for themselves. Only intensive physical exercise allows the body to tolerate large quantities of meat. Otherwise, there is a risk of losing the balance and acidifying the body.

- People with blood types A and AB have a stronger preference towards fruit and vegetables, but this should also not be taken to an extreme. The majority of meals should consist of boiled or steamed meat accompanied by vegetables with added spices. We should always remember that eating too much meat can affect the natural balance within the body.
- The products presented in the book as most beneficial for Americans can be harmful for people from different countries, cultures and climates.

People with blood type O are strong and resistant to illnesses and physical exhaustion. They offload their stress and emotional tensions through physical exercise, running, working in the garden or doing chores at home. Meat gives them a feeling of stability and calmness.

People with blood type B are also strong and resistant to many external factors. But in order to release their power they have to first deal with their emotional problems hidden deeply within their subconscious. Living under constant stress, they have to feel active and creative all the time. They can easily lose themselves to it and become workaholics.

People with blood type A are completely different. They are not as stable as those of blood type O. They are sensitive, prone to stress and frequent headaches. They regenerate from extreme levels of stress only through relaxation and sleep. They tend to switch off from the outer world and sleep through their problems.

People with blood type AB are as sensitive as blood type A people – they are also prone to illnesses and stress.

People with blood type O and B are much stronger that those with A and AB blood types. Has it something to do with the fact that they eat more meat than those of the group types? Throughout history there are cases of whole nations going extinct due to a diet scarce in meat. For example, the Incas, who knew methods of saving lives with the use of certain mysterious substances, were unable to protect their health when exposed to a totally meat-free diet.

I will remind you here that our immunity depends on the blood-forming process and, from my own experience, I can tell you that some broth, steak or liver is very helpful in this process.

In summary: in order to benefit fully from this book we should always have in mind the universal knowledge of the nature of particular food products that are used in our kitchen; let's be conscious of the climate we live in and honest about the "sins" we commit against our body. I know that pineapples are recommended for my blood type (A); but I also know that they do not grow in the climate of the country I live in. I am also aware of my own body's condition and know how I have treated it over the forty years of my life. Therefore, even though I like pineapples, I eat them very rarely and in small portions.

Why do we age?

Is ageing of the body a necessity or is it rather a derivative of our life choices? It is surely the latter. Our death or, putting it in slightly different words, the moment of our transition and passage on to a different energetic level, does not have to be preceded by so much suffering and frailty as we have observed so far. Ageing is not a matter of necessity but choices. **We become ill not because we are getting older; rather, we are getting older because we are ill**. This phenomenon is determined by cultural, religious, social and customary factors. We are used to the image of life which ends with illnesses, ageing and death. It is a pity, though. By acknowledging that we can have influence on our body and its regeneration, we could make our life much nicer and more dignified.

Let's assume, then, that we do not have to age. The biggest impact on the process of ageing is the loss of Yang energy (Chi and warmth) and its inappropriate protection and supplementation, which in consequence makes the regeneration of bodily tissues impossible.

In order for our bodily organs to fulfil their functions, they need to be continuously strengthened by an appropriate quantity and quality of energy and to undergo a constant process of regeneration. Such bodily organs as the stomach, spleen, pancreas, kidneys, intestines and liver become "used up" very quickly and their regeneration is conditioned by a proper and well-functioning metabolic process. The requirement for amino acids and a whole range of accompanying catalysing substances is unavoidable in the process of regeneration. Regeneration is a continuous process. Therefore, the supply of energy and appropriate substances should happen regularly.

Complete protein can only be found in meat (always be aware of the nature of meat, though) and eggs. The rest of the food products used in a meal should create a varied but harmonious composition, making all of the products easier to digest and absorb. The food should always be varied and of a neutral-warming nature; it should simultaneously contain proteins, carbohydrates, fats, vitamins and mineral salts.

When there is not enough energy or the proper kind of proteins or any of the other nutrients (e.g. carbohydrates) in our food, or when our meals are mono-flavoured (sour or salty) and of a cooling nature, then our bodily organs are not able to regenerate properly and simply start malfunctioning (cold). Any organ in such a state cannot function properly and will only cause problems with metabolism. In other words, first we become ill and consequently we start ageing.

The closest to an ideal dietary model is the one derived from multigenerational culinary traditions which value such things as intuition, sensitivity and ability to keep the balance of flavours. Many nations are still proud of their traditions. Therefore, they do not suffer as many illnesses as other nations and their old people are physically more capable and vigorous. On the other hand, in countries where various scientific methods and fast foods are popular, people are more obese and the scale of illnesses is unimaginable. The fact that they live longer has nothing to do with their own health but with medical and pharmaceutical treatment.

Even though academic medicine has achieved quite a lot in the field of health and life protection, a much better way of extending people's lives in a more humanitarian way would be through expanding their consciousness and reducing the quantity of various medicines and vitamins that we use routinely.

Ageing depends on our perception and expectations and is caused by certain dietary mistakes combined with a destructive lifestyle. We do not have to age, unless we want to.

Sport

Sport and physical exercise have been totally natural for me since my early childhood. I grew up with the idea of doing sports for pleasure.

And if we do it for pleasure or simply to improve our condition, we should not overstrain ourselves. When we feel we have had enough, we should stop immediately. But if we treat sport as a form of competition, then sooner or later, we will become enslaved by it. Every type of competitiveness evokes the wrong kind of emotions. We are all different; one person is more physically capable than another. Therefore each time we compare ourselves to somebody else we lose balance. By comparing ourselves to somebody stronger than us we start feeling inferior, and when we compare ourselves to somebody weaker, then we start feeling superior.

It is said that sport is a form of healthy competition. However, such a thing does not exist. Every competition is based on fear and Ego. Anything we do we should really do it for ourselves and not to prove something to others. Our intentions are the most important thing. We compete with others when we lack self-worth. Otherwise, we feel good the way we are and we do not have to prove anything to anyone. Only then does sport become a pleasure.

It is different, though, when we struggle against ourselves, e.g. by going on a lonesome run or expedition. **But we should always remember that our intentions determine the quality of our deeds.**

When we practise sport for ourselves and without overstraining the body, we benefit from it greatly; it strengthens our body, helps to unblock contracted muscles, stimulates blood circulation, improves metabolism, shapes our body, improves our movement and co-ordination as well as our general health and resistance to stress.

Every form of sport boosts the level of Yang energy. And, as we already know, there can never be enough Yang. But we must not forget that the body regenerates best during relaxation and sleep. By comparing those who do exercise or practise some kind of sport (even leisurely) with those who do not do any exercise, we can tell that, even though they may both follow a similar diet, the first group of people will be much healthier than the second. This proves that exercising (energy), stimulating your blood circulation and unblocking the muscles leads to a better condition. Therefore such proverbs as "a sound mind, sound body" always remain true.

The situation looks slightly different with competitive/professional sports. If we go over the reasonable bounds and overstrain ourselves, we destroy our body. It should be wildly advertised that competitive sports are just another way of making money. The Olympics have become an element of our social life. But they usually evoke negative feelings. Therefore, do not fool yourselves that competitive sports are a noble activity leading to better health and positive attitudes.

When do competitive sports become harmful to the body? The destruction of the body happens extensively and rapidly when sportspeople eat mostly food of cooling properties with the addition of various artificial supplements. A wrong diet and extensive physical exercise prevent regeneration and rejuvenation of the internal substance. Only a well-balanced diet of a neutral nature can secure the proper regeneration of the body. And only an appropriate number of meals per day and enough relaxation can prevent destruction of the body. Being a sportsperson one should be especially watchful of all (even the smallest) external factors and their emotional states, as they can have an even stronger effect on a body exploited by extensive physical exercise.

The first organs to be destroyed within the body of a sportsperson are the spleen and pancreas, followed by the liver, heart and kidneys. The majority of sportspeople have an enlarged spleen and heart, but also problems with lumbar vertebrae, blood circulation, indigestion, with frequent colds and rheumatism occurring; a lot of them suffer from allergies, asthma, diabetes, knee contusions, tendon contusions and joint problems. Physical exhaustion of the body is not the only cause of such a state. Failure of several bodily organs, caused by eating the wrong kind of food (excess of cold drinks, fruit, fresh salads), is also responsible. Due to such hostile conditions – excessive physical effort and cold food, the spleen and the liver do not keep up with the production of essence and regeneration of tissues (blood, muscles, bodily organs, connective tissue). This leads to cardiovascular diseases, diabetes and lung diseases.

An especially dangerous activity/sport for the body is swimming. It weakens the liver and the spleen. The liver does not like the cold at all; therefore, together with the wrong kind of diet, cold water has a negative effect on the joints and connective tissue. Rheumatism, or, in other words, a disease of coldness, is an occupational disease among swimmers.

Footballers suffer from an enlarged spleen, heart and lung problems. The spleen enlarges due to increased heart exploitation, as both of these organs are interconnected (a mother–child kind of relationship exists between them). A weakened heart does not support the spleen, but rather exploits it instead.

Cyclists, on the other hand, often suffer from kidney, heart and liver problems.

Weightlifting leads to problems with lumbar vertebrae and joints. Also, the liver does not tolerate such an extreme effort. The destruction of the liver is one of the first side-effects of weightlifting.

All sportspeople suffer from spinal problems, which are usually caused by extreme effort as well as the emotional tensions and the kind of food (colds drinks, sour, raw and cold food) that affects blood circulation (pericardium).

Muscular contractions and emotional tensions are characteristic of every single sporting discipline. These two factors, plus those mentioned above, lead to destruction within the body. In this regard, I would like to point your attention towards bodybuilding, and I am not talking here about such extremities as using artificial, anabolic supplements for the rapid growth of body mass. This particular sporting discipline is still unappreciated and has little popularity. However, slowly and with time it is beginning to become more and more popular. The majority of bodybuilding enthusiasts do exercise in order to improve their health and shape their bodies, which has an immense influence on their self-worth and self-esteem. They wrestle and exercise for pleasure. They learn how to respect their bodies and observe their transformation. This does not happen in any other sporting discipline. Wrestle, then, but not for the sake of achieving goals and better results, but for the body's own good.

Why do I recommend bodybuilding? This kind of exercise enables us to maintain the right proportion of the body. If we are sensible and exercise under the eye of a qualified specialist, then we can achieve a correct and stable body posture. Besides, all our emotions, tensions and stresses are encoded not only in our consciousness but most of all in our connective tissue. This leads to such symptoms as all kinds of contractions and blockages of blood and energy circulation. In effect, it results in very serious health conditions. The strengthening exercises stimulate both sides of the body equally and put the same kind of pressure on muscles on both right and left sides, causing their contraction and extension. It is absolutely invaluable for regeneration of muscles and their relaxation. Intensive training also increases the level of energy (vibration), and because this energy is shared equally on both sides of the body, it has the power of "ejecting" all the accumulated emotions of the day, both in our conscious as well as in our subconscious.

Would we be able to achieve similar effects doing professional competitive sports where the body is treated as an obstacle and a sportsperson is manipulated firstly by the sports business and secondly by the constant pressure of always achieving better results?

Very often those who practise extensive physical exercise or sport are prone to colds, i.e. catarrh and sore throats. Why is this? It is an entirely physiological process. Due to consuming the wrong food or drink, the spleen turns "cold" and weak and starts producing pathological mucus and moisture. This initially accumulates in the lungs and sinuses, and if the body does not receive enough "warmth", it simply remains there. During exercise and physical effort, the level of our Yang energy goes up and the body is strong enough to rid itself of the mucus. It is very good for the body but has the effect of producing catarrh. We should therefore think twice before reaching for a cold drink or a fruit. Very harmful in this case would also be using antibiotics as they block the natural defence mechanism of the body, only intensifying the production of mucus. The most beneficial medication here would be simply using aspirin and a cup of the "killer" tea.

A sore throat, on the other hand, is a typical symptom of a weak liver and contraction within the smooth muscles, which react very quickly to the cold food and stress.

The frequent and painful contusions of sportspeople are simply a symptom of malfunctioning of specific internal bodily organs. For example, knee contusions are a symptom of stomach and intestinal problems; pains in the lumbar vertebrae turn eventually into sciatica, as they cause blockages of blood circulation (pericardium) and gluteal muscles; pains in the heels and the Achilles tendons are a symptom of problems with the kidneys or the triple heater and the liver. And it all has its beginning in wrong dietary habits.

Illnesses

Treatment

According to a dictionary, "medical treatment" means medical care given to a person in order to fight an illness, to prevent an illness, to improve health with the use of medicines and medical procedures, to eliminate or soothe the symptoms of an illness or to heal. "Curative", on the other hand, means "of healing properties".

According to Chinese medicine, "to heal" means to restore the Yin–Yang balance within the body.

How should we refer to the process of eliminating the symptoms and simultaneously ignoring the causes of an illness? Well, it is simply elimination of symptoms and not healing. Professional doctors all over the world are convinced of their exclusive right to treat people, even though we all know that in most cases they do not manage to do so – they do not rid people of the true causes of their illnesses and, what is more, they do not know how to prevent them. As an example, look at the number of diseases of affluence that are beyond curing; available treatments help to keep patients alive but they do not cure these diseases (asthma, allergies, diabetes, kidney diseases and diseases of the liver). Using the word "treatment" is some kind of misunderstanding in this case, as we all know that conventional medicine has not yet found a cure for most of these diseases (allergy, asthma, diabetes). We cannot talk about curing an illness when we know that using medication for one health condition leads to other ailments. It often happens that the side effects of using a certain medicine do not occur for a long time; and when they eventually show up, we do not even realize that they could be related to the preceding treatments.

There are middle-aged women who come to me. Their health is usually in a poor condition, yet they believe that this is directly related to the process of ageing. Their contact with medicine initially starts with rather trivial health problems. But within the next ten or twenty years, due to not eliminating the true causes of their ailments, the whole problem escalates – their bodies become deregulated and their bodily organs destroyed.

I will give you an example. There was a woman who underwent hormonal fertility treatment. Her infertility was, however, caused by overcooling of the body. The treatment turned out to be successful; she was finally able to give birth to a daughter, but at the age of fifty she was so ill that she could no longer enjoy life and her motherhood. She was very upset because nobody had told her that an inappropriate diet and excess of all kinds of medicines, mostly hormonal, could lead to such a state.

If we decide to go for a treatment, we have to think about the effects it might have on the whole body. An illness is just the tip of an iceberg. If you suffer from heart problems, then most likely you also have liver and spleen problems; if you suffer from asthma, it means that your middle heater is malfunctioning; skin problems, on the other hand, signal dysfunction of the lungs and liver, tooth decay, weak kidneys, etc. It is no longer a problem to cure an illness once we discover and eliminate its true causes.

By eliminating the true causes of an illness and introducing changes to our diet, our body will reach a state of balance and thus avoid all kinds of side effects.

Infections

We often use the expression "to catch an infection". It is very convenient to use it as it covers up the fact that the infection was caused by our own imprudence, thoughtlessness, dietary mistakes, inappropriate lifestyle, taking the easy path and lack of knowledge. We are convinced that it has nothing to do with our behaviour. We blame viruses and bacteria instead.

We have been brought up in this way of thinking and it is constantly being consolidated by the health service. I think that it is high time to abandon old stereotypes and start using our knowledge and consciousness.

I remind you here once more – an illness is no more than a Yin–Yang imbalance blocking flow of energy and blood. It is most often caused by a deficiency of Yang (warmth and Chi), which in turn weakens inner Yin – a deficiency of blood, mucus, enzymes, hormones and bodily fluids. The major causes of such an imbalance are an excess of sour, raw and cold food, exposure to cold and emotional problems (stress and fear). If the body is exposed to these external factors for a long period of time, then it loses the ability to defend itself. The body then becomes susceptible to all kinds of viruses and bacteria, which, by the way, are in us and around us all the time.

We often confuse the activation of our "inner thermostat" (high body temperature) – which is supposed to balance out our internal environment – with common infections. By taking antipyretic, antibacterial and antiviral medicines, we destroy our defence system and weaken and deregulate our body even more.

In order to make all the invading germs within our body harmless, we should simply work on retrieving the Yin–Yang balance. The most important process for this is the matter of warming the body from within, which can be achieved by activating the middle heater (stomach, spleen, pancreas and liver).

Spring fatigue

In recent years, “spring fatigue” has been one of those constantly recurring subjects. I do not know if it was brought up as often before the Second World War as it is now. It has been noticed that with time people feel worse and worse around the spring season. Therefore the problem seems to be mounting.

Medical diagnosis sums it up as vitamin exhaustion within the body. This is a typical example of a misleading diagnosis. Especially nowadays, when access to all kinds of fruit, juices, fresh salads and vitamin supplements is so easy all year round, one should not point at the lack of vitamins as the major cause of spring fatigue! It is rather obvious this problem has nothing to do with vitamins.

In order to illustrate this better I would like to point your attention to the changes in Nature (and consequently in our bodies) which happen during spring. According to the laws of Nature, after the period of maximal condensation of energy and its stalling, or, in other words, winter Yin, spring is the time of awakening back to life and activating the flow of energy. The trees become active from within; the energy of spring moves their juices upwards so they can foliate again, and their seeds sprout in the soil and grow towards the sun.

A good gardener knows that the quality of harvest in summer or autumn depends on how they take care of their trees during the previous season. In spring, the trees have enough energy and juices to produce germs, which will then transform into fruit. The period of accumulation of the energy and juices happens between the last harvest and spring. There would be no time for it in spring, as spring is the season of activation and exploitation of the energy and juices. Using fertilizers during spring supports the system of formation and ripening of fruit. Similarly, a farmer who aims for a good harvest in summer or autumn has to take care of the soil during the spring and make sure that the seeds they use are of good quality.

The same kinds of dependences apply to us, too, as after all we are also a microcosm. Our state of being and general condition in spring is simply a derivative of our behaviour during the preceding seasons.

The fact that our liver becomes active in spring (see *Philosophy of Health*) leads to the conclusion that its condition affects our general wellbeing. The lungs also have a great impact on our health, as during spring they reach their energetic low. A strong liver translates as a cheerful and open mind, great tolerance and imagination, ability for good planning, quality circulation and sex and proper protein, carbohydrate and fat transformation. A weak liver, on the other hand, means proclivity for depression, sensitivity, irascibility, apathy, tiredness, feeling sleepy all the time, susceptibility to colds and allergies and problems with metabolism.

The liver can only activate in spring if there is enough accumulated energy and essence. On the other hand, if our body is weak and filled with moisture (a result of eating the wrong kind of food during the preceding seasons) then we will be more prone to allergies, asthma, stomach problems, poor blood circulation, skin problems and, of course, the most noticeable – tiredness and apathy. Due to the lack of appropriate knowledge on human physiology and its connection with Nature, as well as on the methods of regeneration and protection of our body, spring fatigue turns into an unsolvable problem. The health condition of contemporary man is therefore in decline. And it has become noticeable that other seasons have started causing similar problems – our bodily organs slowly "refuse" to function properly and our body seems to have become a painful ballast. So, would you still like some of those vitamins?

What are the true causes of spring fatigue?

- The preceding spring – the excess of spring vegetables (lettuce, radishes, cucumbers, tomatoes), excess of raw, sour and cold food, starvation diets, detox diets, meat-free diets or excess of pork, chicken, ham and sausages, excess of cold drinks, water, juices, teas of a cooling nature, overly refreshing meals, a drastic switch to light, cold, refreshing, low calorific and fat-free food;

- The preceding summer – avoiding sunlight, wearing clothes in inappropriate colours (white, blue, grey, green), overcooling the body with large quantities of cold drinks (water, beer, juices) and ice creams, excess of fruit and yogurts, bathing in cold rivers, lakes and seas, poor quality meals, fast foods;

- When on holiday in hot countries, we often lose our mind and sense of moderation and instead of going for the traditional, local cuisine we go for fruit and cold drinks. Then after coming back we cannot understand why we feel so bad;

- The preceding autumn – not ridding oneself of the moisture accumulated during the spring–summer follies and continuing to eat large quantities of fruit, fresh salads and sour food and drinking cold drinks;

- The preceding winter – pretty much the same thing as in the other seasons: fruit, fresh salads, juices, fruit yogurts, cold drinks, too much chicken, ham and sausages, fish, cakes and, most of all, gluttony at Christmas. And the biggest problem here is not how much traditional Christmas food we eat but the amounts of apples, citrus fruit, fresh salads, juices, fruit yogurts, sweets, cakes and cold drinks.

So, what should we do in spring, then? First of all, we should think about the following spring and not weaken our liver. We should eat well-balanced and warm food with added spices. We do not need as much meat and fat as during the winter, as the demand for energy within our body is smaller in spring. Let's remember that the element of Wood (liver) depends on the essence coming from the Earth. The essence that is necessary for the functioning of the liver is produced in the spleen and comes from well-balanced food of neutral-warming energy. As mentioned in the *Philosophy of Health*, the spleen is able to produce moisture (essence) only when our food contains the energy of all flavours. Similarly, the Earth is able to "give birth" to life only thanks to the co-existence of all climates (wind, heat, moisture, dryness and cold). So, how can we presume that by drinking large quantities of water we will be able to refresh and regenerate our liver? Water has cooling properties. Water is not the essence produced by our spleen!

The liver and lungs in spring

According to the Five Elements Theory, spring is the season of increased activity of the liver and gallbladder. It is the time of the element of Wind. Because there are many theories on the subject of the spring cleansing of the body and loss of the "old shell", it is high time to find out what this really means.

The spring activeness of the liver is physiologically indispensable. It is supposed to stimulate the mechanism that has been almost dormant for over half a year. The winter concentration, stillness and sleepiness is supposed to turn all of a sudden into activity. This can only happen through the stimulation of the liver. The circulation of blood, energy and essence, as well as the functioning of the nervous system and the process of metabolism, all depend on the energy and efficiency of the liver. In other words, the condition of our liver is responsible for the quality of our life, our open mind and emotional stability until the next spring.

The Yang energy of the liver depends on the energy systematically delivered with warm food balanced with all the flavours, spiced with the appropriate spices and cooked on an open fire. This kind of energy is indispensable for the production of essence in the spleen. This essence, on the other hand, strengthens and regulates the liver.

The most characteristic thing about the liver is its expansiveness and the power it has to move energy upwards. This can be achieved by adding the appropriate quantity of the sour flavour to our food. But it is absolutely forbidden to make the sour flavour dominate over the other flavours and to concentrate on food with no Yang energy. Otherwise the liver will not be able to fulfil its very important function and, consequently, our wellbeing during the other seasons of the year (weak lungs, heart and kidneys) will be affected.

In spring we can lift the pressure from the liver by reducing the size of food portions, the amount of fat (especially fat from pork) and meat or even eliminating certain kinds of meat from our diet (pork, chicken). It is also helpful to avoid sauerkraut, gherkins, fresh salads and fruit.

After many years of this so-called “healthy diet” (sour, raw and cold food, large quantities of drinks and sweets), in spring we can suffer from all kinds of ailments characteristic of this particular season: ulcers, stomach contractions, nausea, vomiting, muscular contractions, epileptic seizures, headaches, migraines, constipation, skin problems, rashes, allergies, psoriasis, catarrh, coughs, asthma, cardiovascular diseases and emotional problems such as depression, irritability and mental illnesses.

According to Chinese medicine, the liver is the “mother” of the heart and the “child” of the kidneys. Therefore its condition has a direct impact on the functioning of both of these organs. The liver is also a twin sibling to the pericardium (blood circulation/sex); a weakened liver can cause circulatory problems. The liver together with the spleen are members of the control system and lift the spleen’s energy towards the lungs. A weak liver can cause all sorts of ailments, such as flatulence, typical indigestion, the feeling of a full stomach, weakening of the lungs, asthma attacks, heart and skin problems.

Looking closely at the activity of the liver during spring, one can notice that whilst it reaches its energetic peak around this time, the lungs reach their energetic low (autumn). And we know that the lungs, when they are appropriately strengthened, control the functioning of the liver and regulate its expansiveness throughout the whole year. If it ever should happen that in spring we ate mostly sour food (the so-called refreshment of the body by eating large amounts of spring vegetables), then we would not only destroy our liver but enter the so-called depressive flow of energy characteristic of weak lungs. With this kind of diet our energy would not be able to reach the lungs (weak liver) and we would end up with all kinds of health problems: allergies, skin problems, catarrh, coughs and asthma.

We can openly call depression one of the diseases of affluence. It “wakes up” around the time of spring and reaches its apogee in the summer. According to statistical data, it is around that time people commit most suicides. Maybe what I say now will shock you, but this situation is directly connected to the fashion for drinking beer and cold water, as well as eating large quantities of fresh salads, fish, fast foods and ice cream.

You simply cannot live without a bowl of potato soup!

Allergies

An allergy is a syndrome of many difficult and awkward symptoms experienced nowadays on a massive scale. The most frequent symptoms are catarrh, coughs, itchy eyes, all kinds of rashes, which turn into inflammatory conditions (normally caused by a weak middle and upper heater). Some of the allergies lead to asthma and diabetes; this signifies a major destruction of the bottom heater as well.

Catarrh

Catarrh is one of those wonderful ailments which accompany us from birth. If it was possible we would probably already start sneezing in the womb. Why do I say it is wonderful? Simply because catarrh is a symptom signalling our bad dietary habits and their weakening effects on the spleen, liver and lungs. That is why we end up with rashes and catarrh. It is very bad when we put our "beloved" catarrh into the category of "viruses and bacteria" and start treating it like a dangerous enemy with antibiotics and steroid medication. Catarrh is our ally! Thanks to catarrh we can prevent allergies, asthma, diabetes, gastrointestinal problems, decreased level of absorption, cardiovascular diseases, and so on. Treated accordingly and in time, catarrh is not a danger to our body.

They say that catarrh, treated or untreated, always lasts the same amount of time. What does this tell us? Well, it tells us that the only cause of catarrh is a weakened spleen and lungs (food, cold). If it was otherwise, then we should see improvement after taking antibacterial or antiviral medicines.

The destructive factors within the body prevent regeneration of the internal bodily organs; this leads to weakening of the spleen, liver and lungs and the inflammatory condition of the pancreas. The initial symptom of this state is hay fever, which at the beginning occurs only around particular times of the year (the energetic low of the lungs in spring), but eventually turns into a chronic condition. If instead of changing our dietary habits we decide to go for pharmaceutical aid, then it is just a matter of time before we start suffering from asthma, diabetes, hepatitis and a weakened immune system. This process mostly affects children and the young; although it has been observed recently to affect mature people more often, too. It is the tragic consequence of a failure of our imagination.

The initial, innocent, form of catarrh is most often caused by an excess of sweets, milk and sour food (fruit, yogurts, juices, cheeses, chicken). The sour flavour activates the production of mucus and has a concentrating and blocking effect on energy circulation. This prevents the proper functioning of the spleen and liver and leads to production of pathological mucus, which is then stored in the lungs. Every single episode of catarrh is also a problem with the lungs.

Any sort of catarrh, including the allergic one, can be got rid of by eliminating all sour, cold and raw food, milk, cheeses, yogurts, sweets, chicken, ham and sausages and introducing cooked, well-balanced and warm food.

From observations, we know that the first symptoms of hay fever usually appear when we are in intensely green woods, in a garden or a room with many plants in it or among a crowd in a closed space. Therefore people prone to catarrh should avoid woods, gardens with many trees and bushes, rooms with green-coloured walls and green clothes. This applies mostly to children and the young. The green colour, like the sour flavour, fills the body with the concentrating kind of energy which weakens the liver and prevents the nutritious energy from reaching the lungs.

Coughs

A cough, similarly to catarrh, is a "positive" ailment, as it signifies that the process of ridding the lungs of mucus has started. Of course, we are talking here about the wet kind of cough. Coughs are not diseases. They only assure us that our lungs have still enough energy to rid us of accumulated mucus. There are also cases when the accumulation of mucus does not cause any symptoms, and this is very dangerous indeed as it can lead to sudden dyspnoea attacks, e.g. asthma.

We can eliminate coughs by providing the lungs with Yang energy and stimulating regeneration of the spleen, so it can start producing the appropriate strengthening kind of essence. It is also essential to eliminate excesses of sour, salty and sweet flavours. This unblocks the liver and allows it to move the Yang energy and the essence towards the lungs. Very inadvisable in this case is consumption of cold drinks and cold food.

It is a rule that a few days after catarrh we end up with a cough. This is the typical order in the case when we normally eat sour, cold and raw food. However, if we avoid this kind of food after the first symptoms of catarrh, then there is a chance that we will not have the cough, as by changing what we eat we prevent further accumulation of mucus within the lungs.

The cough will disappear only when we rid the lungs of the mucus. If we want achieve this by taking medicines (antibiotics, astringents, anti-inflammatory drugs, hormonal drugs or syrups of all kinds), then we will never solve the problem of a weak spleen and lungs. As a result of this, in the future we can expect even more serious complications.

There is also the dry type of cough. It is not as common as the wet cough and concerns mostly older people with a destroyed middle heater and a deficiency of Yin. In this case, we should focus on regenerating the spleen by introducing food composed of all flavours and containing the Yang energy, and ensure proper blood circulation and physical exercise (especially exercise of the upper part of the body).

Dry coughs signal a deficiency of the essence and the right kind of moisture in the lungs; it can occur as a reaction to emotional aggravation, a strong overcooling of the body or an excess of cold and sour food. This leads to inner contraction (muscles and spleen), which, especially within a body with Yang deficiency, can cause the split of energy – Yang goes up and all the fluids down. Emser salt (applied 2–3 times) makes the two energies concentrate together again; this activates the wet cough which means that we are getting rid of the mucus and beginning the process of warming up the lungs.

If a child normally fed with yogurts, sweets and juices suffers from this kind of dry cough, we should also give them (1–2 or even 3 times) Emser salt diluted in a small quantity of warm water, until the cough has become wet. Then we start the process of warming the child's body by replacing the sour, raw and cold food with a warm and well-balanced kind of food.

Asthma

Asthma is a direct consequence of treatments for catarrh and coughs that do not focus on eliminating the true causes of these minor ailments. In other words, asthma is caused by an imbalance within the spleen, liver, lungs and kidneys. The middle heater suffers from a deficiency of Yang energy and has a problem with the production of essence. This means that the lungs are also deprived of both of these. The symptoms of asthma (breathing difficulties, dyspnoea) are connected with contractions of chest and back muscles which make it harder to breathe and which block the flow of energy. This kind of contraction is simply caused by an excess of sour, salty and cold food as well as stress and cold.

Asthma is a disease of the lungs. Therefore, the process of production of pathological mucus by the spleen and its accumulation in the lungs also occurs. This happens when the body is suffering from a constant deficiency of Yang energy and nourished with the wrong kind of food. The accumulated mucus affects the function of the lungs and shortens the breath. We start suffocating as the lungs have not got enough capacity due to the accumulated mucus. Another reason is the contraction of the smooth muscles of the bronchus, which is caused by an excess of certain flavours of a contracting nature, as well as cold and stress, and the contraction of the chest muscles (a weak liver).

The two major problems for people suffering from asthma are mucus in the lungs and their contraction. And here I ask again: how long can we function on steroids and dilatory medication? Is this how our life is supposed to run?

In all diseases, even the most serious ones, the most important thing is to identify and eliminate their causes. Those suffering from asthma should avoid especially the energies of flavours of concentrating and contracting properties (sour and salty), but also watch the quantity of fat and sweets they consume, as they cause blockages and stimulate production of mucus. One should also not forget about the impact of emotional problems. This applies especially to older people, who are often incapable of separating themselves from their past; they are regretful and sorrowful, and thus more susceptible to problems of the lungs. I remind you here that the lungs belong to the element of Metal (the energy of autumn = the time of dying); therefore, lung treatment should provide the dispersive kind of energy (bitter and spicy flavours) always accompanied by Yang energy (the cooking process) and appropriate composition of spices and other flavours.

In order to rid our lungs of mucus and improve the quality of breathing (elimination of the muscular contractions) the most important thing is to warm the body up. We can also apply strong pressure to certain points on our chest: between the ribs, just under the sternum and along the middle line down from the clavicle/chest bone. If we suffer from a disease of the lungs then this kind of pressure will cause us great pain and almost immediately stimulate a wet cough. Also very important in this case is physical exercise of the upper part of the body (energetic arm movements) accompanied by deep breathing (you can use weights – 1–2 kg).

It has been shown that sportspeople are very prone to asthma. This is the natural consequence of excessive physical exercise (weakening of the spleen), contractions of the chest muscles, inappropriate diet – cold drinks, fresh salads, fruit, vitamin and other supplements (weakening of the whole middle heater) and stress caused by constant competition. Even though the best kind of treatment in this case would be to acknowledge the energy of the destructive factors and simply change their lifestyle, or at least dietary habits, all sportspeople and others suffering from asthma are instead being treated with all kinds of steroid inhalers which relieve their symptoms.

Itchy eyes

Another symptom of allergies is itchiness of the eyes. The initial itchiness starts normally around summer time (May/June – see *Philosophy of Health*). According to Chinese medicine, summer time begins during the second half of May. It is a season of the element of Fire, which means increased activity of the heart, pericardium (circulation/sex), the small intestine and the triple heater.

The activity of the element of Fire should be balanced out by a stronger Yin energy; that is by an appropriate quantity and quality of essence (strong spleen). If by some means (bad diet) our spleen has been weakened and we suffer from a deficiency of blood, mucus, fluids, enzymes and hormones, then it is possible that an excess of Yang within the Fire element will eventually occur. Every weakening of the spleen causes a split between Yin and Yang; the fluids move downwards and the energy upwards. This will always lead to obstructions, blockages and stalling within the circulatory system.

One thing is the fact that summer is the time of activity of the element of Fire and all the bodily organs ascribed to it. Another thing is that this particular element and all the bodily functions associated with it become weakened by a general deficiency of the Yang energy within the body that is already affected by an allergy. The element of Fire (heart) is being created by the element of Wood (liver), and we already know how weak a liver can be if the body is overcooled. We experience it every time we are under the influence of spring fatigue. The conclusion is that even within the element of Fire, there is a deficiency of Yang. In order to understand the cause of the itchy eyes even better one should consider that the element of Fire, when it is energetically low, starts "eating up" the energy of the element of Earth (stomach, spleen, pancreas).

From my observation, the weakening of the liver and gallbladder has a direct impact on the eyes, causing them to itch (inner corners of the eyes). The problems mentioned above, those concerned with the element of Fire, seem to confirm the validity of this deduction. The heart will also start using up the energy of the element of Wood. This problem normally occurs around the time of June when we start feeling the side effects of our spring follies of indulging ourselves with too many fresh vegetables and strawberries; this can eventually turn into a chronic problem. One of the functions of the liver and gallbladder is to move energy within the stomach-spleen meridian. If these bodily organs are weakened and lack the Yang energy, then we are most likely to get all sorts of allergic symptoms on our face (around the eyes), such as eczema, redness of the skin, itchiness and rashes.

Summarizing this topic: itchy eyes are a symptom of a disturbed flow of energy and of an imbalance within the elements of Wood, Fire and Earth, which can also cause blockages of the bladder. In other words, this rather trivial ailment is really and truthfully an alert of an imbalance within the whole body. If we do not do anything about this, then our eyes will be constantly red, swollen, filled with tears and pus, sensitive to sunlight, and our eyelids will become flaky.

We have a choice here between applying a standard, often hormonal, medical treatment or ridding our diet of the products which destroy our body. The latter method is not only safer but more effective. We can also help ourselves by applying methods of acupressure, by applying pressure to the number one point on the meridian of the large intestine, the number one point on the gallbladder, the number one point on the bladder and point numbers two and three on the liver, and introduce some physical exercise, which should improve the quality of breathing.

The symptom of itchiness of the eyes intensifies around the time of pollination of grasses and trees. However, this is merely a coincidence, as pollens and sunlight have not just appeared in modern times. They have always been here, and it is only our bodies that are different now – they are simply destroyed and deregulated. If there are energetic blockages within our body and our mucus membrane is not regenerated sufficiently and our lungs are weakened and the liver cold, then we will always react badly to any additional "pollution" of the air and exposure to sunlight. The true cause of our allergic suffering is the excess of both the sour and salty flavour, cold food and drinks, as well as our fascination with fresh vegetables and fruit, increased consumption of ice cream, overcooling the body by exposing it to the first rays of spring sunshine, as well as open-air bathing in lakes and rivers, physical and mental exhaustion, lack of exercise, and stress.

Rash

Rash is a symptom similar to catarrh or cough. It warns us about a Yin–Yang imbalance within the body and indicates that there are problems with blood circulation, stalling of energy and blood and a deficiency of nutrients necessary for the regeneration of tissues.

The fact that it appears on the skin surface signifies most of all an imbalance within the lungs and liver. Rashes usually appear around the meridians connected to the lungs and their functions and in situations when energy blockages occur within these meridians. These are the meridians of the large intestine, liver and lungs.

And so, a rash on the upper part of the facial cheeks in children signifies weakened lungs, a deficiency of energy and good quality essence and is often treated with cortisone (oh, horror!), although the best advice would be to simply change the diet. A rash on the skin of the hands – dry, cracked and very itchy skin – signifies problems with a weakened spleen (deficiency of moisture), dry lungs and an inefficient functioning of the liver. A very itchy rash on the arms (the area around the elbows) signifies problems with the spleen, lungs and the large intestine (an excess of emotions). A rash on the chest means that the lungs are filled with mucus; eczema on the face – a weak middle heater (stomach, spleen, pancreas, liver); acne on the back, shoulders and face – stress, a blocked blood circulation, cold and mucus within the body, but especially in the lungs and head; itchy eczema on the buttocks – problems with circulation, cold and contraction of the gluteal muscles. A rash on the genital area, on the underbelly and around the knees, signifies liver and circulatory problems and cold within the body.

There are two kinds of rashes: the so-called cold rash – red, very itchy spots which with time become leathery; and nettle rash notable for blisters. The first type should be treated as a signal alerting us about coldness and an insufficient activity of the bodily organs, which means that the body needs warming from within (under no condition should one use cortisone or calcium). The second type of rash warns us about a blockage of energy and a temporary excess of the Yang factor, which we can easily eliminate by drinking some water with lemon or eating a slice of white cheese.

In order to better understand the mechanism of formation of a rash, we must go back to the information from the chapter on thermoregulation and the defence system. Negative stimuli penetrate the body (an excess of energies of certain flavours, stress, cold), activating contracting reactions which block the flow of energy, blood and production of essence; the rash is just a tiny and not dangerous symptom of some more serious problems within the body. If we concentrate on ridding the body of the rash and ignore the problems within our body, then within a short period of time, we can expect all sorts of skin allergy problems and asthma.

By introducing a well-balanced diet of the appropriate energy, it is practically certain that we will finally rid ourselves of all of these burdensome ailments.

To avoid allergies and asthma simply remember this advice: we do not treat catarrh, coughs and rashes with hormonal medicines, desensitizing drugs or immunizing vaccines! That is the shortest route to all sorts of diseases of affluence: diabetes, cardiovascular problems, cancers, kidney and liver diseases and obesity.

Diabetes

All diabetes-related problems are like a "pathological grinder". Therefore, I would advise everyone to read this chapter, and especially parents.

I do not know whether we should be more afraid of HIV, mad-cow disease or rather the dangers related to diabetes affecting the young. The people responsible for the health of our children are usually stuck in their stereotypical thinking modes which prevent them from seeing the importance of changing our dietary habits. It is very easy to neglect our children's health and then, as a consequence, force them to undergo costly treatments. But it is very difficult to truly protect them! It is not an easy task to learn how to secure the proper development and healthy upbringing of our offspring from the moment of their birth. I can tell you from my own experience that what mothers-to-be eat during their pregnancies and the way they feed their newborn babies and small children is directly related to their future proneness to diabetes-related diseases and most other health problems.

Would a woman who finds out that her child has diabetes and is at risk of becoming disabled be brave enough to take complete responsibility for its health (as there is a chance of a successful treatment) when faced with doctors constantly repeating that it is impossible to cure diabetes? But has anybody actually tried to cure a child from diabetes yet?! Has anybody attempted to analyse the true causes of this disease? Can giving insulin to a child be called a treatment? As far as I know, the whole issue of diabetes revolves around improving the quality of insulin and undergoing a rigorous regime of its application or application of its so-called substitutes. Do not seek the cause of this disease in genetic factors. In fact, even genes can change under the influence of external factors.

Diabetes among juveniles apparently leads to the complete destruction of the pancreatic beta cells which are responsible for the production of insulin.

Apparently – as in most cases nobody checks whether all of these cells are in fact dead. If not, then it is justified to think that under a special treatment they could eventually regenerate. Is insulin then a medicine?

We know that each case of diabetes is pre-dated by a period of pancreatic inflammation, which eventually turns into a chronic condition. A drawn-out inflammation of the pancreas leads to its fibrosis and a reduction in its body mass. The inflammation is usually caused by steroid medication, as well as by hyperparathyroidism, irregularities in fat metabolism (insufficient activity of the liver), allergies, colds, malnourishment and, most of all, by protein deficiency (lack of essential amino acids).

Those who apply the rules of Chinese medicine in the analysis of bodily organs and their functions realize that inflammations are most likely to occur in cold and insufficiently active bodily organs with a deficiency of Yin. Inflammation means, in other words, an activation of the alert system.

If we have problems with beta cells of the pancreas and their regeneration, then it is more than likely that we suffer from a hormonal imbalance within the whole body. This is the order of things.

There is this opinion that our body treats beta cells like antigens and fights them with antibodies. But if so, then the question is, why? Is it caused by a dysfunction in our immune system? And if so, then again, why? Perhaps the whole process of regeneration of the beta cells is wrong. But why is it?

The body of a young person has great regenerative strength. We also know that each bodily organ is able to regenerate. One should merely secure appropriate conditions for this process to happen. And here is another question: why do we treat beta cells as being already dead? If there is at least one healthy cell in the pancreas, then a child has a full chance of recovery!

A deficiency of insulin in the blood is not the only cause of diabetes. The disease is also connected to problems with digestion and absorption; metabolism of proteins, fat and carbohydrates; irregularities in the process of blood formation and the whole immune system; but most of all, it is linked to a deregulated endocrine system.

Chinese medicine treats diabetes as a dysfunction of the middle heater – the stomach, spleen, pancreas and liver, as well as an insufficient activity of the lungs and kidneys. Generally speaking, we can say that people with diabetes have a body that is wholly deregulated. Can we then treat diabetes only with insulin and its substitutes and think that we have solved the problem?

We must also not forget about the impact of emotions. A deregulated body functions like a deregulated clock. This leads to a positive feedback or a chain reaction where one effect causes the next one. And so, emotions appear that are related to the so-called false fire (deficiency of Yin), such as aggression, irritability, hyperactivity and constant excitement, or emotions that are totally opposite to these, such as depression, apathy, unwillingness to live. Children with a Yin deficiency evince high intellectual talent (intellect = fire). But neither parents nor children realize that it is very dangerous for them, as excessive intellectual activity additionally destroys their inner Yin. This fact is often difficult for parents to understand and accept. They would rather be proud of their child's intellectual capability. But the fact is that only one year free from school and intellectual work would be enough for their body to start regenerating.

I once met this wise older woman who told me about her three-year-old granddaughter: "Of what use is her intellect if she is unable to poo properly?" The process of the destruction of the body, leading eventually to diabetes, lasts many years. Therefore if the disease affects small children, it means that their mothers have committed cardinal dietary mistakes during pregnancy. Another factor could be multigenerational weakening. The symptoms of diabetes are very explicit, but neither parents nor doctors realize that they themselves have something to do with this disease. I will not even go on about such aliments as catarrh, allergies, asthma, stomach aches or indigestion. I am talking here most about the high level of sugar in the blood. I am convinced that in children who constantly suffer from allergies, asthmas, permanent inflammation of the pancreas, the high level of sugar should raise concerns long before the disease actually manifests itself. Improperly fed children will always have abnormal tests results. There is only one conclusion in this case: they have a deregulated metabolism and malfunctioning bodily organs. There is only one cause of such a state – an overcooling of the body. And we already know what causes this overcooling – it is the wrong kind of diet, cold and stress.

I will give you examples of the diets of those pregnant and breastfeeding women whose children got diabetes and the diets of small babies and children who also ended up with this disease:

- Pregnant women – large quantities of fresh salads, fruit yogurts, cheeses, apples, ice cream, cakes, ham and sausages, pork, water, juices, gherkins, lemons and red wine;

- Breastfeeding women – fresh salads, fruit, soya milk, fruit yogurts and rice puddings, juices, chicken, sauerkraut and cheeses;

- Babies – infant formula, soya milk, artificial porridge which does not involve cooking, ready-made soups, sponge fingers, fruit, juices, fruit yogurts, homogenized cheeses;

- Small children/toddlers – processed cheeses, fruit yogurts, cornflakes with cold yogurt or milk, ice cream, cold water, cold drinks, chips, fast food, ham and cheeses, fish, fresh salads, large quantities of sweets.

This kind of nutrition, both for the mothers and the children, is very dangerous as it directly leads to the diseases we are talking about here. The products mentioned earlier prevent the proper development of children in the womb as well as immediately after birth.

So, what is especially harmful for people with diabetes? The doctors say that gluten (cereal protein) and ham and sausages (the chemical compounds they contain) damage the beta cells of the pancreas. Such a statement does not say anything good about us. I think that adults should be more honest and responsible, as this concerns all our children. The gluten case presents a problem similar to the way we treat our cows, thinking that we can trick Nature by feeding them with meat and bone. By modifying wheat genes we have actually produced a high-gluten type of wheat, which brings huge profits to the producers of floury products, but is very dangerous to people. So, there is much said about the harmful effects of gluten and the toxic compounds it allegedly contains. At the same time, there is much said about avoiding gluten in food and treating health problems caused by it. Would it not be enough to simply ban the production of high-gluten wheat? After all, gluten is harmful to us all!

The side effects of eating processed hams and sausages during diabetes are quite obvious. Even the producers of hams and sausages have doubts as to whether they can still qualify them as meat products or maybe rather as substitutes for meat. There is one sure thing about it – they do not taste like they used to. Besides, all hams and sausages are dominated by the energy of the salty flavour, which is absolutely inadvisable for people with diabetes; similarly wheat, which is also sour.

Apart from these two very bad food compounds, one should also mention fibre, which also has a weakening effect on the bodily organs, especially on the spleen, pancreas and liver. Fibre deactivates insulin by bonding with zinc. And a deficiency of zinc causes production of insulin that is incapable of transporting glucose to the cells of the body and transformation of glucose into glycogen. In this situation, the beta cells of the pancreas are constantly stimulated by the high level of glucose, which leads to their exhaustion and eventual death. Zinc is also needed to release vitamin A from the liver. This particular vitamin is responsible for the regeneration of every kind of tissue, including the beta cells of the pancreas. Besides, zinc is an important component of many enzymes as well as DNA and RNA. Therefore, consumption of large quantities of uncooked cereal (muesli), wheat bran and fresh salads is one of the leading causes of diabetes. Chromium also plays an important role in preventing diabetes, as its deficiency leads to problems with insulin tolerance.

Cheeses, fruit and juices are therefore bad in this case as they do not provide important mineral salts, such as magnesium, iron, zinc and chromium, all of which are important determinants of the quality of blood, the function of the liver and activity of insulin.

The organs of the medium heater can be destroyed by consumption of cold drinks, fruit yogurts, fruit, sweets, ready-made baby soups, infant formula, gherkins, sauerkraut, calcium supplements for allergies and colds, and antibiotics which deregulate the natural immunity of the body and stimulate production of mucus, which is then accumulated in the lungs, causing problems with the flow of energy, breathing and transportation of oxygen to the cells of the body. A deficiency of oxygen, on the other hand, creates the situation of insufficient usage of glucose. This leads to the exhaustion of the beta cells of the pancreas as they are forced to produce excessive quantities of insulin. Also very harmful are anti-inflammatory steroid medications. Other than this, not eating breakfast or warm meals, stress, intellectual exhaustion, lack of exercise, unventilated rooms, the white colour, cold and excessive physical exercise are also very harmful too.

Diabetes and all diabetes-related diseases can become an iceberg of our nonchalant behaviour and a rich subject for scientific exploration. There is still so much to discover and understand about it! Saying that diabetes is a genetic disease is equal to indicating the effect and not the true cause of this disease.

In order to better explain the changes that happen within the body under diabetes, I will remind you here briefly about homeostasis. Homeostasis means the maintenance of a stable state of the inner environment within our body despite continuous changes in the outer environment. As long as the defence mechanisms are functioning properly, the inner environment is in a state of balance. Once they are destroyed or simply overused, the function of the cells of the body is deregulated, which leads to their exhaustion and death. It sounds rather simple. But homeostasis is none other than the well-known Yin–Yang balance that we are familiar with.

Going back to the beta cells of the pancreas – let's think why they behave so strangely and become destroyed by the body.

Why does it happen? The body that reacts in this way is usually overcooled, malnourished and its internal organs do not function properly. Therefore, such symptoms as catarrh, coughs, tonsillitis, colds, allergies, asthma, inflammation of the pancreas and kidneys, chronic stomach aches and intestinal pain are simply a warning to us about a deficiency of Yang energy within the body. The body needs warming up by consumption of the appropriate kind of food. But unfortunately, in most cases, we do not even try to warm up our children from within and energize their bodies by introducing changes to their diet. Instead, we try to "cure" them with antibiotics and anti-inflammatory medicines, which are based on glucocorticoids – that is, hormones which are normally produced in the adrenal cortex. They belong to the group of steroid hormones, and hydrocortisone is an example.

Glucocorticoids affect metabolism of proteins, sugars, fats, water and mineral compounds. They also raise the level of glucose concentration in the blood (because of the intensification of glycogenolysis); through having a direct impact on the beta cells and blocking production of insulin, they reduce the consumption of glucose. They also accelerate decomposition of proteins in muscles and bones, maintain muscular activity, have anti-allergic and anti-inflammatory properties, and restrain synthesis of prostaglandins, which play an essential role in the process of biological thermoregulation of the body. Glucocorticoids also decrease the number of leucocytes and lymphocytes and badly affect the activity of the lymphatic glands and thymus. No more needs to be added here! Therefore all the different kinds of medicines and antibiotics we so easily give to our children, apart from dealing with inflammation, also deregulate the whole body. These medications make beta cells lose their identity and physiological individuality.

Perhaps a child who was secured with decent conditions for development whilst in the womb and after birth was breastfed with milk coming from a mother whose body is in a state of balance and was given food appropriate to its age would not have to suffer from the negative reactions to the aforementioned medicines? But what are we even talking about here? Such a child would not need any medication at all.

There is one thing that really interests me here. Are those mothers who let doctors treat their children with all these medicines fully aware of the side effects of this kind of treatment? And do those doctors who prescribe them so freely remember the Hippocratic Oath they swore by and the sentence "never do harm to anyone"?

And what does Chinese medicine have to say on diabetes? It qualifies this disease as a state of Yin–Yang imbalance, with very typically a deficiency of Yin; that is fluids (blood, enzymes, hormones, mucus) and substance, and consequently an excess of Yang (false fire), which, as we already know, always occurs when the other factor (Yin) is missing.

It does not matter what kind of condition we are talking about here– excessive excitability, accelerated metabolism, over-activity of certain glands – the prime cause of all these states is always a dysfunction of bodily organs destroyed by the cooling kind of diet, external cold or stress. Health problems caused by cold and insufficient activity of bodily organs become the routes to diabetes; the negative impact of the external factors and progression of the disease create the so-called false Yang.

In the *Philosophy of Health* I already explained what the deficiency of Yin can mean and how this state manifests itself within the body. But I will remind you of it again: the essence, also called the prime matter, is normally produced by the spleen, but this can only happen in optimal conditions; so, there needs to be an appropriate temperature of the body, food and the environment, as well as an appropriate energy of the food (the energy of all flavours and energy of the fire – Yang) and emotional balance. If deficiency of the essence (Yin) occurs or the essence is of a poor quality, then it means that the spleen and pancreas do not function properly. As we have already become accustomed to the Universal Rules of Yin and Yang, we can easily indicate the causes of the ailments and illnesses that can develop from here.

In the analysis of diabetes according to the rules of Chinese medicine, it is very helpful to investigate the function of the triple heater. We have to remember that insufficient activity of the middle heater and deficiency of the Yang energy within this area (stomach, spleen, pancreas, liver), if not treated in time, will always lead to insufficient activity of the upper heater and deficiency of energy within that area as well (lungs and heart), followed by the same kind of reaction within the lower heater (kidneys).

In diabetes, the lungs have a very important function in speeding up the process of recovery as they are the major player in the process of oxygenation of the whole body. Therefore, one should investigate first the posture of a person suffering from diabetes, as well as the quality of their chest and back muscles and the quality of their breathing. Then one should introduce a set of systematic and specialist physical exercises. Because of the initial poor condition of the muscles and of the whole body, extensive physical exercise should be avoided at first (football, tennis, cycling, swimming). In fact, these kinds of exercise are not good for the spleen and pancreas. Let's not forget that a person with diabetes should be treated more like a convalescent and not like a healthy person. By introducing the appropriate kind of exercise we will stimulate the elimination of accumulated mucus from the lungs and improve the quality of breathing, and oxygen – as we already know – is invaluable for those affected by diabetes.

I would like to mention here that hormones play a very important function in diabetes. They work like bio-catalysers, similarly to enzymes and vitamins, but unlike these, hormones can only exist within a living organism. Hormones are carriers and relayers of information, and when they reach cells, tissues or particular organs, they change their functions. They are indispensable in the process of life, even though it is possible to live without certain hormones. This does not mean, however, that the function of the body will stay unaffected. In fact, a hormonal imbalance will lead to a deficiency of Yin.

The secretion of hormones is regulated by nervous, psychological and mood impulses – that is, by chemical compounds and other hormones present in the blood. The hypothalamus and pituitary gland, as well as other endocrine glands, are very sensitive to physical and chemical changes within the blood (sugar level, salt, hormones, temperature, stress and energy of the flavours). Stimulation of the detectors affects the activity of the hypothalamus and pituitary gland and other endocrine glands dependent on them. The so-called psychological influences that directly affect the cerebral cortex are simply our emotions, which are a direct derivative of the state of our bodily organs. We know very well that our emotions cannot be controlled by our will, but they certainly can be by our consciousness. And consciousness depends directly on the state of our bodily organs.

The endocrine glands which are responsible for the production of hormones can sometimes be overactive or insufficiently active. These states of imbalance cause all kinds of problems within the body, as a deficiency or an excess of even one of these hormones initiates a chain reaction leading to deficiencies or excesses of other chemical compounds within the body. And diabetes is one of the results of such hormonal imbalance, which is originally caused by improper nutrition, cold and stress. The high level of glucose in the blood should tell us that there is something happening with the supply of insulin and its activity. But this does not necessarily mean that the beta cells of the pancreas will be destroyed.

One of the most important hormones is the growth hormone produced by the pituitary gland. It stimulates the metabolism of proteins, fats, sugars and mineral compounds, enabling the process of anabolism which is crucial for the growth of a young organism and sustaining the body mass of a mature organism. The growth hormone is a long-chained polypeptide constructed of essential amino acids. It enables transportation of amino acids to the cells and synthesis of proteins; it increases the level of glucose in the blood and stimulates secretion of insulin.

Negative external factors, such as cold and even a minimal drop of blood temperature, lead to the almost immediate activation of the thyroid. This is the second most important endocrine gland that can in a manner be related to diabetes. Hyperthyroidism can also be caused by a deficiency of vitamin A, D and E (soluble in fats). Increased activity of the thyroid leads to a greater consumption of oxygen, secretion of hormones by the pituitary gland, metabolism of proteins, sugars, fats, cholesterol, mineral salts and water. The hormones produced by the thyroid activate metabolic processes and hyperthyroidism leads to nervous hyperactivity and increased metabolism that can be very destructive for the body.

Another important endocrine gland is the adrenal gland. The adrenal medulla is responsible for secretion of adrenaline. Adrenaline is created from phenylalanine. It is usually secreted when we find ourselves under the influence of very strong stimuli, such as alert and stress stimuli. This hormone has an influence on metabolism, blood circulation, breathing, digestion, excretion and the central nervous system. It increases the level of glucose in the blood and accelerates the breakdown of glycogen. It should also be noted that it stimulates mental activity, accelerates metabolism, slows down secretion of insulin, and in effect leads to a lesser consumption of glucose. The state of chronic activity of the adrenal gland can be very dangerous for all those exposed to permanent stress. It is especially dangerous for children and young people and contributes to diabetes.

The adrenal cortex produces, among other things, cortisone, which has an influence on the metabolism of proteins, sugars, fats, water and mineral compounds. It increases the level of glucose in the blood through the process of increased synthesis of glycogen in the liver with a simultaneous intensification of glycogenolysis and reduced consumption of glucose.

There are situations when the whole mutual regulation of hormonal activity eventually becomes disturbed. In this case, the pituitary gland and all the other endocrine glands that are subject to it start secreting the maximal amount of hormones. This happens under the influence of such stimuli as hunger, injury, pain, fear and stress, all of which, instead of protecting our body, turn into destructive chronic states.

The aforementioned situation can also relate to the pancreas, which is an independent bodily organ as well as an endocrine gland. It produces digestive juices which are then transported to the duodenum to help in digestion of proteins, carbohydrates and fats. It also produces two hormones: insulin in the beta cells and glucagon in the alpha cells. Insulin is a polypeptide built of 51 amino acids, including essential amino acids. It is successively caught by cells within the whole body, but this process is determined by the presence of zinc. Insulin has an anabolic influence on the different cells and especially on the cells of the liver, skeletal muscles and the adipose tissue. The mechanism of the function of insulin is very complex and depends on many factors, such as the aforementioned presence of zinc or chromium.

All of these analyses lead to a conclusion that the whole endocrine and nervous system regulates the level of glucose in the blood. So, it is not only insulin that is responsible for the right level of glucose but also glucagon and hormones produced by the adrenal cortex and the adrenal medulla, as well as those produced in the anterior pituitary and the thyroid. Therefore diabetes-related ailments can become a nucleus of all sorts of diseases (not only diabetes). It is obvious, though, that in the body affected by diabetes many other ailments will eventually occur as side effects. These are: emotional imbalance, problems with digestion and absorption, circulatory problems, and lung and kidney disease. Therefore, in the case of such a serious health dysfunction, should we reduce our treatment merely to application of insulin and claim that it is all related to pancreatic problems?

What then can we recommend to people with diabetes? Garlic, onion, leeks and fennel are especially good to improve metabolism and reduce the level of glucose. Animal products such as veal and young beef, giblets and eggs are also indispensable as they contain chromium, iron and zinc, which are invaluable in dealing with diabetes, and protein, which is the source of the essential amino acids, deficiency of which can lead to hormonal imbalance. We should introduce to the menu the "heavy" kind of products, such as peas and beans, onion, garlic and the green parts of vegetables. From time to time, one can cook some chicory or blueberries as they contain compounds which have an influence on the body similar to that of insulin.

I would like to stress here, though, that diabetes requires a total elimination of all sour, raw and cold food and an introduction of a balanced diet with a lot of added spices. One should also try to relax when possible, avoid stress and eat regularly.

Shingles, chickenpox, herpes

These ailments are normally caused by a virus which can be activated by problems with a malfunctioning and weak liver, and an insufficiently active and cold body. Shingles and chickenpox usually occur at the end of winter or at the beginning of spring. Let's remember that, according to the Chinese calendar, spring starts as early as the middle of February.

Shingles normally manifests itself in the appearance of the characteristic skin rash around the waist area, as well as on the face and buttocks. The rash appears usually in the coldest places of the body. And so, the most common shingles, which appears around the waist, signifies coldness within the liver and the whole middle heater. Shingles on the face appears around the meridian of the stomach and gallbladder, and shingles on the buttocks is a symptom of a deficiency of energy in the pericardium (circulation/sex) and a weak blood circulation.

Shingles is not only characterized by a painful rash and sensitivity to touch but also emotional hyperactivity.

If we are going to treat shingles pharmacologically without changing our diet, then we can be almost sure that the bodily organs which caused this condition (cold stomach, spleen, pancreas, liver) will soon remind us of their presence through much more severe symptoms. On the other hand, treating shingles with a well-balanced diet will perhaps take longer, but once it is gone we can be sure that we have eliminated the true cause of the disease and brought back the energetic balance within those bodily organs.

Until recently, shingles was characteristic of older people. Unfortunately, in recent times this condition is also affecting children more often. It is a very serious warning as a young organism should normally have a large supply of Yang energy.

Chickenpox is perhaps less burdensome. But the fact that the virus activates every year, mostly around the same time (early spring), proves that it is caused by a weakening of the liver as a result of our dietary follies during the previous summer, autumn and winter (especially Christmas!!!).

Oral herpes, commonly known as a "cold sore", usually appears around the so-called stomach-spleen places on the body – that is, on the upper lip and nostrils. It can also appear on the face alongside the stomach meridian or on the cheeks (lungs). The conclusion is simple – the middle heater is suffering from a deficiency of the Yang energy (warmth and Chi).

If affected by any of these ailments, one should immediately start the process of warming up the body. The first thing we should do is to eliminate all sour, raw and cold food. I remind you that these are all raw fruits, juices, fresh salads, cheeses, yogurts, sour food products, chicken, cold drinks, ice cream and sweets. Instead, we should introduce a well-balanced diet of a neutral-warming nature. We should also start wearing red, yellow or orange underwear.

Psoriasis

Psoriasis is a disease of the skin. Its characteristic symptoms are inflammation, dryness, flaking of the skin, pain and itching. These are all external symptoms of internal problems. A decisive role is played by the liver, stomach, spleen, pancreas and lungs in this disease. Psoriasis is a symptom of liver and lung fire (deficiency of essence – Yin) caused by an insufficient activity of the stomach, spleen and pancreas. One should also remember that psoriasis goes hand in hand with cirrhosis (replacement of liver tissue by fibrosis).

The liver governs our subconscious. And as all our emotions and feelings are stored in our subconscious, they consequently affect the quality of the connective tissue and muscles. Therefore, apart from all the basic dietary mistakes, which cause problems with metabolism, psoriasis can also be caused by serious emotional problems, often present since early childhood. The dominating emotion responsible for psoriasis is stifled sorrow and sadness, which is often passed from one generation to another.

In order to cure psoriasis one should take into consideration all of the aforementioned factors and try to consciously avoid them. Very helpful in this case is intensive physical exercise (even with the use of weights), which effectively improves the quality of breathing and the function of the lungs, and by improving the blood circulation, it helps to take the weight off the liver. Only then can the process of eliminating emotional blockages truly begin. Any kind of exercise will improve blood circulation, nutrition of the body and consequently stimulate cellular regeneration, including the regeneration of the skin.

Psoriasis is a disease of metabolism and thus it requires special attention to be directed towards preparation of well-balanced food. Only then, through the process of digestion and absorption, will the body obtain appropriate nutrients which will then stimulate regeneration of the skin. An indispensable element here is the Yang (fire) energy, which by strengthening the middle heater will also strengthen the liver, blood circulation and the connective tissue. Therefore, all kinds of sour, cold and raw food are inadvisable in this case, as they possess the contractive kind of energy which then slows down the blood circulation and consequently the distribution of appropriate nutrients. One should thus eliminate from one's diet milk, cheeses, yogurts, juices, fruit, fresh salads, chicken and pork.

Food should be composed and prepared in a way that would assure strengthening of the spleen and regeneration of the liver. It should be of a neutral-warming nature. Only then can the inner substance be properly rebuilt. We should use in our menu all kinds of vegetables, veal, turkey and many spices, remembering always to keep the flavour balance. I remind you here that the leading flavour enabling the regeneration of the inner substance is the sweet flavour (but not sugar). All meals should be warm, cooked and varied, and include the so-called "heavy" food products. For drinking, I would recommend teas regenerating the spleen, pancreas and liver. In the treatment of psoriasis, fish liver oil and fatty sea fish (halibut, mackerel), green beans, a brew made of bean pods, Jerusalem artichoke and parsnip are very useful, using almost exclusively olive oil or rapeseed oil with an addition of butter.

It has been claimed that psoriasis is incurable. Nobody really knows the true causes of this disease; however, it has been said that psoriasis is a derivative of a bad metabolism. After introducing a well-balanced diet and solving all the emotional problems, the body should go back to the natural state of balance and all the different kinds of ailments should disappear. The skin will then start regenerating and the problem with psoriasis will disappear too.

One of the proofs that psoriasis is mostly caused by deficiency of the Yang (warmth and Chi) energy and, connected to it, problems with metabolism, is the fact that some kind of healing effect in psoriasis can be achieved through exposure to infra-red light and sunlight.

Coeliac disease

Apart from the basic information on coeliac disease, which I have already mentioned in the *Philosophy of Health*, I would like to add here a few more things. From my own observation, I can tell that the bodily organ directly connected to the symptoms of coeliac disease is the liver. The problems are caused by a severe dysfunction of the liver and fat metabolism. It is quite obvious that destruction of the liver happens under the influence of sour, raw and cold food, which does not provide the body with a sufficient quantity of nutrients responsible for regeneration of the intestinal mucosa (mostly vitamins A, D, B and zinc and magnesium). But I have also noticed that the disease can be activated by eating large quantities of fat by breastfeeding mothers or by the child themselves. After noticing the first symptoms, diarrhoea, one should immediately introduce a restrictive diet that eliminates all sour food, such as fruit, juices, fresh salads, yogurts, cheeses, chicken and sweets, and also all food based on wheat flour. Until the symptoms go away, we should feed the child with only carrot soup mixed with porridge and then slowly start introducing home-cooked and well-balanced food.

Why is it, then, that gluten is thought to be the main cause of coeliac disease? In my opinion, the intestinal mucosa is damaged by inappropriate nutrition during pregnancy and then straight after birth. Gluten is merely one of the compounds of food which happens to be of an irritating nature. Therefore, one should eliminate from one's menu not only all wheat products but also all of those which contain energy of the sour flavour, cold and raw food, sugar and an excess of fat.

Fungal infections (mycosis)

All fungal infections appear in a body dominated by moisture. They are connected to the weakening of the middle heater (stomach, spleen, pancreas, liver), problems with metabolism, circulation, activation of production of pathological mucus and, most of all, a deficiency of the Yang energy. The major cause of this state is the consumption of sweets, cakes, dairy products, overly fatty food, cheeses, milk, yogurts, fruit, cold drinks and fresh salads.

Fungal infections are characteristic of people eating an unbalanced food with not enough of the bitter and spicy flavour. I would like to warn you here that some of the products of the bitter flavour useful for treating fungal infections can have a strongly cooling effect on the body. They may be very helpful in treating fungal infections but can at the same time cause other problems, such as lung diseases and digestive and circulatory problems.

Circulatory problems

Why do doctors, as well as ourselves, think that circulatory problems are exclusively related to diseases of the heart, such as coronary artery disease or high levels of cholesterol, high blood pressure, blood clotting and strokes? In fact, circulatory problems signify much more than this. They are connected to problems within the whole body, such as deregulation of the basic physiological functions, problems with metabolism, energy, cellular regeneration and excretion, and deregulation of the whole endocrine system. But most of all, circulatory problems signify a weak and dysfunctional liver and the whole middle heater.

If, all of a sudden, we start suffering from atherosclerosis or heart problems, then it is very likely that for years we have been trivializing and ignoring the signals our body has been sending us. Like cancers, cardiovascular problems are an example of a disease of affluence, which are only the tip of the iceberg of much bigger problems hidden somewhere within our body. The destruction of the body in all of these cases is usually serious and difficult to treat, as it always relates to emotional problems. It seems that only preventive treatment would make sense in this case.

The treatment of circulatory diseases and its effectiveness depend on our consciousness. The supplements and medications we take every day can keep us alive but, as I have said before, they are not the cure. In order to bring back the necessary balance within our body we should first try to identify those destructive factors which lead to this kind of devastation (stress, tiredness, eating cold, and sour, cold and raw food) and eliminate them. Only then will our treatment make sense. Taking medicines translates merely as vegetation and keeping oneself desperately alive, but, at the same time, it means ignoring the responsibilities for one's own decisions. Therefore, let's change things now, while we can still do it!

There are plenty of various wonderful medications coming onto the market. They often come from countries such as Russia or China, where people still cultivate original traditions. Each one of these medications is a treatment for a specific illness and can save the lives of many people. But if we do not get rid of all those destructive factors and mistakes, then even they cannot bring back the Yin–Yang balance and health. We can only get our health and balance back once we change our dietary habits and lifestyle.

In order to better understand the physiology of our body and the whole process of blood circulation (blood, lymph and interstitial fluid) I will refer here to the book by E. Mietkiewski (*Medical Physiology*):

> *In order to acquire energy and build its own structure, every living cell must absorb matter from the surrounding environment. At the same time the cell excretes all kinds of waste. Therefore, within the cellular environment, the amount of substances needed to keep a cell alive is decreasing whilst the amount of harmful side-products of metabolism is increasing. (...) Within the body a large number of cells live in a very small volume of interstitial fluid. The consumption, and consequent contamination, of this fluid would occur very quickly if there was no mechanism of continuous and sufficient regeneration. (...) Through this fluid the blood delivers all kinds of substances required for the maintenance of cellular life, but it also collects the final side-products of metabolism. In order to avoid losing all nutritious substances by the blood and prevent its contamination by side-products of metabolism, the blood needs to be constantly replenished with nutrients and at the same time cleansed by certain bodily organs which rid the blood of all metabolites, excrete them out of the body, or at least turn them into less harmful substances. The bodily organs responsible for this process are the lungs,*

digestive system, liver, endocrine glands, kidneys, skin and the intestinal wall. The blood plays the function of a carrier – food supply transportation.

If there are problems with our blood circulation, then the whole body is affected. The quality of blood (process of blood formation) and its quantity become deregulated. The bodily organs responsible for distribution or accumulation of blood, such as the liver and muscles, can cause temporary fluctuations of its flow. A bad quality of blood blocks the process of cellular regeneration and cleansing of the intercellular spaces. In the first instance, this affects the internal bodily organs, which play such an important function within our body.

And all of these problems start because of a deficiency of the factor which stimulates the processes, reactions and movement of all bodily fluids within the body. This factor is Yang energy (Chi and warmth). Should I remind you once more why this happens and what kind of mistakes cause such a state? I think, my Dear Reader, that you already know the answer.

Atherosclerosis leads to a degeneration of coronary arteries and blood vessels. The cells in the walls of these vessels accumulate toxic moisture (caused by inappropriate nutrition and stress) and start degenerating (scarring). Then, together with the progression of the degeneration process, these scars get covered with so-called atheromatous plaque. Due to inappropriate dietary habits, the toxic moisture can be accumulated in the lungs, sinuses, head, arteries, blood vessels and other bodily organs.

The situation can get very dangerous when the pathological production of moisture is accompanied by serious circulatory problems. It is obvious that a mountain river with a vigorous current always has a clean, rocky riverbed; but once the river hits a plateau the water starts flowing slowly and the riverbed becomes muddy and the riverside becomes overgrown by bulrush and grasses. Therefore we should know that even though we eat mucus-forming food but do physical exercise or some kind of sport, our body will get rid of the mucus on its own (catarrh, cough), as the body will have the active Yang factor (movement). But it is very bad when we start treating these symptoms with all kinds of antibiotics, vaccinations or anti-inflammatory medicines based on steroids. On the other hand, if we do not do any exercise, then the accumulation of mucus progresses, blocking all of the internal organs.

The smooth muscles, which build the walls of blood vessels have a specific construction that can directly affect the character of atherosclerosis. The scarring of blood vessels can be affected by the fact that each cell of the smooth muscle is equipped with a separate nerve fibre. These cells are then prone to the same kind of contractions as the skeletal muscles and react as separate motor units to all kinds of external stimuli (stress, nutrition). If the stimulating (contracting) factor affects the cells for a long period of time then it can cause functional changes within those cells or even their necrosis. The most dangerous factors that cause destruction of blood vessels are stress, calcium and the sour flavour. These factors lead to contractions, destruction of the cells and often production of mucus within the whole body. They simultaneously affect the circulation of blood and cause accumulation of toxic mucus in the areas where the scarring of blood vessels occurs (cholesterol).

The liver is also responsible for the degeneration of the connective tissue of the blood vessels. We have to be aware that the body affected by these kinds of disorders suffers from a weak and insufficiently active liver. This state is also connected with a deregulated functioning of the pericardium (circulation), or, in other words, with deficiency of Yang. Therefore, high blood pressure is always a symptom of a bad condition of the middle heater.

The major factor leading to such conditions as embolism, strokes and heart diseases is a deficiency of Yang, usually caused by an excess of cooling-type food, stress, emotional problems, cold and lack of physical exercise. All of these factors cause:

- Weakening of the spleen and, connected to this state, excessive production of pathological moisture (mucus) as well as proneness to haemorrhages;
- Deregulation of the whole process of metabolism;
- Liver failure and circulatory problems.

Dietary mistakes which contribute significantly to such states as atherosclerotic changes, coronary artery disease, circulatory problems, strokes and other heart diseases, are:

- Fatty pork, porky hams and sausages, sauerkraut, gherkins, fruit compotes, cold drinks, yeasty cakes, herring, cheeses;
- Floury products, such as dumplings and pasta; sour soups, cakes, cheeses, and some fruits;
- Chicken, fresh salads, juices, fruit, yogurts, water;
- Hams and sausages, bread, cheeses, some fruits;
- And the food that we normally consider "healthy", such as: in the morning, a white bread roll with some margarine and processed cheese, ham or jam, accompanied by black coffee with sugar and cream, a glass of carrot or orange juice or some fruit; for lunch, a cake or sandwich with some processed cheese, accompanied by fruit juice or coffee; for dinner, sour soup (e.g. tomato soup), a piece of chicken or fish with some fresh salad or sauerkraut, accompanied by fruit juice or lemon tea with sugar, and some fruit, then followed by coffee and a cake; for supper, some fresh salad, white cheese or ham sandwich with gherkins or tomatoes; and in between having some snacks, such as fruit yogurts or drinking large quantities of water, or simply having an apple just before bed time; all of the foods, of course, without all the necessary spices.

What kind of food could then help us to prevent all of these diseases or restore the necessary balance within our body once we are already affected by them? Well, it is mostly home-cooked food, balanced with all flavours, and with added spices. It should be mostly based on veal, young beef or turkey, and all kinds of vegetables. But we should most definitely eliminate all foods and food products of the sour flavour, such as tomato soup and other sour soups, gherkins, marinated herring, fresh fruit, fruit juices, cold water. We can, however, eat as much as we want of all kinds of grains, well-spiced legume dishes, olive oil, rapeseed oil, butter, fish-liver oil, boiled eggs, fatty fish, wheat-rye bread, or even dark rye bread (but without any added seeds).

Circulatory problems and atherosclerosis used to be related only to old age. But nowadays they also affect children and the young. Our children need most of all the energy of love, acceptance and safety, which can balance out in some way the growing stress in their lives. In order to prevent all of these diseases, we should not only eat healthily but also include in our daily routine some physical exercise, long walks or at least isometric exercise (muscle stretching).

Heart attack

Heart attack is caused by a Yang collapse within the body – a very serious deficiency of energy which blocks blood circulation and the functioning of the heart. The energetic emptiness within the middle heater causes the energy to go down instead of up.

Heart attacks are characteristic of people living under constant stress, who use up their Yang energy, suffer from chronic tiredness, eat irregularly and, most of all, commit the most fundamental dietary mistakes (excess of cold food, cold drink, sweets, cheeses, fruit, hams and sausages, chicken, etc.).

The most characteristic feeling that signals an impending heart attack is the feeling of general cold within the body, cold sweating and panicky fear. In order to save such a person, one should immediately serve them a drink of a strongly warming nature (the "killer tea", or hot tea with a shot of vodka).

Very often heart attacks are followed by jaundice, which is not caused by a virus but is rather the consequence of a cold and destroyed spleen. There are also other conditions which may follow a heart attack: hernia – the symptom of a cold liver, pneumonia – the symptom of a dysfunction within the middle heater. In the meantime, an allergic reaction can also appear and eventually another heart attack.

Venous thromboembolism

Venous thromboembolism is related to circulatory problems caused by a poor quality of blood (too thick), blood deficiency and deficiency of Yang energy within the whole body. Without the right kind of knowledge, one might think that, in certain cases, venous thromboembolism is caused by an excess of Yang. But it is not, for sure. Venous thromboembolism usually affects those suffering from a destruction of the middle heater (stomach, spleen, pancreas and liver). It happens as a result of long-term dietary mistakes (sour, raw and cold food) and long-term stress (tension = contraction). It leads to a further destruction of bodily organs and weakening of the lungs and kidneys.

Venous thromboembolism is a very serious disease, as it signifies a large deficiency of both Yin (essence) and Yang (Chi). The first symptoms of this condition are usually a constant feeling of cold, cold feet and hands (but not always), digestive problems, hyperactivity, irritability and, most of all, nerve root pains and leg pains. Nerve root pains are one of the most indicative symptoms of circulatory problems. But we often do not connect the two. It is a pity, though, as we could prevent a lot of suffering and serious diseases, or even premature deaths.

What do nerve root pains have to do with circulatory problems? Well, in our buttocks are located the so-called pericardial muscles. Therefore, when we eat food of the kind of energy that can block circulation (pericardium, liver), such as food of sour, salty and sweet flavour, cold food, fatty or raw food, the pericardial muscles contract, causing pressure on the sciatica. This kind of condition is very common. If the pain is not too "old" then we can help ourselves by pressing a point on the pericardial meridian (point no. 7), warming the pericardial muscles (buttocks) and introducing changes to our diet.

If we decide to treat the nerve root pain in a traditional way, that is by applying certain medicines, then the destructive factor destroys our body, mostly the spleen and liver, and deregulates all of the other internal organs. By saying that nerve root pains are caused by problems with sciatica or deficiency of the B vitamins, we refer to the symptoms and not the true cause of this state. The true cause of nerve root pains is much more serious and can even become dangerous to our health if we let it develop into a chronic problem. At this point, problems with venous thromboembolism may also appear, especially when the body is seriously weakened.

One of the most unpleasant symptoms of venous thromboembolism is popping (bursting) of the blood vessels, which is a symptom of a weak spleen and, of course, circulatory problems.

Venous thromboembolism also causes the blood to become thick and sticky, which in no way (!) should we try to thin by eating more fruit, fresh salads, yogurts, fruit juices or water. The problem may only get worse, as this kind of food blocks the blood circulation and the production of essence by the spleen. We should instead eat warm, home-made and well-balanced food, which would enable the spleen to retrieve its balance.

To improve the quality of blood and lower the risk of blood clotting, one should apply spices such as cloves, ginger, cinnamon, coriander, cumin, liquorice, turmeric, thyme, garlic and onion. All of these spices stimulate the factors responsible for breaking down blood clots and simply help in the process of digestion.

Hyperacidity and heartburn

Hyperacidity and, very often related to it, heartburn can become a real nuisance. I know how determined people affected by these conditions are to find a way to get rid of the pain. They start using a number of medications, as a change of diet has not brought them any relief. Every single meal in this case leads to stress because they simply do not know which food products cause the pain.

The condition of hyperacidity has not been sufficiently explained yet. According to conventional medicine, the food products which cause hyperacidity are meat and fatty foods, whilst fruit, fruit juices, yogurts and milk are thought to be helpful with this condition. But from my own observations, I can tell you that fruit, juices, cheeses or milk can cause hyperacidity as much as fatty and heavy food.

Contemporary dietary recommendations, which stress eating large quantities of fresh salads, fruit, yogurts, chicken, fish, frozen food, ready-made food, only escalate the whole problem. Hyperacidity is connected to a weakening of the spleen and, related to this, a deficiency of neutralizing fluids and mucus in the stomach and inappropriate regeneration of the stomach lining.

It is very convenient to say that hyperacidity, and the peptic ulcers caused by it, are a consequence of multiplication of bacteria in the stomach. But we already know that in order for bacteria to multiply, there need to be specific conditions. According to American researchers, the most acidifying food products (destructive for the spleen) are milk, beer and fizzy drinks. I would also add here sugar, wheat flour, and cold food with no added spices, and fruit.

Hyperacidity in the stomach does not necessarily lead to acidification of the whole body, although it can be the beginning of the process. Also, acidification of the body does not necessarily mean that there is a problem with hyperacidity in the stomach. The biggest nuisance with hyperacidity are not only peptic ulcers but everyday problems, such as the feeling of burning (heartburn), hunger pains, painful flatulence, anxiety, nervousness; headaches, muscle pains, vomiting, diarrhoea or constipation can also appear.

In order to get rid of hyperacidity and its related problems, one should apply certain dietary discipline. Most of all, we should eliminate all sour, raw and cold food, fast food, snacks (crisps, salt sticks, ice cream, biscuits, nuts, raisins, seeds) and introduce food cooked on a real fire, as well as well-balanced food with a lot of added spices. Despite the common opinion, spices ease and get rid of hyperacidity, even though initially we might think that we are "adding oil to the fire". Spices stimulate digestion, absorption of nutrients and circulation. This way we stimulate the spleen and accelerate the regeneration of the stomach lining.

Stomach juice is a combination of hydrochloric acid, alkaline substances and mucus. The parietal cells are responsible for the formation of hydrochloric acid, and the non-parietal cells for the formation of the alkaline substances and mucus.

The concentration of hydrochloric acid in the stomach is so high (pH) that it kills even the most dangerous germs and denaturizes all kinds of proteins. The formation of stomach juice depends on the person's general health, as well as on emotional factors, taste and temperature. These are known as exogenous (external) and endogenous (internal) factors. Strongly stimulating factors include stress, calcium ions (Ca), which activate secretion of gastrin, and acetylcholine and histamine. Hydrochloric acid is indispensable in digestion of animal protein, as it causes swelling of the connective tissue and decomposition of muscles into singular fibres. The hydrochloric acid also helps in the absorption of iron and calcium.

In the parietal cells, in addition to hydrochloric acid, an internal blood-forming factor is also produced which enables absorption of vitamin B12 (an external blood-forming factor). Vitamin B12 can only be found in animal products. A deficiency of any of these factors leads to severe ischaemia. So we can see that hydrochloric acid is very important, and in order to fulfil its function, it needs the presence of the alkaline substance and mucus, which protect the delicate lining of the stomach against self-digestion and microorganisms.

There are many factors that can cause ischaemia of the stomach lining, poor secretion of mucus and neutralizing fluids as well as an improper regeneration of the stomach lining. These factors are inappropriate food, emotional problems and cold. If any of these factors is present, then it can stimulate multiplication of bacteria and penetration of the stomach lining by the hydrochloric acid.

So, in the case of hyperacidity and heartburn, should we then merely take medicine which neutralizes the acid and temporarily gets rid of the pain? This kind of behaviour can in fact deregulate the process of digestion and absorption of important vitamin and mineral compounds. In this condition, it is very important to stimulate secretion of the neutralizing fluids and mucus and proper regeneration of the stomach lining. We can only achieve this by introducing into our diet the well-balanced kind of food.

Everything that can be harmful to the middle heater, and especially to the spleen and pancreas, has an acidifying effect on the stomach and damages its lining. Heartburn gives a feeling of burning in the stomach and oesophagus.

Hyperacidity can also cause reflux. Therefore, if the stomach content does not contain enough neutralizing fluids and mucus (caused by a weak spleen), and thus is more acidic, then once it comes into contact with the already sore and congested lining, it causes a very painful sensation. When the lining is healthy, then releasing the gases out of the stomach brings relief rather than pain.

When the natural balance in the stomach is lost (deficiency of Yin), we have a state of so-called false fire or, in other words, an excess of Yang. This is directly related to a malfunction of the spleen, pancreas, liver and gallbladder and leads to flatulence and a very painful release of the gases.

Very often, heartburn and hyperacidity cause a strong and dull pain within the chest area, which is mistakenly related to a dysfunction of the heart. Once we regulate the functioning of the middle heater (stomach, spleen, pancreas, liver and gallbladder), we also stimulate the energy flow within the meridians ascribed to all of these organs. And this is how we eliminate this condition. We can achieve this only by changing our diet.

The causes of heartburn and painful flatulence are the same as in the case of hyperacidity. These are: sour, raw and cold food, alcohol, beer, sweets and milk.

In other words, a long-lasting deficiency of NaCl (cooking salt) in the food reduces, or even stops, the production of hydrochloric acid. Should we then put salt into our food? Well, let's think first what we need the hydrochloric acid for and not act in haste.

Rheumatism

Rheumatism is a disease of the kidneys and liver (cold and wind). In this case, the body is usually overcooled and the bodily organs start malfunctioning. There are also deficiencies of internal fluids and blood, circulatory problems and general contraction within the body.

Deficiency of Yang energy activates the thermoregulatory system; this leads to the so-called rheumatic fever and inflammation of the weakest part of the body. This may be a group of muscles, joints or bones. Under no circumstances should one treat this state with antibiotics or anti-inflammatory medicines based on steroids. Rheumatism may be accompanied by spontaneous depressive states or aggression. Like many other health problems, rheumatism is the result of a destroyed middle heater.

Rheumatism is characteristic of people who are either exposed to cold for a long period of time or whose diet is of a strong Yin nature. I will give you an example: there was a 14-year-old boy who ate nothing but bread rolls with hard cheese throughout the whole of spring. Once the autumn came he was taken into hospital for a few months due to serious rheumatic fever.

The most common dietary mistakes that lead to rheumatism are: consumption of pork together with gherkins and sauerkraut, large quantities of fruit, fruit compotes, fresh salads, cold drinks, cheeses and chicken.

Rheumatism signals contraction and a general malfunction within the middle heater. Therefore, one should try to warm up and relax the body. We do not have to do this by applying a fatty-meat diet or apitoxin, or medicines. It is enough to start eating well-balanced food with large quantities of spices, based on food products of all the appropriate flavours. Foods with strong anti-rheumatic properties are: cloves, turmeric, ginger, onion, garlic, liquorice and chilli.

Another example: a woman in her forties had suffered from rheumatism since her childhood; every single year she had to go to a sanatorium, as her state was very severe; once she applied the diet recommended in the *Philosophy of Health*, all of the symptoms disappeared.

Rheumatoid arthritis

Rheumatoid arthritis is also a disease of the middle heater and kidneys. The destruction of the stomach, spleen, pancreas and liver affects the quality of synovial fluid and connective tissue.

If one is affected by rheumatoid arthritis, then one should immediately eliminate from one's diet: sweets, cakes, floury food products, cheeses, yogurts, milk, chicken, pork, fresh salads, fruit, juices and cold water.

Nipple cancer and other cancer-related diseases

Every case of cancer signifies a weakening of the body and low immune system; it is a consequence of a Yin–Yang imbalance and a dysfunctional middle heater. These kinds of diseases appear when our Centre suffers from the so-called energetic emptiness, and the destructive external and internal factors overcome our defence system.

Immunity is a defence system of the structural and chemical identity of the body against penetration by external factors that can stimulate the creation of detrimental and poisonous substances within the body (especially those of a protein nature). Examples of such external factors are: bacteria, viruses, fungi, and organic fluids. Once they enter the body they can damage the cells and even cause their death; cancerous cells and multi-molecular side-products of metabolism may also appear. In order to protect the body against exogenous and endogenous factors, a system is needed that is able to locate, identify, neutralize and dispose of them from the body.

I have already mentioned in the *Philosophy of Health* about the impact of a free flow of energy and fluids (the so-called Taoist emptiness) on general health. Such a free flow of energy is especially important in everyday mobilization of the self-defence system which enables the lymphocytes to reach the potential danger.

What influences the quality of factors protecting us against cancer and helping us to maintain the Yin–Yang balance? It all depends on our Centre (stomach, spleen and pancreas) and the right quality of the process of blood formation – especially lymphopoiesis (formation, differentiation, growth and specialization of lymphocytes). Let's not talk here about personal determinants such as "endless" energy which allows a person to fool around for a long period of time without any visible consequences. Cancer-related diseases appear due to spleen failure. Our body enters a state of total "anarchy", as the spleen is the major distributor of all the energy acquired from the outside (breathing, food, colours, emotions). All of it goes through the spleen which decides and distributes it to all bodily organs in the form of essence and energy.

In order for the spleen to produce a sufficient quantity and quality of essence (the basis for the entire internal substance: blood, lymph, nutritious fluids, mucus, digestive juices, hormones), it needs to be supplied with appropriate nutrition (matter) containing the appropriate quantity of energy of all the flavours and the Yang (fire) energy. The chemical composition of the matter (proteins, carbohydrates, fats, vitamins, mineral salts) is not the most important factor responsible for the appropriate transformation of energy into matter and matter into energy. Paying too much attention to this particular factor can have a destructive effect on the body, as has been shown.

The production of internal essence cannot be measured by cognitive methods. Science has admitted this. Therefore we should not dwell on solving this mystery but rather try to find an answer to making this process efficient. Food, by supplying the spleen with the appropriate matter, energy of flavours and Yang energy, will activate other bodily organs. They will start functioning properly and consequently will stimulate the flow of energy and fluids. Therefore, if we want to stimulate the process of blood formation and the self-defence system, we should first strengthen the stomach, spleen and pancreas.

Cancer does not appear from nowhere. We should remember that this process takes years. It usually starts with simple problems with metabolism which cause very innocent symptoms. Exposure to cold, tiredness, not enough sleep, hard work, stress, emotional problems, malnutrition (eating either too much or not enough), irregular meals and inappropriate diet – all of these factors can eventually lead to cancer.

The saddest thing is that we simply ignore all of the signals our body sends us for years. We should remember that we live because of our bodies. Constantly running forwards and simultaneously ignoring the basic needs of our body can stop us midway and cause a lot of suffering or even death.

By enabling the Centre's (spleen, pancreas, stomach) efficient self-creation and regeneration mechanisms, we simultaneously strengthen our defence system. Let's think of this system as an efficient anti-terrorist brigade. Perhaps this kind of metaphor will help us to understand how important it is to take care of our body. Any anti-terrorist brigade is more efficient when it receives decent support from headquarters (Centre) and when it is decently remunerated, fed and equipped. We all know of the kind of effects that can be caused by unnecessary economizing, stupidity, laziness and the so-called half-measures. We know what kind of effects can be caused by disorder, lawlessness, powerlessness or inability to move fast or communicate. And this is what happens within our body. The weakening of our Centre leads to anarchy; the flow of energy and fluids gets blocked by a deficiency of such energy, but also by mucus and waste products. Therefore, what kinds of effects should we expect when we introduce merely half-measures and do nothing to improve the whole system? The choice is ours. Only we can decide what kind of energy and resources we should deliver to our "headquarters".

We cannot prevent nipple cancer by a prophylactic examination of our own breasts or mammography. I wonder whether those who advise this kind of prophylactic behaviour realize the stress of the whole thing ("Do I have a lump? No, not this time, yet…"). It is like Russian roulette and causes unnecessary stress. Therefore, I tell you – mothers, wives and lovers – if you want to avoid this kind of stress, you should simply take care of your "anti-terrorist brigade". Do everything you can to take proper care of your own immune system.

What does this imply?

- simply – cook
- learn how to prepare well-balanced meals

- eat regularly
- take care of your body: relaxation, showers involving massage of the chest and breasts, physical exercise (Tibetan rituals, stretching exercises)
- discipline your thoughts, speech and behaviour: talk a little, think calmly, concentrate on what you are doing
- be patient and trustful in everything you do.

Factors leading to nipple cancer:

- emotional problems, frustration, chronic stress, depression
- irregular meals
- chaotic and frequent slimming diets
- excess of the sour flavour in food, which blocks circulation and metabolism (juices, fresh salads, fruit, sauerkraut, chicken, cheeses)
- fatty food and food that stimulates production of mucus (cakes, creams, fatty meat, processed cheese) combined with sour food (for example – fatty cake followed by drinking some juice or a portion of fatty meat combined with fresh salad or sauerkraut)
- cold and raw food which does not contain enough energy but stimulates production of mucus and consequently blocks circulation (ice cream, cold water, juices and other drinks, beer, fruit, fresh salads, sauerkraut, gherkins, hams and sausages)
- biscuits, chocolate, chocolate bars, halva
- crisps, salty sticks, crackers, nibbles, nuts, seeds

- mono-flavoured food or food based on one product
- excess of pork and chicken
- excess of hams and sausages
- lack of physical exercise (moving around at work and in the house is not enough)
- long-lasting exposure to cold
- surrounding oneself with "cold" colours (white, green, blue, grey, black); too many potted plants around
- water veins.

A general dysfunction of the spleen and deficiency of energy are not the only ailments which accompany nipple cancer. There are also other symptoms, such as pain and a tingling sensation in the chest area, a stabbing pain in the chest (often misjudged as heart pain), back pain (especially under the right shoulder), shoulder pain, indigestion and flatulence accompanied by a dull pain in the chest area, painful breast areas under the armpits and around lymphatic glands, and headaches related to a weakening of the gallbladder. We may also experience mood swings, difficulties with concentration, calming down and distancing ourselves from things. All of these problems are evidently related to circulation, liver, gallbladder and pericardium.

Among other ailments preceding nipple cancer are also pains of the lumbar vertebrae, usually caused by contraction of pericardial muscles and the large intestine. They may also be accompanied by problems with the mobility of the pelvis, hip stiffness, diarrhoea and constipation.

All of the ailments mentioned above can eventually become chronic problems and turn into the so-called "lurking state". This is especially dangerous because instead of getting rid of the problems we get used to them and in the meantime the malfunction and destruction of the middle heater progresses even more. Consequently, this may lead to serious deficiencies of nutrients, enzymes and hormones. Usually at this point the process of formation of cancerous cells begins, but the body and the immune system are too weak to fight them.

The increasing number of cancers nowadays is directly connected to certain destructive factors in the life of the modern woman (too much work, tiredness, stress). Another reason for it is the totally misunderstood concept of a healthy diet, followed by underestimating the importance of home-cooked meals.

In the situation where there is a need for a mastectomy, one should absolutely support the body with proper food to prevent progression of the disease.

To improve health and strengthen the body after a mastectomy one should:

- implement everyday physical exercise which will stimulate blood circulation and alleviate the muscular contractions
- introduce well-balanced and warm meals with added spices
- in cooking – use only rapeseed oil, olive oil and butter
- eat all kinds of so-called "heavy" products but with added spices
- absolutely eliminate cold, sour and raw food
- absolutely eliminate ham and sausages, pork, chicken, sea fish, sweets, cakes, fruit, water, ice cream, juices, beer
- strengthen the process of blood-formation by taking small doses of herbal mix by Paprzecki (see recipes) – half a teaspoon, two times a day followed by warm thyme-liquorice-ginger tea.

One should remember that cancer-related diseases will always appear in a body that has been acidified, with a deregulated middle heater and malfunctioning bodily organs. Food that is harmful to the stomach, spleen and pancreas most likely has acidifying properties. If we know that our body is acidified, and if such a state lasts for a longer period of time, then we should absolutely change our dietary habits and start eating food that is well-balanced and contains the energy of all flavours.

It is not advisable, though, to introduce strongly warming food if suffering from cancer. The problem here is not a deficiency of internal substance or the bad quality of essence or stalling. We should instead try to regenerate the substance with food that is energetically balanced. It should be mostly food of a neutral or neutral-warming nature, with added spices which will stimulate metabolism and circulation. If we provide the body with too much Yang energy without balancing it out by the Yin factor (that is, an appropriate quantity of vegetables, grains, meat) then we may experience emotional problems, which will only destroy the newly regenerated substance. Therefore, it is recommended to separate a person suffering from cancer from all kinds of factors that cause stress. Especially useful in this case is direct contact with Nature.

The most important food products that help in the prevention and treatment of cancers:

- green and yellow vegetables, which contain large quantities of beta-carotene (I remind you here that beta-carotene does not decompose during cooking) and chlorophyll: parsley, dill, celery leaves, watercress, kohlrabi leaves, leek leaves, chives, spinach, broccoli, carrots, sweet potatoes, parsley root, pumpkin, peppers, pattypan squash, parsnip; also all kinds of cabbage, Brussels sprouts, kale, cauliflower, kohlrabi, celeriac, fennel and all kinds of legumes (except soya beans)
- grains – millet, buckwheat and oats
- herbs – basil, thyme, tarragon, rosemary, sage, marjoram, fenugreek, liquorice

- spices, which should be used at all times – ginger, turmeric, cardamom, chilli, cayenne pepper, cloves, mustard seeds, cumin, cinnamon, nutmeg
- fish-liver oil, olive oil, rapeseed oil, butter, eggs
- onion, garlic, leeks, fennel.

From all these products we should be able to prepare well-balanced meals, which should always be accompanied by a small piece of meat of an appropriate energy, such as veal, young beef, turkey (especially the dark meat) and freshwater fish. All other kinds of meat, as well as hams and sausages, are in this case absolutely forbidden!!!

Multiple sclerosis

According to conventional medicine, multiple sclerosis is a disease of the nervous system related to damage of the insulating covers of nerve cells. The doctors claim that lymphocytes treat these insulating covers as enemies; they attack and damage them, which leads to hardening of the connective tissue and blockages of the flow of nervous impulses.

I do not think that the only cause of this disease are lymphocytes. If they treat the connective tissue (insulating covers of nerve cells) as an enemy then either there is something wrong with the tissue itself or the process of lymphopoiesis is somehow disturbed. The connective tissue depends on the liver. And as a matter of fact, MS is usually accompanied by problems with liver cirrhosis. Due to a deficiency of essence and energy, the liver stops the process of regeneration of the connective tissue and the insulating covers of nerve cells. A dysfunctional liver also leads to problems with the subconscious. Emotional blockages are one of the leading symptoms in MS. This disease is also accompanied by diabetes, which is directly related to spleen, pancreas, liver and lung problems. In conclusion, MS is a disease of the middle heater and our consciousness (misunderstanding of reality, lack of acceptance).

In this analysis of MS we discover the original cause of the whole sickness process. It is, in fact, a malfunction of the stomach, spleen, pancreas and, most of all, the liver and the whole circulatory system. If the food we are eating is destructive for the middle heater, then the liver cannot secure the appropriate quality of connective tissue and consequently of the whole nervous system. Also, our consciousness is not able to control the incomprehensible emotions which come directly from our subconscious.

We can then determine the external factors that cause weakening of the most important bodily organs, which together with congenital predispositions and emotional problems lead to this very serious disease. Among these factors are an inappropriate diet and an exposure to cold and stress.

MS does not happen instantly. It is in fact a long process of degradation and destruction of the body, and only our own consciousness and appropriate prophylactic treatment can help us prevent it.

MS is a real challenge for an ill person. Perhaps thanks to all of the difficulties experienced by sufferers, they will be able to find within themselves the will to live and fight against the disease in order to give themselves a chance of a dignified life. There is always an option to choose. So, either we give up and suffer severely, often missing the true sense of existence, or we generate within ourselves the power and energy to face this challenge. Therefore, it is indispensable in this case to treat our consciousness seriously and try to understand the mechanisms of the emotions and their qualities. I think that people affected by MS have a problem with the correct perception and acceptance of reality. I am talking here about their living conditions as well as the people around them. This reality is supposed to inspire them to internal transformation in order to understand themselves and the suffering they have to go through.

Yes, it is undeniable that people with MS have to face a lot. And a proper diet (no sour, cold and raw food), which is supposed to protect the spleen and liver, will be very helpful in this case. It can bring unexpected positive effects, such as regeneration and strengthening of the spleen, liver, inner substance (Yin) and stimulation of metabolism and circulation (Yang). It is a process requiring a huge sacrifice and patience. People with MS should also not forget about physical exercise; isometric exercise is especially recommended in this case.

Osteoporosis

Vitamin D2 can be found in plants, whilst vitamin D3 is created in the skin under the influence of ultraviolet light. The effect of vitamins D2 and D3 is the same – they are both biologically inactive, stored in body fat and are absorbed thanks to bile. Their transformation into active metabolites happens in the liver and kidneys. And it is only the active vitamin D3 that enables absorption of calcium in the small intestine.

Active vitamin D is also called the kidney hormone, which is stimulated by the hormone produced in the parathyroid gland. But deficiency of magnesium within the body can prevent its synthesis. The body is able to adapt to a low-calcium diet. When the level of calcium drops, the kidneys and liver start activating vitamin D3; this enables maximal absorption of calcium from food. Activation of vitamin D in the kidneys is supported by oestrogens and the growth hormone. This increases the process of absorption of calcium even more.

Conclusion: we will not prevent osteoporosis by eating dairy products and taking calcium supplements. In fact, in this way we can only destroy our internal system. We can prevent, or even stop, the progression of osteoporosis by doing the following:

- taking care of all internal bodily organs and the whole body in general
- eliminating all sour, raw and cold food
- eliminating from our diet: cheeses, milk and yogurts (the more you eat them the bigger the chances of osteoporosis)
- regularly eating butter, eggs and fish-liver oil
- eating warm and well-balanced meals with added spices and meat of an appropriate nature (bitter, sweet and spicy flavour)

- being exposed to sunlight for at least 15 minutes a day, every day
- practising physical exercise (at least 30 minutes a day) – I recommend Tibetan rituals and strengthening exercises with small weights (1–2 kg)
- eliminating stress and trying to understand and accept everyone and everything
- introducing warm colour into our life (red, orange and yellow), especially in the closed spaces we work and live in, but also by wearing underwear of these colours.

Headaches

Long-lasting and frequent headaches signify our misjudgement of energetic stimuli: emotional tensions, stress, frustration, sorrow, inappropriate flavours, climates and colours. Headaches can appear suddenly and are usually caused by years of exposure to destructive factors that we originally thought to be harmless. For example: long-lasting stress (tension) can all of a sudden manifest itself in the form of a headache. It is difficult, then, without the appropriate kind of knowledge about the energy of emotions, to understand that this condition can be caused by accumulation of certain factors, which lead to muscular and blood vessel contractions, or ischaemia and asphyxia of the brain. Also, by eating food of strongly cooling properties (juices, fruit, cold water, cheeses) over many years, thinking that they are good for us, we are not paying much attention to our general health, which gets worse and worse over time (obesity, indigestion, flatulence, sleepiness, constipation). The headaches finally "wake" us up; but even then we do not realize that it has something to do with our dietary habits.

Susceptibility to headaches is an individual matter. Therefore the same destructive factors can cause different effects in different people. It depends on our condition, character, our psychological state and other negative factors.

From my observation, I know that the people most prone to headaches are those with blood type A. They are simply more sensitive to the stimuli of a low energetic vibration, such as stress, cold, and sour food.

Women are more susceptible to headaches, especially when they are tired and have emotional problems (stress, frustration, sorrow). It is quite obvious in this case, as any kind of tension blocks the flow of blood through the reproductive organs and causes contraction of the blood vessels responsible for supplying blood to the brain. It is a state of typical ischaemia and asphyxia of the brain. Emotional tension within the reproductive organs also blocks the flow of energy. This state is very difficult to overcome, as it is caused by permanent cold within the body and our limited consciousness that such things as a bowl of hot soup and free and happy sex are the best medicine for headaches, as well as for good humour and beauty.

Men are more fortunate in this case – getting rid of emotions (energy) is much easier for them. Besides, women suffer more often from a deficiency of blood – another cause of headaches.

But it does not really matter which case we are analysing here. The fact is that the major cause of headaches is a Yin–Yang imbalance, followed by circulatory problems, blood and energy stalling, and contraction within the body. It is a signal that there are some dysfunctions within the whole body and in every bodily organ.

All the energetic meridians of all of the bodily organs end in the head. Therefore, a headache can be a symptom of dysfunction within any of the bodily organs: liver, gallbladder, small intestine, large intestine, stomach, bladder, triple heater and heart. If pain recurs constantly in the same place, then it may signify that we are under the influence of the same destructive factor.

Chronic headaches are a problem not only for adults but also for children and the young. If during her pregnancy a mother-to-be eats mostly food of a cooling nature (fruit, fresh salads, cold water, hams and sausages, yogurts, cheeses, and so on) and is under permanent stress, then it is more than likely that her child will have a certain predisposition to suffering. Once we put our children on a well-balanced kind of diet, their problems with headaches should disappear with time.

Headaches can take away from us the will for living and motivation to do things; they make us sad, depressive and sorrowful. This tells us that headaches are a typical ailment of an overcooled body which is also suffering from a deficiency of Yang and blocked circulation. It is dangerous to trivialize the pain and the factors that cause it, as they can be the nucleus of a much more serious problem.

Of different character is the so-called neuralgia, or simply – nerve pain, connected mostly to the trigeminal nerve and facial nerves. Inflammation of these nerves gives very strong pain. It is normally caused by overcooling (deficiency of Yang) and malnourishment (deficiency of good quality essence – vitamin and mineral salt deficiency). A major role in this case is played by the liver, of course, which, deprived of good quality blood and proper nutrients, affects the quality and function of the nervous tissue. Affected by this kind of pain, one should most of all take care of proper nourishment and try to warm the body.

Headaches caused by tiredness and stress can be eliminated by applying pressure to points 1, 14 and 20 on the meridian of the gallbladder, points 8 and 36 on the meridian of the stomach, and also points on the "stomach muscles" – muscles of the neck, shoulder and breast muscle. All of these muscles contract under the influence of not only stress, but also flavours and cold. This leads to a blockage of the flow of blood and energy towards the head and very often affects the function of other muscles and bodily organs. Neck muscles, on the other hand, are part of the "drainage" system in the head.

Recurring headaches can also be a derivative of problems in the large intestine. Because this condition affects a bigger group of people (and we know that a malfunctioning large intestine signifies also a malfunction of the majority of the bodily organs), we should approach the problem of headaches more consciously. We cannot get rid of headaches only with painkillers, massages or acupuncture. We should most of all try to find the true cause of this condition, eliminate the destructive factors and restore the balance within our body by introducing a proper kind of diet and the aforementioned supportive actions. Our body does not like it when we ignore its alarm system, and we can be sure that within a certain period of time it will put us back on our feet again.

I remind you here once more of the main causes of headaches:

- Energetic blockages in the meridians
- Pain in the forehead – problems with the gallbladder and stomach
- Pain between the eyes – problems with the bladder and stomach
- Pain in the temple – problems with the triple heater and gallbladder
- Pain in just half of the head – problems with the small intestine
- Pain at the top of the head – problems with the liver
- Pain at the back of the head – problems with the gallbladder, pericardium and kidneys
- "Jamming" sensation in the head – problems with the liver
- Problems with the large intestine – constipation, diarrhoea
- Deficiency of Yang – weak circulation, malfunctioning liver and gallbladder
- Deficiency of Yin (deficiency of blood – anaemia) – cold spleen
- Contraction of the muscles of the head and blockages of the energy and blood – excess of stimuli causing contractions.

All of the aforementioned blockages of the meridians and problems with bodily organs and blood circulation appear under the influence of factors such as stress, excesses of particular flavours and cold. These factors cause specific symptoms which then result in headaches (the so-called vicious circle).

In summary, the middle heater and all of the bodily organs within this area (stomach, spleen, gallbladder and liver) are responsible for most headaches. It is the central system of creation and stimulation within the body. All of these bodily organs are also responsible for our emotional states (conscious and subconscious). In a situation when our body is under the influence of a destructive factor which is causing blockages and damage within the middle heater, we can start suffering from all sorts of problems, as our stomach is unable to "prepare" the food content for further digestion and the spleen is unable to produce the essence and starts producing toxic moisture instead. The gallbladder is also unable to push the energy of the stomach downwards, which causes the feeling of fullness and flatulence in the stomach and consequent headache. The liver, on the other hand, is too weak to lift the moisture and the energy from the spleen, which would otherwise strengthen the lungs. Besides, the weakening of the spleen and the stomach leads to an even bigger deficiency of blood and Yang of the liver. This can cause a number of headaches linked, for example, to emotional problems, which appear in the situation of a deficiency of blood or problems with the circulatory system – and these are always related to a deficiency of Yang and an excess of moisture.

Urinary incontinence and overactive bladder

Problems with the bladder and urinary incontinence can also be added to the group of diseases of affluence. Both of these ailments, probably in most cases treated by one and the same doctor, are related to completely different physiological determinants.

Urinary incontinence can affect people of all ages – young and old, who most likely have similar predispositions. Initially this condition is not dangerous, but only if we recognize the symptoms in time (and, of course, if it is not a derivative of a much bigger problem, e.g. MS).

The most common causes of urinary incontinence are a weak and overcooled body, poor blood circulation, and a deficiency of blood and nutritious fluids. Trying to define this state of imbalance according to the rules of Chinese medicine, we can say that it signifies a malfunctioning middle heater (stomach, spleen, pancreas, liver). We already know that the spleen is responsible for the quality of the muscles, blood and other bodily fluids, and the liver for contractions and expansions as well as the circulation of energy within the spleen meridian.

If the middle heater is deficient in Yang (this relates mostly to the spleen) then the energy within the body gets split – the fluids and substances go up, and the energy goes down. This leads to stalling in the legs, a "sliding down" of the lower part of the abdomen and dislocation of bodily organs. Also responsible for this state is the liver, which is also responsible for the quality of the connective tissue.

The bodily organs responsible for gathering, storing and excreting urine are made of smooth muscles (bladder) and striated muscles (urethra), which are controlled entirely by the liver. A significant role in this condition is played by the dorsal hip muscles, muscles at the bottom of the pelvis and the muscles of the abdomen. Contractions of the gluteus (pericardial muscles), which can cause pressure on the sciatic nerve, weaken the nervous centre located between the lumbar vertebrae and the spinal cord. The nervous centre, on the other hand, is responsible for gathering urine in the bladder.

The endocrine system and its response to common external factors such as cold, stress and excesses of particular flavours has a certain impact on urinary incontinence. Exposed to all of these factors, the endocrine glands become insufficiently active and start malfunctioning. And it has been proven that a deficiency of oestrogens can lead to the muscles becoming limp.

Urinary incontinence is usually caused by our negligence. It is more than obvious that if we do not use certain muscles they simply become limp and eventually may even disappear. Let's have a look at body posture. I am more than certain that most of us do not "hold" the lower part of the abdomen and the bodily organs within this area. Therefore, isometric exercise (contraction and extension of the muscles), which can be done in any place and at any time, is the best way to quickly regenerate this part of the body.

Hyperactivity of the bladder, despite all appearances, is a serious problem. And its increasing occurrence should raise concerns. On the one hand, it means that stress can affect anybody regardless of age, as it affects children and adults equally. On the other hand, it means that our body gets badly affected by the overcooling type of diet and continuous exposure to cold.

Hyperactivity of the bladder leads to frequent urinating (usually accompanied by pain) and also pain in the lower abdomen. These kinds of problems can stay with us for life. It has actually happened that somebody was treated for this condition for over thirty years, not realizing that it was mostly caused by continuous stress, exposure to cold and, of course, their diet based on sour, raw and cold food.

When under stress, the pain that accompanies urinating signifies activation of the defence system which protects our heart from the excess of Yang. Energy of this type is intercepted by the small intestine and bladder. Stress has a blocking effect on the body; it leads to contraction of our outer coat (skeletal muscles, spleen, kidneys, head), whilst simultaneously the inner organs (heart, liver and pancreas) increase their metabolism and consume the essence to obtain more energy. It is difficult to consciously control our stress level. Therefore, this defence system which protects the heart is a blessing in disguise. The problem of painful urination goes away when we relax our body sufficiently by taking a rest or implementing some massage techniques, exercise involving core strength and flexibility, acupressure and, of course, by introducing a well-balanced diet.

Each of these three factors – that is, stress, exposure to cold and inappropriate diet, lead to deregulation of all of the bodily organs, but most of all to a weakening of the spleen and kidneys. If this turns into a chronic state then it can also badly affect the endocrine system (e.g. deficiency of vasopressin). This can lead to problems with the secondary absorption of urine which has the effect of frequent and profuse urination. This condition is characteristic of women of all ages who suffer from a large deficiency of Yin. They can experience unexpected heat rushes, often completely unnecessarily ascribed to the menopause.

Some of the pains in the bladder and during urination can be caused by cold (external cold and cold drinks). But I would not recommend treating these conditions with antibiotics or anti-inflammatory medication. Otherwise, this state can become chronic, as this kind of treatment can deregulate our immune system and cause an accumulation of mucus. At this point, the question of activating bacteria is not so important; we have to work on retrieving the state of balance within our body first. I would especially recommend in this case broths based on veal, parsley root (or parsnip) stock, onion soup, steamed carrots, and elimination of all sour, raw and cold food.

Painful urination can also be an initial symptom of inflammation of the prostate, which is also caused by a deficiency of moisture. Hyperactivity of the bladder and problems with urinary incontinence are derivatives of a general weakening and insufficient activity of the middle heater (stomach, spleen, pancreas, liver), always accompanied by a severe deficiency of Yin and Yang.

To summarize, I would like to remind you here once more that hyperactivity of the bladder is mostly caused by stress. It is also worth mentioning that this condition, caused by this specific factor (stress), can be followed by other symptoms, such as sudden headaches, especially in the forehead and at the back of the head. These kinds of headaches are most likely to appear in the morning when we feel strong pressure and activity of the bladder.

Dislocation of bodily organs

This condition is characteristic of people affected by an insufficient activity of the middle heater, and especially the spleen and liver. The problem is related to the quality of the muscles and the connective tissue. If any of these organs is weakened by a deficiency of Yang energy or an inappropriate energy of food (excess of sour, salty and sweet (sugar) flavour), then the substance (muscles and connective tissue) stops fulfilling its function and loses its tone. The problem with dislocation of bodily organs is caused not only by a weak middle heater but also by insufficient activity of the lungs and kidneys. In this case, other problems can also appear, such us prolapsing of the bodily organs, intestinal adhesions, urinary incontinence, hyperactivity of the bladder, joint stiffness, and poor quality of all skeletal muscles and the skin. This may also be accompanied by circulatory problems, hyperactivity, sensitivity, sleeping problems and generally poor health.

Major causes of this condition are stress, tiredness, lack of physical exercise, but most of all sour, raw and cold food, which overcools the body, leads to contractions and poor quality of substance (muscles and connective tissue).

Depression

Depression is one of the emotional states. But it is also often related to the general physical condition of the body. It is characterized by a loss of vitality and the will to live; the body and the psyche stop reacting to stimulating factors. This state is usually accompanied by a lack of appetite, and aversion to movement and contact with the environment.

Depression also has another meaning – it means "below a certain level". And this relates to our life, too. Deficiency of the Yang energy (Chi and warmth), poor blood circulation, and movement of the energy mostly downwards – all of these things make us feel smitten, stoop-shouldered; we do not have the strength and the will to breathe, talk and move. We can only think of the bleakness and senselessness of existence. Other symptoms of depression are a lack of acceptance of the environment and oneself, followed by suicidal thoughts which quite often lead to death.

We already know from the *Philosophy of Health* that our bodily organs can manifest positive and negative emotions. It all depends on the state of balance within the body. Depression is a state of our emotions and our body, too, connected directly to the functioning and the energy of the lungs and kidneys. The kidneys accumulate the whole life energy (Yang) and essence (Yin), which stimulate the will for living. Both of these bodily organs move the energy downwards and are associated with concentration and dying. But, on the other hand, when the lungs and kidneys are in a state of balance, they manifest a great will for living, openness and vigour.

If not treated in time or treated incorrectly, depression can lead to serious mental disorders and destruction of the bodily organs. Very often a seemingly controlled depression, under certain conditions such as severe overcooling, a traumatic experience or even inappropriate diet, can explode unexpectedly, leading to shocking results, such as destructive sadness or even suicide.

Nowadays, depression is a big social problem and it always intensifies during the summer. This is because at this time of the year we consume large quantities of overcooling foods (ice cream, cold drinks).

The causes of depression:

- A sudden and tragic experience. Sadness and sorrow have the energy of autumn, which is directed towards the Earth – it is the energy of dying. It affects the lungs, causing blockages in the flow of energy which then lead to difficulties with breathing. If this state lasts for a long period of time, then the feelings of sadness and sorrow are usually followed by depression, which at this point is still not too dangerous. Therefore, if someone is dwelling on these emotions for a long time, we should discretely feed them exclusively with warming types of food. In order to prevent the stalling of energy, it is advisable to occasionally serve them ginger tea, or the "killer" tea, or even a shot of cognac. On the other hand, juices, fruit, fresh salads, cold drinks, ice cream, an excess of sweets, sour food or a starvation diet are in this case absolutely forbidden.

- Mono-flavoured food or food based on a single product, sour and raw food. The most destructive are food products of the sour and salty flavour (chicken, pork with no added spices, hams and sausages, herrings, gherkins, yogurts, cold drinks, ice cream). Trying to neutralize the negative influence of the aforementioned products by drinking alcohol (energy of the spicy flavour) leads to alcoholism. Some people try to neutralize this problem by eating sweets.

- Slimming diets – they lead to a permanent deficiency of energy; they only cause mood swings and recurring depressive states.

Do believe me that depression happens involuntarily. But it is mostly a lack of knowledge of the nature of the factors affecting us that makes us emotionally imbalanced. I think that children and the young especially deserve special attention in this case.

It is also very likely that depression is triggered by our personal or family-related emotional problems – that is, lack of warmth, acceptance, love, compassion of the people closest to us. It is strange that, despite all this suffering, we are unable to learn to give to others what we would want to receive from them in return. But it is we adults who should realize that there are people around who wait for our touch and a smile. Even though we may not have experienced this kind of affection during our childhood, we should try and make such moments a daily occurrence.

The best treatment for any kind of depression or emotional problem is elimination of the cooling type of food (sour, cold and raw) and an introduction of home-cooked food, well-balanced with all the flavours and added spices. We should also realize that proneness to depression is an emotional problem which we should try to understand and learn to deal with. Let's think if we hold any old grudges and sorrows, probably rooted in our childhood. If so, then we should try to understand and transform them into the energy of joy, openness, acceptance and tolerance. Try to think that, without this sadness or sorrow, you would be unable to activate the energy of love. It is our suffering, after all, that provides the best lesson.

Fear

Fear is an emotional state related to the kidneys. As much as depression (sadness, sorrow) leads in most cases to anxiety disorder, fear leads to aggression. Fear signifies a low vibration and concentration and dominates overcooled and malnourished bodies.

The energy of fear is intertwined into our subconscious and consciousness from birth, the same as love. The energy of love means natural trustfulness, an ability for self-sacrifice and acceptance; it is a feeling of unity with everything and everybody around us. At least, this is how children feel it.

Fear should only exist for our security, in order to protect our individuality, identity and physicality. It is our Ego. Ego is always scared or fearful. If we feel swamped by thoughts, then it is simply our Ego reminding us that perhaps we will be late, perhaps we will not learn enough, perhaps something will kill us, perhaps we will not be accepted, perhaps we will not be liked, perhaps we are too fat, perhaps we will lose our job, perhaps we will be unappreciated, perhaps, perhaps, perhaps… From this chaos of warnings we should choose only the most useful ones that can truly protect us. The rest we should tame. In order to do this, we should refill our body with the Yang energy.

Every single fear tries to pull us to their side; it wants to become the most important one. There was a woman going through a divorce from her alcoholic husband. I asked her: "What are you afraid of?" "I am afraid that I will not manage on my own." Great. Ego is capable of predicting and taking care of us. But let's not go crazy. Maybe we should initially force ourselves into feelings of joy and trustfulness. Only then will we be able to get used to them. Another example: a young man desperately wanted to go to a summer camp. But before going, instead of being happy, he constantly worried whether he would be accepted by his peers, and in this way he diminished the joy of preparation, and afterwards, of being in the camp. Sometimes we lose contact with our partners; we stop talking to them because our Ego injects into our mind the most incredible scenarios which only make us feel miserable.

Fear can reflect on our emotional state and our body; it can become a positive factor protecting our life, releasing strength in situations of danger. Our body usually then secretes adrenaline, which causes muscular contractions and raises the blood pressure, heartbeat and the level of glucose in the blood. This state always activates our metabolism. It is a temporary and very positive mobilization of the body.

However, when this strong excitation turns into a chronic state, it usually leads to the destruction of our body. Tense muscles block the free flow of energy and blood, and thus the liver starts suffering from a deficiency of blood (Yin), and this consequently leads to aggression. In such a state, Yin and Yang are being successively consumed, as the regeneration of substance gets blocked. This kind of tension also absorbs our energy and leads to "burning out" of our inner substance and the state of "fire". If this kind of tension and stress lasts too long, we can end up with some serious consequences: heart attack, spleen puncture, haemorrhages, stroke, high blood pressure, peptic ulcers, etc. It is a typical emotional syndrome characteristic of people holding high and stressful jobs: bosses, directors and businessmen.

Every fear is of a Yin nature. But its intensiveness varies depending on the situation: fear of an alcoholic father is different from a fear of aggressive colleagues or a fear of losing your job. It is an incapacitating kind of energy accompanied by hopelessness. It blocks the functioning of the bodily organs, metabolism, blood circulation and normal functioning of the body. Consequences of this include: heart attacks, obesity, hernias, problems with the lungs, indigestion, diarrhoea and headaches.

In both the first and the second cases above, only proper nutrition can neutralize even the biggest emotional tension. In a natural sort of way, we start distancing ourselves from the problem that has been eating away at us. A well-balanced diet can protect us from the consequences of long-term stresses and fears.

By introducing everyday discipline, finding time for relaxation, physical exercise, strengthening meals consumed in a friendly atmosphere and plenty of sleep, we will manage to cut ourselves off from all tormenting thoughts and free ourselves from the destructive energy of fear.

There is one more type of fear which relates to the element of the heart and is a manifestation of mental disorders. It appears in a body with an insufficiently active spleen, deficiency of the internal Yin and a deficiency of blood (affecting the heart). The mind is usually very stimulated in this case.

This state also signifies a deficiency of blood in the liver, which leads to a "release" from the subconscious of all kinds of fears and phobias. When the liver is in a state of balance, all of these fears remain hidden; this is the normal state. We have to remember that our subconscious accumulates an unbelievably large number of feelings and emotions and we should never try to get to the bottom of them and eject them. In fact, when we are in a state of balance, all of these emotions are harmless to us. It is a mistake to try to fix them, as we can never be sure that our body will withstand this kind of trial.

In the situation when the fears of our subconscious start entering our mind, one should immediately think of restoring the inner Yin and retrieving balance within the bodily organs (liver, heart). We can do this by eliminating from our diet all kinds of overcooling food and replacing it with well-balanced and warming food. It is also important to get rid of the muscular tensions which are an involuntary reaction, appearing even ahead of the thinking process. But I do not think that an ill person will be able to deal with all of this by themselves.

Spine

Spinal problems can affect each one of us from time to time. They are a derivative of all that happens within our body and a reflection of the condition of the bodily organs and skeletal muscles. It is a total misunderstanding to treat the spine as a separate and self-sufficient "organ". Pain in the spinal area is usually a symptom of muscular tension and dysfunction of a particular bodily organ. Pain may be located in a specific area or it can emanate from a larger part of the body.

In order for the spine to function properly, all of its parts should be of an appropriate quality – that is, all of the vertebrae should be well-formed and the connective tissue (discs) should be elastic and moist. Because the spine has to "work" all the time and the discs are always under great pressure and subject to friction, they can be used up quite quickly. Therefore, their regeneration and renewal is one of the most important processes within the body.

And again I go back to the basic argument, which we have mentioned many times before: in order to make the process of tissue regeneration run smoothly, it needs to be supplied by the blood-specific building, energetic and regulating factors. Thus, the blood needs to be of an appropriate quality and quantity. Indispensable in this case is the Yang energy, which stimulates the spleen, blood circulation and lymph glands. The lymph glands here play a major role as they collect all the used-up cells created during the process of regeneration of the discs. The liver, as we already know, is responsible for the renewal and regeneration of the connective tissue, and the spleen for the basic building essence.

Another very important factor for securing the proper functioning of the spine is the body posture. Straight body posture enables circulation of energy within the central canal and consequently within the whole body. The posture should be symmetrical and proportional. We can maintain it by eating wisely, introducing strengthening kinds of exercise and disciplining our emotions.

A good and straight body posture relies on the skeletal muscles. Therefore, whether we hunch our shoulders, drag our legs, or are bent over and asymmetrical is dependent on their condition. These muscles are responsible for our outer appearance and body shape. Let me remind you here that the quality of muscles depends on the spleen, and the liver is responsible for their motor functions (contraction – extension).

According to the research and analysis of J.F. Thie, all the bodily organs have "their own" muscles located in different parts of the body. And so, a disorder of a particular bodily organ or a strong emotional stimulus causes contraction in the muscle ascribed to this organ. If the contraction lasts too long, it can lead to blockages of blood and energy circulation.

Muscular contractions usually happen after eating very fatty, sour or cold meals. They can occur both in the area of the dorsal hip muscles as well as around the cervical vertebrae and thoracic vertebrae. Other symptoms may also appear, such as chest pains, difficulties in breathing, rheumatic pains in the hands, thighs, calves and heels.

Dull pains in the spine, between the fifth and sixth thoracic vertebrae, and in the lower thoracic vertebrae, usually accompanied by vomiting and headaches, signify a weakening of the liver. A weakening of the liver, which affects practically all of us, manifests itself as a continuous, burning and itchy pain under the right scapula, between the fifth and sixth thoracic vertebrae, 2.5cm right from the spine. The spot affected by the pain may be slightly reddened and sensitive to touch. By applying pressure on this particular spot, we will feel instant relief around the dorsal hip muscles, the legs, shoulders and head.

We can eliminate the problems related to spinal pains by disciplining ourselves and introducing a proper diet and physical exercise (minimum half an hour a day). This kind of discipline guarantees elimination of the pains which are caused by blockages and insufficient circulation within the joints and muscles. The most important thing is not to be afraid of the pain caused by the physical exercise. By stretching and tightening the muscles they will become more elastic and will thus regenerate more quickly. Everyday exercise (not only 2–3 times per week) will secure for us a great condition for the whole day.

Cellulite

Cellulite is caused by a degeneration of the connective tissue of the fat cells and deposition of lymph in the intercellular spaces. The external appearance of the skin reminds one of an orange peel. It is not an independent condition, but, like other ailments, it is a result of metabolic disorder caused by factors such as:

- irregular and cold meals
- excess of fast food and sweets
- excess of sour and raw food (gherkins, fresh salads, apples, juices, fruit yogurts, cheeses)
- excess of cold drinks
- mono-flavoured food or food based on a single product (cheeses, fruit yogurts, fruit, juices)
- exposure to cold (wearing a mini skirt regardless of the weather)
- stress and emotional problems
- lack of physical exercise
- slimming diets.

Cellulite signifies a weakening of the stomach, spleen and pancreas, problems with digestion and absorption, or problems with cellular regeneration. If the spleen does not produce essence of a good quality, it starts producing pathological moisture instead, which then dwells in different parts of the body. Inappropriate food and deficiency of Yang weaken the circulation of energy, blood and lymph, which makes cleansing of the intercellular spaces from the by-products of metabolism and moisture practically impossible. This leads to stalling and a degeneration of the connective tissue of the fat cells. This is all caused by a deficiency of building and energetic factors.

The liver, as we already know, is responsible for the process of regeneration of the connective tissue and circulation within the whole body. Cellulite is the first symptom of a weakening and malfunctioning of the liver. So, it is almost certain, Lady, that you will soon be affected by much more serious health problems (digestive problems, obesity, problems with reproductive organs and breasts). Such is the order of things. You cannot improve the condition of the liver by applying various creams and body balms.

What, then, can help in this case? Definitely not drinking large quantities of water or eating large quantities of fruit and fresh salads, but:

- everyday flexibility and strengthening exercises
- warm food of the Yang energy, which will stimulate circulation
- food well-balanced with all the flavours and spices, which can stimulate metabolism.

Constipation

According to conventional medicine, constipation is not a disease but a symptom caused by certain factors. The major cause of this state is habitual atonic constipation or spastic constipation. Atonic constipation manifests itself through a weakening or total cessation of movement of the appendix and spastic constipation through painful contractions. Factors which from a medical viewpoint are seen as causes of this ailment are in fact the results of much more serious disorders of metabolism and Yin–Yang imbalance within the body. Medicine often forgets that problems with constipation can lead to serious diseases of the large intestine, which increasingly are affecting more people. Constipation and diarrhoea can be categorized as social diseases.

The large intestine is not a separate organ functioning independently of the whole gastrointestinal system and other bodily organs. The large intestine reflects the functioning of the stomach, spleen, pancreas, the small intestine, liver, kidneys, lungs and circulatory system (pericardium). However, the majority of responsibility falls on the stomach, spleen and pancreas (Centre), as these organs are responsible for the whole digestive process and secretion of internal fluids and mucus. The large intestine belongs to the group of hollow bodily organs; it is Yang, and in order to function properly it needs energy and moisture (mucus).

The major function of the large intestine is moving – thanks to peristalsis of the smooth muscle – undigested or digested but still unabsorbed food content, and the formation and excretion of stools. This process is accompanied by a simultaneous absorption of water and some mineral salts, as well as enzymatic digestion of the rest of the undigested food content from the small intestine. This additional enzymatic digestion occurs when the gastrointestinal system is overcooled and the whole food content moves through it too quickly. The large intestine is also responsible for absorption of some of the amino acids, but only if their concentration is right. Mucus is the element indispensable in the proper formation of stools. The substances which cannot be excreted with urine (iron, calcium, magnesium, phosphorus, mercury and bismuth) are excreted through the wall of the large intestine.

Germs in the large intestine take part in the process of fermentation mainly of sugars and rotting of the undigested protein. The hydrogen released during fermentation enables various chemical transformations based on reduction, e.g. transformation of bilirubin. Rotting can cause a lot of harm to the body (toxic contamination), especially when the stools stay in the large intestine for too long and the final product of this process cannot be neutralized as there is too much of it. In normal conditions, the poisonous substances are neutralized by the wall of the large intestine or in the liver.

Peristalsis is caused by the mechanical stretching of the walls by the food content and stimulation of chemical receptors. This process is directly dependent on the nervous system and on stimulation of the parasympathetic fibres of the vagus nerve and sympathetic fibres of the coeliac nerve and on the functioning of the smooth muscles of the intestine. The liver is responsible for all of these interdependences. Tension of the smooth muscles and movements of the intestines, as well as stimulation of the parasympathetic nervous system, can be increased by bile and many chemical substances and decreased by sympathetic impulses, adrenaline and atropine. Therefore, the so-called "light food" products, such as juices, fruit yogurts, fresh salads, cheeses and sweets, tame peristalsis and make the intestine lazy.

The process of excretion of stools from the large intestine is directly connected to the energetic function of the kidneys. Deficiency of the Yang energy and essence in the kidneys manifests itself as intestinal disorder. The stools should be well formed and have a homogeneous consistency. A loose consistency of the stools, with bits of undigested food in them, signifies a certain disorder and weakening of the spleen, stomach, pancreas and intestines. Constipation occurs when we do not empty our bowels for two or three days.

Gases, which usually cause us great discomfort, depend not on the function of the large intestine, but on the small intestine and its digestive capacity. Undigested food content from the small intestine undergoes the process of fermentation in the large intestine. Another cause of digestive problems, which can then lead to problems with too much gas, is a deficiency of Yang in the stomach, spleen, pancreas and the small intestine.

Strong contractions in the lower part of the abdomen caused by the disorder of the large intestine signify blockages of energy circulation within its meridian. A very helpful method in this case is to apply pressure to certain points on your hands. This blockage of energy has a direct influence on the functioning of the stomach. By eliminating blockages we can improve the functioning of the stomach.

Carefully analysing the problems of the large intestine (constipation, diarrhoea), we come to the conclusion that they can be intensified by cold, sour and raw food and the deficiency of Yang energy in this type of food. By consuming large quantities of fresh salads, fruit, sour dishes, cold water, beer, juices, cheeses, pastas, rice, white bread, chicken, hams and sausages, pork, sweets, and chocolate, and, of course, by neglecting spices, we create ideal conditions for all kinds of diseases of the large intestine (mostly related to damage of the mucosa or deficiency of mucus in the intestine): ulcerous inflammation, haemorrhoids, fistulas, cancers and simple constipation.

Remember:

- If the process of excretion of the stools from the large intestine depends on the kidneys and their Yang energy, then most surely by eating fruit, fresh salads and drinking cold water we will only decrease this energy.
- If peristalsis of the intestine is distorted – and normally this is connected with the function of the liver (smooth muscles and nervous system) – then eating sour and cold food can cause even more problems.

- If the large intestine is forced to digest the food undigested by the stomach and the small intestine, then cold food with no added spices will only augment this problem.

- If the large intestine needs mucus produced by the spleen for its proper functioning, then starvation diets, enemas, detox diets and eating large quantities of fruit and drinking cold water will only destroy the mucosa of the intestine and deprive the intestine of mucus (deficiency of vitamins A, D3, E, magnesium, zinc and iron).

The advice of many so-called "specialists" to implement frequent enemas, detox diets, starvation diets and use special mixtures, drinks and herbal remedies can be very dangerous for our health. Of course, we can do so once, but only when we have definitely decided to change our dietary habits and lifestyle. Only then will the detox process make sense as it enables us to break away from the "old" and enter the "new" with much better psychological comfort.

It is time to realize that our body is perfectly constructed and all the processes and transformations happening within it depend on continuous strengthening of the energy, replenishment and regeneration and self-sufficient detoxification and excretion.

It is strange indeed how we relate to the power and love of our Creator. On the one hand, we admire Him; on the other hand, we always doubt His reliability and competence. Did He disregard something and in creating us in His image forget that this wonderful body has to excrete waste? Let's think whether we do enough to enable our body to self-cleanse and excrete all the by-products of metabolism.

If we just do our duty then we will no longer have problems with constipation and excretion of toxins. Some people claim that many deposits (so-called soaps) become accumulated in the intestines. Yes, sure. But the fact is that they are the side effect of poor metabolism and deficiency of the Yang energy, always caused by a wrong diet. Inability to compose the right combinations of flavours, cooking with no spices, using the wrong combinations of different food products (eliminating some and favouring others), can lead to production of toxins during the process of metabolism which cannot be removed from the blood and the gastrointestinal system due to a deficiency of the Yang energy.

Enemas have been known since antiquity. They can alleviate suffering but cannot become the way to healthy living and should never be applied daily. If we think that we need them more than usual due to accumulation of toxins in our body, then it simply means that we have committed some cardinal dietary mistakes and have problems with metabolism. This kind of dysfunction causes constipation and can eventually lead to serious diseases.

I remind you here once more that, if our body is in a state of balance, eating meat (protein) never leads and will never lead to the harmful process of rotting; however, the meat should be always balanced out with all the flavours, and the nature of the meat itself must also be taken into consideration. The process of rotting happens only in two cases: if the meat is part of an unbalanced meal with no added spices and accompanied by raw and sour vegetables and fruit, juices, cold drinks and sweets, and if the body is weak, overcooled and suffering from deficiency of the Yang energy.

Another very important fact is that the process of rotting never happens in the stomach. Food can only dwell in the stomach for a little longer than usual. This is caused by a weakening of the stomach, small intestine, pancreas and liver. The rotting process, if it ever happens, will then usually happen in the large intestine. Therefore our fear of meat is completely unjustified.

Doctors warn against using laxatives. They say that under their influence the intestine becomes lazy. What, then, is an apple eaten before going to bed or water drunk first thing in the morning? It is nothing else but such a laxative. The nature of this kind of laxative is strongly cooling and makes the undigested food matter simply "flow" through the intestines. And most likely it does not clean the intestines properly, leaving small pieces of food in some parts of them. Apples and water cannot regulate the digestive process and the functioning of the large intestine. Instead, they can actually make it lazy.

The functioning of the large intestine depends on the strength and energy of the stomach, spleen and pancreas, on the condition of the small intestine and on the efficiency of the liver and kidneys. An important role is also played in this case by the circulation (pericardium), which enables transportation of energetic and building factors crucial in the regeneration of the intestines; also, around the dorsal hip muscles are located pericardial muscles which can contract and thus cause blockages of blood circulation and affect the functioning of the intestines. This condition can be augmented by contractions of the muscles of the large intestine, which can also be located around the dorsal hip muscles.

Faced with problems with the large intestine, one should:

- eat only warm, home-cooked and well-balanced food
- use different spices regardless of any intestinal problems
- in your meals use mostly food products of the sweet flavour: carrots, parsley root, parsnip, pumpkin, pattypan squash, courgettes, potatoes, fish-liver oil, butter
- eat small portions of meat (veal, young beef, dark turkey meat); it will enable stimulation of those hormones which regulate metabolism and regeneration of the intestinal tissue
- be careful with fibre – excess of it (for example, oat bran) stimulates bonding of precious mineral salts, weakens the functioning of the bodily organs, irritates the intestinal mucosa and can also affect the level of insulin
- be careful with gluten (wheat protein), which has a destructive effect on the intestinal mucosa

- be aware that stress and an excess of sadness and sorrow can lead to very serious complications

- remember that every weakening of the Centre leads to problems with the lungs and large intestine.

As I have already mentioned, constipation can be the beginning of much more serious diseases, which eventually occur when our body is in a state of the so-called "false fire". And this fire, as we already know, is a consequence of serious damage or weakening of the Centre, and most especially the spleen. This leads to a deficiency of the digestive enzymes and mucus and poor quality of blood, all of which has an impact on the digestive process and the functioning of the large intestine.

Bleeding of the large intestine signifies problems with the mucosa and its dryness (deficiency of mucus), which makes it impossible to regenerate (hormonal, vitamin and mineral deficiencies). The liver is responsible for regeneration of the mucosa and sufficient quantity of vitamin A in the body. However, bursting of blood vessels is dependent on the spleen. Once we switch to a well-balanced diet all the haemorrhages will pass. But they are likely to come back if we start eating again, for example, raw fruit or gherkins. Very helpful in this condition are saunas based on cirsium.

Portion of reason

Diets

Diets are particular methods of nutrition based on quantitative restrictions, selective implementation or complete elimination of certain food products. Diets should only be applied in extreme cases, when our health condition requires it. Due to a growing number of health problems nowadays, many varied dietary methods have appeared.

Some of them take their origin in traditional dietary recommendations, which were concerned with taking special remedies for a certain period of time in anticipation of a full recovery. Modern recommendations very rarely warn people about the consequences of a thoughtless and overly extended treatment regime. Traditional recommendations on treatment of specific diseases are often used nowadays as a starting point in creating the so-called "diet of/for life" or in order to find new ways of nutrition and health restoration. However, one should notice that the causes of diseases are different nowadays from what they used to be in the old days. Therefore, even though there are methods of successful treatment, or even saving life, we should not see them as recipes for life which are good for everyone. We have to remember that ridding oneself of a disease and saving one's life is not the same thing as preventing diseases and maintaining good health.

Prolonged application of even the most miraculous remedies can lead to serious disorders, because after reaching the ultimate aim of balance, the body can quickly lose it again and become incapable of self-defence. We must remember that every remedy is treated by our body as a concrete energy of a concrete function.

Our health depends on many external factors, but most of all on regular, varied, appropriately prepared and warm food.

Traditional remedies may bring relief of suffering, or even save life, but they will not secure inner balance and consequently good health. The most advisable thing would be to combine the treatment with a well-balanced diet that would enable restoration of inner energy and essence as well as inner balance, which is crucial to the process of recovery.

Diets can be supportive of treatment by different remedies. But they should be applied for a specific purpose and should last only for a certain period of time. Selective nutrition applied for a long time can only distort the balance within the body and lead to dysfunction of bodily organs and emotional problems. Diets should never be treated as a lifestyle. Their function is to restore the energy within the body.

Detox diets, starvation diets, vegetarianism

Do you create or destroy? Dag Hammarskjöld

Is fear a good adviser, especially when it comes to our life and body? Our choices are influenced by our intentions; both send us various pieces of "advice". If we carry within ourselves fear caused by questions on the purpose and sense of life, we start emanating energy of a specific frequency. This means that we will only attract specific kinds of situations as well as people. Everything starts from us. If we do not trust ourselves and do not accept who we are and what we have experienced or who we have become, or if we do not know how to strengthen our body without destroying it at the same time, then we will never be able to "find" ourselves, we will not be able to love and the word "love" will have a hollow ring.

If we truly loved ourselves, we would not destroy our body, even if some spiritual guru was trying to convince us to do so. In fact, we are our own gurus. We carry within ourselves the wisdom of the whole Universe. We should slow down and listen to our body. It will tell us all we need to know.

Starvation diets have become very fashionable. And detox diets have turned into some kind of obsession. In normal circumstances, if our body was provided with an appropriate quantity and quality of nutrients and Yang energy, these kinds of procedures would be unnecessary – the body would be strong enough to cleanse itself.

During the first phase of a starvation diet, the body starts using up all the stored material – mainly fats and the protein structures of the living cells. During the second phase, a shortage of sugar occurs, which means that fats cannot be burnt properly and the body becomes contaminated with ketone bodies; the usage of proteins drops down to a minimum. During the third phase, all energetic deficiencies need to be covered at the cost of one's own proteins; this leads to destruction and wearing out of the muscles, endocrine glands and other bodily organs. The strongest organs are the lungs, heart and nervous system. All of these phases lead to a strong acidification of the body and contamination with the by-products of bad metabolism. The body then starts emitting a very unpleasant smell.

The content of fat in a healthy liver is around 3%. In certain circumstances – a high-fat diet, starvation diet, physical exhaustion, diabetes, reduced quantity of choline and methionine (due to not eating eggs or eating a diet based exclusively on large quantities of raw vegetables and fruit) – the liver can even contain 30–40% fat (fatty liver).

Do we know what is responsible for the accumulation of these toxins? It is easy to explain. It starts when our metabolism does not operate at the appropriate energetic level. This means that biochemical reactions cannot be finalized, and in effect this contributes to creating by-products and supplementary compounds. On the other hand, poor blood circulation, weakened due to a deficiency of Yang energy and malfunction of the bodily organs, causes accumulation of the products of metabolism within the intercellular spaces, all of which should be absorbed firstly by lymph and then by blood and be neutralized or excreted from the body. Problems with metabolism lead to serious hormonal disorders. All of these disorders can be stimulated by emotional problems and stress.

Any kind of detox, whether it is based on water, or juices and fruit, or herbal remedies, will only increase our health problems, as it additionally overcools the body, weakens blood circulation and deregulates metabolism. Yes, it is true that we will rid our body of most of the toxins, but detox only lasts for a short period of time and we eventually go back to the normal level. We start again but this time we take off from a lower level. We have less substance – Yin and Yang energy. And during the process of metabolism new toxins start being produced, but our body is too weak to get rid of them. And so they start accumulating again. Then we go through another detox diet and drop down another level again. Our mind enters a state of chaos.

Some people feel very bad after detox; they feel cold, weak, have problems with digestion, suffer from headaches and generally feel shattered. Other ailments also appear – all to do with the weakening of the body. Starvation diets and detoxes generate gigantic Yin, which destroys balance within the body. And Yang means spirituality. How can we achieve the right body form when we undergo starvation diets and detox? We must remember that our body is capable of self-cleansing; we need only to take proper care of ourselves, protect our body against cold and excessive stress and feed it with well-balanced food rich in Yang energy.

Some people may experience the state of false Yang, especially when they have starved and overcooled themselves many times. During starvation, the function of the spleen gets blocked, which leads to contraction of skeletal muscles. This activates the so-called emergency metabolism within certain bodily organs (especially the heart, lungs, liver and pancreas). As a result of this, energy is released at the cost of these organs' moisture. It is this particular energy that gives the effect of detoxification of the body and the illusion that the body is stronger and healthier. But it is a short-lasting feeling. Due to the deficiency of energy and matter, the spleen stops producing essence and moisture. The body starts drying out. But we should still have within us our Yang of birth. The balance disappears and the fire starts dominating. What happens then? A person undergoing this process can become euphoric, excitable, full of energy, and may experience some kind of "high". They may also be rid of certain illnesses of cold (colds, catarrh, flues, tonsillitis, allergies). Everything seems to be wonderful. This state lasts for some time. Then they try to eat a normal meal and the body rejects it. So they start eating just fruit, raw or cooked vegetables, and drinking large quantities of water and juices. After some time, their condition worsens, so they decide to undergo another starvation, and then another and another… Each time, they have a feeling that they are so close to reaching their ultimate goal. Unfortunately, serious health problems start to appear, as well as emotional problems, and the process of ageing speeds up. They burn out from within. And all of their efforts turn out to lead to a dead end. They start regretting it and blaming others for their state. But the fact is that they went on this road because they wanted to be…

Vegetarianism and macrobiotics are both methods of nutrition based on elimination of animal products. They differ in their selective approach towards plant products. A macrobiotic diet is mostly based on grains and cereals, whilst vegetarianism includes all plant products. The macrobiotic diet, similar to a vegetarian diet or diet based on fruit and vegetables, leads equally to acidification of the body. It might appear shocking but it is true, despite common opinion that only meat products acidify the body and plant products are more alkaline. But this should be shocking only to academic specialists and not to us, as we already know that all that weakens the spleen has an acidifying effect on the body.

Both of these diets, applied for a longer period of time, can lead to serious dysfunction of the middle heater and consequently dysfunction of the whole body. The macrobiotic diet is especially dangerous in that the energy leads to blockages and stimulates production of mucus. And a vegetarian diet overcools the body due to eating large quantities of fresh salads and fruit and drinking cold drinks. Both of these diets damage the spleen and thus affect the process of regeneration of the body and especially the blood-formation process. But the biggest problem here is the poor quality and quantity of blood. How can we even talk about spirituality when the nest of the Spirit – the blood – is in danger?

If we decide to apply a starvation diet, detox, vegetarian diet or any other diet based on nutritional restrictions, we do so because of our convictions and of our own free will. Yes, we have the right to do it. But do we really know our original intentions behind it? Do we realize what kind of stereotypes and schemes we are following? Well, Dear Readers, we are usually manipulated into feelings of guilt and fear of rejection and condemnation. We have been stuck in these schemes for centuries and they take away the joy of living and creation from us. We feel guilty that our body is filled with toxins, impure and defiled; we think this prevents us from reaching the higher level of spirituality; we think of ourselves as ill and ugly. We feel we have to detoxify our body and this eventually turns into an obsession.

And what is the truth? Truly toxic are the convictions and thinking modes which block our soul (subconscious) from being open to the Good News, the world, ourselves and love. We live in fear. Let's raise the vibration of our body and we will see what kind of impurities will start coming out of us. We will see how much suffering and emotions our body has accumulated.

We kill animals in order to eat meat; then we start feeling guilty as we know that killing is wrong. We fear God's anger and in order to tame Him and please Him we sacrifice our own body. We choose asceticism, starvation, detox, vegetarianism. We stop killing animals, but do we realize that we start killing ourselves, our own body and God within us? Our mantra, chosen by us, is to create ourselves and God within us. We do it out of respect to all we have been given; we work on creating the right kind of essence within us – the essence which will elevate us spiritually and make us in God's image. We must not kill! But we also must not kill ourselves within us. We must not kill God within us. We should experience the world through our body. God does not need our sacrifice; He wants you to experience the joy of life.

Going back to killing – we must not kill for pleasure! And we should not treat farm animals the way we do nowadays. This is the thing we should learn.

The proof that through asceticism we only drift away from God is the fact that by lowering our vibration (through vegetarianism, starvation diets, detox diets and other diets) we activate our Ego. Our consciousness becomes unable to control our pride, feeling of superiority, self-contentment, lack of tolerance, fear, guilt, aggression, sadness and sorrow. It is very difficult to feel empathy or accept others, to trust and feel joy, to reach a feeling of self-worth. We can only feel all of these emotions once we reach the higher level of vibration, when our Ego and all the feelings connected to it become subordinate to our new consciousness, freed from all the old thinking modes.

"Be aware of all those who claim that through a special kind of nutrition or through special methods of fakirs concerned with special kinds of food and breathing techniques one can reach a higher level of spirituality."

Slimming tablets

Obesity is a disease – that is a fact. Conventional medicine claims that obesity is the main cause of diabetes, arteriosclerosis, heart attacks, blood clots and high blood pressure, kidney or liver diseases and so on. But by saying so it only proves that it still knows nothing about the subject. Can a disease be a cause of another disease? It can, but only when its first symptoms are initially ignored.

Nobody becomes obese because they want to. Even the people who say to everyone around that they feel good being overweight, that they are happy because of it, are really crying inside. It is not true that obesity can bring happiness.

One cannot demand that an obese person simply lose weight and claim that it is their only hope of being healthy. If a doctor gives such an ultimatum, they should also indicate the proper and efficient way of achieving this goal.

What do they normally propose? They say "stop overeating" or suggest the 1000-calorie diet or simply prescribe some pills. How can one "stop overeating" when one's body needs energy? And we already know what kind of effect the 1000-calorie diet can have on the body.

What about the tablets, then? Until recently, there have been two kinds of tablet on the market – one kind was a derivative of amphetamine and the other one had a similar effect. After twenty years of "helping", they have been finally withdrawn from the market, as they cause very serious side effects.

In recent years, other kinds of tablet have come on the market. The producers and health services claim that they are much safer and cause only minimal side effects… One of them was supposed to cure depression but turned out to be ineffective(!) so somebody decided that it would be much more effective as a slimming tablet instead (!). With this tablet you can "eat what you want" and feel satisfied even after small portions of food. The supposedly "safer" side effects these tablets cause are increased sweating, dryness in the mouth, insomnia, sometimes high blood pressure or a faster heartbeat. The producers of this tablet claim that it will not only stimulate weight loss but also inspire people to change their dietary habits. In what way??!!

The other kind of tablet blocks the decomposition of fats within the digestive system; therefore, an obese person is forced to reduce the amount of fat in their food, otherwise they can suffer from steatorrhea. The producer of this tablet also suggests eating large quantities of vegetables and fruit in order to supplement the body in those vitamins which normally dissolve in fats – vitamin A, D, E and K (but none of these vitamins can be found in vegetables and fruits!!!). The only "innocent" side effect is frequent diarrhoea or problems with faecal incontinence. But the producers claim that diarrhoea will force obese people to start eating low-calorific food, such as fruit and vegetables. They also claim that the tablet does not affect the nervous system as it does not enter the blood circulation!

I would like to mention that peripheral nerves are made up of only 10% axons and dendrites, 30% myelin sheath – lipid substance (fat), and 60% connective tissue. Like any other tissues within the body, these tissues require continuous regeneration and renewal, or, in other words, a constant supply of the building, regulating and energetic compounds. In order for this to happen there needs to be proper blood circulation and a sufficient quantity of blood.

So, what do you think about it? I am completely terrified by this total lack of knowledge of human physiology. Just to remind you:

- Dryness in the mouth is a symptom of a weakening and malfunctioning of the spleen due to a deficiency of the Yang energy and matter (food) – the spleen holds the production of essence and moisture and in consequence is unable to moisten the body from within.
- Excessive sweatiness is a symptom of a Yin–Yang imbalance, which can be very dangerous for the heart.
- Insomnia is an evident symptom of a Yin–Yang imbalance and a deficiency of moisture (blood) in the liver and heart.
- High blood pressure – liver or kidney problems are caused by a hormonal imbalance and deficiency of Yin.
- Fat-free food can have a very dangerous effect on the nervous system, endocrine system and metabolism.
- Consumption of only fresh salads and fruit can cause a big deficiency of Yang within the body and lead to premature ageing and destruction of the body; other symptoms are: heart attacks, diabetes, liver cirrhosis, gastritis, asthma, allergies, rheumatism, and so on.

Cooking means creating

Fantasy, imagination, focus, joy – they are all attributes of the process of creation. Thoughts affect creativeness as much as creativeness affects our thoughts. It is a closed circle. A malnourished person will not be able to create; they will not have enough willpower to change their life and the reality around them. They are usually stuck in the thick fog of their own incapacitation.

It is a strange thing, the cooking process. All those societies and cultures which can be proud of their long culinary traditions treat people and their households as priorities not because they have to or have been told to do so, but because they know that these are the sources of joy and happiness. Perhaps it has something to do with their well-balanced cuisine which is perfect for them?

Let's have a look at ourselves. We are often courageous, inventive, have a wonderful imagination and sense of humour. We should be on top of the world. But instead we seem to be stuck in one and the same place. Why is this? Why, instead of following our own dreams, do we tend to always look up and compare ourselves to others? Why do we have so many complexes? Has it got something to do with the way we eat? It is quite obvious that our contemporary cuisine supplies us with energy low in vibrations. But even the cuisine of our grandmothers was poor in warming spices, but due not so much to a lack of knowledge but to poverty and circumstances.

And then we entered the days when it was perceived as shameful to cook, to taste, to feed our loved ones, to take care of them and eat all meals at a table in the presence of the whole family. Households with dark kitchens are the best example of this. The woman was supposed to all of a sudden fulfil herself outside of the house. And in modern days this model is still carried on – it still does not behove to cook, stay at home and look after our own children. We are easily taken in by kitschy culinary methods, ready-made products which significantly speed up the cooking process. In restaurants and pubs, almost all of the meals taste the same. Nobody takes their time to taste and create them properly.

But nowadays we more often experience the effects of our culinary negligence. Let's have a look at the children, adults and elderly people. Their faces can tell us a lot. Why is there so much sadness in their eyes? Why so much suffering? Who is responsible for our children's aggression, unfriendliness and lack of tolerance? Where is our patience towards our children and parents? Why are the elderly so apathetic and hopeless? Did you know that all of these emotions appear when bodily organs are in a state of imbalance? It is a physiological process which can be easily changed!!!

Our reality and feelings are an expression of our consciousness and our energy, which depends on our dietary habits and the beauty of the objects around us; we can also influence them by being friendly and respectful towards others.

We should give in to the magical influence of the energy of music, beautiful paintings or the written word. All these can significantly lift our vibrations, make us happy, elated, euphoric and full of love. Why is it so difficult to accept the meaning of the appropriate energetic composition in our food? This food can also lift our vibration, make us happy and full of a zest for living. We should not neglect our sense of taste – it is very important too! When a painter creates a painting, he or she chooses the most beautiful colours; a musician always listens to the vibration of different sounds; a poet chooses the right words; a sculptor must be familiar with the quality of different materials and decide which one will be best for their sculpture. Whilst cooking, we gather energy which gives life to our loved ones. Therefore, we should ask whether a woman cooking a soup is simply a housewife or more of an artist?

Every artist needs to get to know the secrets of their profession; they study under their masters for many years. Should we not then spend some time learning about the impact of different compositions of flavours?

Nutrition for pregnant women, babies and small children

My Dear Ladies, do you want to give birth to healthy babies and go through a joyful motherhood, seeing your babies blissfully sucking your breasts, then growing up and being happy? Do you? Then get yourself to work and start learning! First, you have to decide what you really want: health or sickness, a good night's sleep or being stressed all night long asking yourself "why is the baby crying?" Then you have to understand the workings of various energies determining our life and learn to cook well-balanced meals.

The condition of a baby is dependent on its mother's nutrition during pregnancy. The baby in the womb is like a fruit up on a tree that grows and ripens thanks to the never-ending essence of the Earth and sun. The foetal stage of prenatal development is very important. It is the time of formation of all of the bodily organs and their preparation for independent functioning. Perhaps they are still not fully developed at the moment of birth, but they allow a newborn baby to grow properly. But only under one condition – that the baby is fed with the milk of its mother.

The nutrition of pregnant women and the energy of the food they eat have an important bearing on the development of the foetus and its bodily organs. And the quality of milk during the lactation period depends on the mother's diet too. The quality of the mother's milk contributes directly to the healthy development of a baby.

Feeding babies with formula is a different matter. From what the producers of infant supplements and institutes of nutrition have to offer, we can see that human physiology is still a mystery and common sense is worth its weight in gold. I would suggest that mothers, or even those specialists, live on baby food for a month, in portions proportional to their body weight, of course. And I am not talking here about the flavours or smells of these popular baby formulas, but most of all about their nature and energetic content. Also, do not forget the fact that babies and small children can be real gourmets.

Knowing the energies of different flavours, we can choose the right kind of food for pregnant women. They should definitely avoid all kinds of food of the sour flavour, such as gherkins, cheeses, yogurts, sour soups, fruit, chicken; this is because all of these products have a contractive effect on the body; they block the development and growth of the foetus.

It is also important to avoid cold food, as it restricts the production of the appropriate quantity and quality of essence and leads to contraction of bodily organs, especially the intestines. All of these problems successively accumulate and affect the mother (e.g. poor health after giving birth, post-natal depression) as well as the baby (intestinal problems, respiratory problems – coughs, catarrh and snuffles).

Pregnant women should not eat raw food, as it is heavy to digest and absorb and leads to dysfunctions of the large intestine, such as constipation and diarrhoea. Fresh salads can help initially with emptying one's bowels, as they have some laxative properties. However, their energy blocks the function of the spleen and prevents production of moisture; this leads to dryness of the intestines. Fresh salads will not regulate the process of excretion or the function of the large intestine. They actually weaken the liver and affect peristalsis of the intestines. Eating large quantities of fresh salads during pregnancy can lead to a deficiency of Yang and circulatory problems, and due to a weakened digestive process, deficiencies of the most basic nutrients – vitamins and minerals – may appear.

Of particular danger for pregnant women are also all kinds of supplements and artificial vitamins, as they simply deregulate the function of the middle heater. The absorption of vitamins and mineral salts is a complex process, and in order for it to happen, the body must secure the appropriate natural conditions and parameters (well-functioning bodily organs).

This kind of condition can be secured by warm, well-balanced and varied food with added spices; this would contain the appropriate energies (flavours), catalysers (spices), Yang energy (Chi and warmth) and all kinds of indispensable vitamins and mineral salts.

Pregnant women should be sensible, conscious and responsible for their own decisions. If they take care of things in time and create a certain hierarchy of actions, then pregnancy has a chance to develop without complications and the whole period will become filled with great joy. Once they know that well-balanced food is the most important thing which is best for them, they can then commit tiny “sins” from time to time and eat something they really crave, following the saying that “a pregnant woman can eat anything”.

But their “little sins” should be of restricted quantity and always neutralized afterwards. We feel like eating biscuits? Great. But we can always sprinkle those ready-made biscuits with ginger, cinnamon, and cardamom and drink boiled coffee with spices or our special tea with them. Apples and pears should be cooked with spices or even red wine. Apples can also be baked, but never served as a dessert, but rather as an addition to meaty meals (as the sour flavour). We should not drink cold water at all, but if we really have to, then we should take one sip and hold it in the mouth, mixing it with saliva, until it becomes warm. The same applies to juices. We feel like eating some white cheese? Go on then. But eat it only for breakfast with a large quantity of spices, onion or garlic, together with a piece of toast and some porridge. You feel like pizza from time to time? Why not? But only with a large quantity of added spices. And the same with our famous tomato soup – cook it according to the recipe with a large quantity of garlic and onion and always based on veal or beef stock.

A woman expecting a baby should remember that the caprices of her taste buds – that is, an appetite for something sour, sweet, salty or bitter – should warn her about a Yin–Yang imbalance within her body. In other words, it is also a symptom of a malfunctioning spleen (deficiency of Yin – moisture), weak or blocked blood circulation and deficiency of the Yang energy. These sudden appetites for different flavours are usually caused by a deficiency of essence (needed for building the baby's body), and all those fashionable foods and satisfying one's own needs only augment the problem. If pregnant women implement a well-balanced diet, they should be able to avoid the aforementioned problems.

Some advice for the beginning of pregnancy:

- Eliminate all raw, sour and cold food.

- If you really crave something sour, then eat a bowl of vegetable soup, have a cup of tea (see the *Philosophy of Health*), eat a sandwich with carrots, veal and chives, eat a plate of freshly boiled potatoes with some butter, some asparagus, stewed vegetables or a salad made of boiled vegetables – this will stimulate the spleen to produce moisture which will then balance out the suffering liver and your craving for the sour flavour will pass.

- If you have an appetite for something sweet, then ask yourself whether you are stressed. If so, then isolate yourself, relax and – the same as you did with the sour flavour craving – try to eat every two hours, a small but warm and well-balanced meal.

- If you crave something salty (e.g. ham or sausages), then eat some bean soup with chickpeas and lentils (remember to add appropriate spices) and small quantities of fish (freshwater fish is the best) and do what you did with the other cravings.

- If you have a craving for coffee, then prepare it according to the recipe – you do not need to worry: boiled coffee does not have a negative effect on the liver or the nervous system. You do not need to worry about your baby either.

- Your main duty is to eat often but in small portions. All your meals should be varied. Each one should contain an optimal quantity of nutrients, such as B vitamins, vitamins A, D, E, and important mineral salts, such as magnesium, zinc, iron, chromium, calcium, and potassium. You must remember that you will not find most of these nutrients in yogurts, cheeses, juices, fruit, sweets, fresh salads, etc. You need meat (veal, beef, turkey and giblets), legumes, large quantities of onion, garlic, leeks, a little bit of cabbage, a lot of carrots, parsley roots, parsnips, pumpkin, courgettes, sweet potatoes, eggs, butter, honey, grains, the green parts of plants; you should only use the sour flavour to balance out your meals.

- You have to tame your cravings because excesses of certain flavours (sour, sweet, salty) can prevent the proper development of your baby; you know well the energy of all of these flavours and you know what a destructive effect they can have on the body. By satisfying your cravings you can cause a significant energetic chaos.

- Do not be afraid of different spices – they are indispensable in a well-balanced meal. Eat frequently in peace and quiet and always eat your fill. Do not think that you might put on weight; with well-balanced food it is actually impossible.

A feeding mother should apply an even more restrictive diet, as the baby reacts to every single flavour; it could be a slice of tomato, a slice of ham, a biscuit, sour soup, too much fat (butter, fatty sauce). You must remember that the energy of the mother's milk is exactly the same as the energy of the food she puts into her mouth.

The baby can react to this in different ways – it can be anxious and start crying; it can express a continuous need for suckling; it can spit, suffer from diarrhoea, loose stools, colic, constipation, snuffles, catarrh, cough, ear pain, rash, or high temperature. The first most worrying symptom is a snuffle – it signifies that the mother's food was of mucus-forming quality (sweets, cheeses, fruit) and that the milk has acquired its nature. The baby's body starts producing pathological mucus, which is then accumulated in the lungs; this weakens the lungs and leads to snuffles, catarrh, then cough and consequently to ear pain.

Do not panic! Your food needs to be simply very carefully selected (no sweets, no fruit and fresh salads, nothing very fatty or sour, and under no condition should you eat cheese, chicken, pork or ham and sausages!); instead eat a lot of garlic and onion, drink tea and also ginger tea or the "killer" tea, and everything will go back to normal. Antibiotics are definitely not necessary in this case. You can cure your baby yourself!

Spitting-up in babies is also a symptom of dietary mistakes made by their mothers. It usually appears after the mother has eaten large quantities of sweets, cakes, puddings, sweet dishes, bread with honey and fatty food.

After the first worrying symptom the mother should realize what kind of food causes such a reaction. She should immediately eliminate these mistakes and introduce to her diet the aforementioned well-balanced food. For example, suppurative spots on the baby's face signify accumulation of mucus in its lungs, and is directly connected to an excess of fat and sweets in the mother's diet.

A breastfed baby can only be cured by its own mother's milk. The baby is what the mother eats and produces. Any form of dysfunction in the baby signifies a dysfunction within its mother's body. Her milk is a quintessence of the energy from her food; it can also be affected by her emotions. And we already know which kind of energy can cure the body – which also applies to the body of a baby.

Let's give ourselves some time for reflection. Not the motherly kind of reflection (her heart has enough pain already) but rather the scientific kind of reflection. Do our imagination and knowledge really have to end on antibiotics, hormonal medicines, genes, transplants and the production of artificial bodily organs?

In fact, the production and accumulation of mucus in the body of a baby, and then treating it with antibiotics and hormonal anti-inflammatory medicines, can form the beginning of much more serious diseases. I remind you here once more what kind of diseases these can be: low immunity, allergies, asthma, cerebral palsies, epilepsy, autism, diabetes, tumours, cancers, cardiovascular problems, kidney and lung dysfunction, problems with digestion and absorption, physical and mental underdevelopment, excitability, apathy, and obesity.

Can we help a two- or three-month-old breastfed baby suffering from catarrh or cough (because the mother eats a lot of biscuits, yogurts and cheeses) to rid itself of mucus by treating it with antibiotics? Absolutely not, because antibiotics can only stimulate the production of mucus and additionally they are of cooling and contracting properties. Antibiotics only help to accumulate more mucus and thicken it, but they do not get rid of it. This leads to an even stronger weakening of the body and destruction of the spleen. The quantity of mucus within the body only rises. The improvement after the use of antibiotics is only temporary. And after some time the mucus manifests its presence again through catarrh, coughs, ear problems or rashes. The problem escalates due to the application of a new series of stronger antibiotics. After a year or two, the physical condition of our child is so poor that it enters the phase of chronic health problems.

I will give you a concrete example of how a wise mother took care of her five-month-old son's health condition. She breastfed him, of course. When she noticed that the baby snuffled she realized that it must have been caused by the sweets she liked to eat from time to time. She knew straight away that the sweet flavour was responsible for accumulation of mucus in her son's body. So, she started a delicate warming up; she drank the "killer" tea (see recipe in the *Philosophy of Health*), then she ate some beef or veal, or lamb broth with added turkey meat, and generally she started being much more careful of what she was eating. The baby started coughing. Initially, it was a dry cough. So, the mother gave her son some Emser salt diluted in a small quantity of warm water. The next day the baby's cough changed and became wet. At this point, she had to rid her son of the unnecessary moisture. How? She did not do it with antibiotics, even though her home health visitor prescribed them twice for him. The mother started drinking small portions of ginger tea, constantly observing her son. From time to time, she also drank the "killer" tea. But most of all, she took care of her diet. Her son was coughing quite intensively initially; he had to be held in the arms more often or put in his bed with his head slightly higher than the rest of his body. Some pus started coming out from his ears. But the mother knew that this was a very good symptom, because the baby was simply undergoing the process of cleansing from within. She only cleaned the ears properly using a few drops of camphor oil.

Is the mucus in the form of coughs, catarrh or ear discharge in children something negative or positive? This kind of treatment was very appropriate, as the mother got rid of the true causes as well as the symptoms of her son's health problems. The best medicine in this case was the mother's different approach to what she ate and drank – the food and drinks rich in Yang energy. They were the indispensable stimuli for ridding the baby's body of the mucus.

The baby started slowly to retrieve his balance; he became calmer, started sleeping properly, was joyful and smiling during the day and had a good appetite. And what was the reaction of the doctor during the next visit? She checked the baby and said that he was absolutely healthy; that his lungs and ears were clear and that he was developing very well. The mother told her about her treatment without the antibiotics. The doctor was very surprised and said that she did not have a clue what kind of method the mother had used but told her to carry on using it.

What mother would do something like this? Only the one who trusts that what she does is absolutely best for her and her baby. And only the mother who knows about all those nuances of the well-balanced diet and has the courage to go against the advice of her family and friends.

A very common ailment in babies is colic and painful flatulence. The baby usually cries because of the pain; it cannot sleep or eat. Only by passing the gases can relief be achieved. Colic is caused by all sour food and an excess of calcium, yogurts, milk, floury products, juices and fruit. All of these factors lead to a dysfunction of the spleen, pancreas and liver, as well as contraction of the intestinal muscles and blockages of the flow of energy and blood. The most common way of ridding the baby of flatulence is by giving them some water with sugar. As we know, the sweet flavour relaxes the liver. But is this kind of sweet flavour appropriate for the liver of a baby? Relief can be bought by the mother eating some carrots. We can also give the baby some carrot soup (as a remedy), followed by well-balanced food of mostly a sweet flavour.

If a breastfed baby cries because of colic, then it is usually caused by dietary mistakes made by the mother. She should not eat fish, cheeses, milk, yogurts, jams, sweets, fruit, juices – all of which are of a cooling nature. Only if the mother decides to change her dietary habits can the child become calmer and sleep much better. We can also give a baby suffering from colic a few drops of thyme-anise-(dill)-ginger tea, which will soothe the problem.

I will give you another example. There was this breastfeeding mother who ate according to the well-balanced diet, but every morning she would unthinkingly add some dried apricots and raisins to her breakfast soup. After some time, suppurative spots appeared on the cheeks of her two-month-old daughter (slightly premature baby). The doctor, of course, prescribed antibiotics, although the baby was suffering simply from accumulated mucus in the lungs and all it needed was for her mum to drink some ginger tea and be more careful with her diet. Everything came back to normal, but after some time the mother made another mistake: together with the breakfast soup she also had some bread with home-made jam. The baby got a much bigger rash on her cheeks and chin this time; the weakening of the spleen, liver and lungs was evident. The doctor decided to prescribe an even stronger antibiotic, as the diagnosis was atopic dermatitis. He also advised feeding the baby with some apple. But the mother decided to change her diet instead, which helped her to retrieve the balance and the baby started feeling fine. I do not think I have to mention here that the mother did not give her baby the antibiotics or the apple. The rash appeared once more when the mother ate too much butter.

Another example. A few-months-old breastfed baby, with proneness (inherited from his mum) to a lower level of blood was diagnosed by a doctor with heart murmurs. The doctor advised feeding the baby with apples and ready-made soups from a jar. The doctor had in mind an improvement in the process of blood-formation (!!!). The conclusion is that if we want to become mothers, we have to be very vigilant and trust our own intuition.

Mothers who carefully observe the reactions of their small, breastfed babies to the food they eat have noticed that, especially after sweet, sour, salty or very fatty food, their babies start suffering not only from physiological problems (constipation, colic, painful flatulence, high body temperature, lack of appetite) but also from anxieties and problems with sleep, especially during the night. The baby wakes up crying and does not want to sleep in a dark room, as if it is scared of something. But as soon as the mother holds the baby in her arms it calms down and falls asleep again. We have to remember that due to a weak liver (this applies to everyone) our subconscious releases our hidden fears, which are totally harmless when the liver is strong.

I do realize that the majority of women will decide to go for the antibiotic treatment; they will be happy that their children do not have the common symptoms, such as coughs, catarrh, or pus in the ears. They will be calm as, according to them, their children are in good hands. But in a month's time they can expect all of the symptoms to return…

It is an undeniable fact that mother's milk is both food and a remedy for a baby. It is a miracle. But without the knowledge of the nature of certain food products this miracle will not work!

If you are a mother, you must remember:

- Do not believe your aunties, grannies, your mother, mother-in-law or your doctor who say that your milk is bad. Change only what you eat and everything will be fine.
- If someone destroys your peace and joy of motherhood, simply hang up your phone and close the door.

- Do not tell anybody whether your child slept well or cried, whether it had problems with pooing or snuffles – these are only yours and your partner's problems. You should always say: "Thank you, everything is well".

- Be moderate when it comes to telling people about yourself, and you should not complain at all. Motherhood is a process of elevating your spirituality and learning to understand the world differently. Motherhood is for you and not for grannies, grandpas, aunties, neighbours or friends. This is your "Five Minutes".

- If you feel weak, experience a bad mood and generally start thinking that nothing makes sense – do not worry, it is not the end of the world; you are simply suffering from depression. Your body was weakened due to pregnancy and labour and your energy has dropped down to the level of your heels. Do not do anything except for cooking (according to the book), eating, sleeping and feeding your baby. Then again – cook and eat, and within a week you will feel much better. Try it; you will see that it works!

- Your baby is you – it takes over your tensions. Therefore, relax and let it go! Do not check all the time if your baby is asleep or maybe not; do not think why it eats every two hours and then all of a sudden every four hours. Your duty is to eat, feed and sleep. And if your baby is crying and demanding to be held and carried close to you, even during sleep – do it. After a few days, it will all go back to normal. The baby will spend some time close to you and then will want to sleep alone again. By caressing a baby one cannot "create" a terrorist or a hysterical person! Such a mode of thinking is a terrible stereotype.

- Breastfeed your baby as long as you can. This will, of course, depend on your inner intention, your well-balanced nutrition, your relaxation and psychological comfort. Remember that your milk is the best way to your and your baby's peace.

- Some mothers breastfeed their children up to the age of two or three years. But it is not compulsory; it is entirely your decision. Once you introduce some solid food, such as porridge or soups, your milk will become a wonderful addition, a drink to quench your child's thirst; you can feed them then in the evening, in the morning and also at night or even during the day, as long as your work allows for you to do it.

- If for some reason you have very little milk, then you can nourish your child additionally with porridge. The proportions depend on the age of the child; the older the child, the more solid food it needs.

- Remember that if you are breastfeeding your child and it seems to develop well, then do not give them anything else, and especially not juices, grated fruit, teas and vitamins. All your child needs is in your milk. All you need to do is to think of what to eat yourself.

- When your baby is 5 to 6 months old, you can start giving it additionally, as well as your milk, some vegetable soups with more carrot in it, and special porridge composed of various grains, also with an addition of carrot soup.

- For the first two weeks, we should cook fresh soups every day. And after two weeks we can cook soups that can last for two days.

- The rules of cooking for children are the same as for adults; only the products need to be different and selected appropriately to fulfil a child's special needs. These products are: sweet flavour – carrots, parsley roots, parsnips, pumpkin, potatoes, sweet potatoes, courgettes, pattypan squash, beetroot (but not too much!), butter, egg yolks, veal, loin of young beef, honey; spicy flavour – always onion, garlic or leeks, fennel, one small leaf of Savoy cabbage or Napa cabbage, one piece of cauliflower or broccoli; sour flavour – the green parts of plants, such as the young leaves of parsley, kohlrabi, celery, beetroot; bitter flavour – fresh marjoram.

- We should use spices of all flavours, but obviously in smaller quantities (always add a pinch of cumin, ginger, salt to taste, and some sour flavour to keep the balance – a few drops of lemon juice, a piece of tomato or one sprig of parsley or other greens and a pinch of turmeric and thyme).

- Soups cannot be based merely on vegetables; they should contain carbohydrates too, that is – different kinds of grains, e.g. buckwheat, pearl barley, millet, oats, cornmeal, and occasionally some rice. We can then add a teaspoon or two of grains, remembering at the same time the order of flavours. For one-year-old babies and older ones we can thicken the soups with some egg yolk and wheat-flour noodles with the addition of turmeric, or simply add some egg yolk, potatoes and, after a few weeks from serving the soup for the first time, we can add some meat (portion as big as a walnut) and then blend it. This kind of meal should be enough for three to four hours. With time, we increase the amounts of particular products.

- Soups should always be blended, but only in the element of the sour flavour. Then we bring the soup to the boil once again and add sour flavour, bitter flavour and always end with the sweet flavour. A very important thing: soups should be tasty! Children are real gourmets.

- In choosing the products for our children's soups we should follow our common sense and knowledge on the energy of products (flavours), e.g. if the soup is based on veal stock (sweet flavour), then we must not add too many sweet products, as it may result in diarrhoea or vomiting caused by a simple energetic blockage, for example: A bad combination – veal, carrots, parsley roots, parsnips, pumpkin (sweet flavour), garlic (spicy flavour), salt, and as the only sour product – a sprig of parsley. This kind of soup is not well-balanced; there is too much of the sweet flavour and not enough spicy and sour flavour (lemon or tomato juice), as well as the bitter flavour (turmeric, thyme).

- A good combination – thyme, veal, cumin, carrots, parsley roots, potatoes, onion, celeriac or Napa cabbage, ginger, half a garlic clove, salt, one sprig of parsley, a few drops of lemon, turmeric. And to thicken the soup we add some ground oats. A good combination – thyme, cumin, carrots, parsley roots, parsnips, cornmeal or millet, turkey, onion, ginger, a piece of Savoy cabbage, salt, a sprig of parsley, one teaspoon of home-made tomato juice or lemon juice. One should always be careful with beetroot – we can add it to soups but in small quantities (e.g. one slice), as beetroot is strongly overcooling and can cause intestinal problems. Similarly with celeriac and cabbages; the most useful in this case is Savoy or Napa cabbage, or a piece of cauliflower or broccoli.

- The best time to start giving our child soups is between 6 and 7 months; we can start spoon feeding around this time.

- Up to three years old, a child should be fed with only cooked, half-liquid, blended or, using a fork, carefully mashed food. Otherwise the child can end up malnourished, as at this age children are not able to chew properly. This is a very important rule.

- As long as a child is breastfed, there is no need to give them any other milk, even when breastfeeding happens only once a day, at night or in the morning; the rest of the meals should be prepared according to the recipes from the book.

- If it is necessary to give a child a few sips of tea after a meal, for better digestion, then we prepare it according to the recipe (thyme-liquorice-ginger) and serve it with a pipette or small spoon.

- An older child who is no longer breastfed can be given before bed time some fresh and full-fat cow or goat's milk with added honey, garlic or ginger; the same kind of milk we add to porridge in a ratio 1:3.

- A child up to three years old should only eat meals that have been specially prepared for them (due to different products and different spices).
- In order to force a child to chew we can give them some wheat-rye and dry bread. It should be given only as an addition to the rest of their menu. Giving them fresh bread can be very dangerous, as the undigested carbohydrates (not enough saliva) can destroy the spleen, pancreas, intestines and liver (coeliac disease).
- Warning: a sandwich with ham or a sausage is not appropriate for a small child!
- A 12–13-month-old child can be given a second course; so, breakfast at 8a.m. (porridge), soup at 12a.m., second course or more soup between 3p.m. and 4p.m., and supper between 7p.m. and 8p.m. (porridge); milk is only served as a drink at night or just before sleep.
- Older children (2–3 years) can be given for breakfast or supper additionally an egg or sandwich with meat and vegetables left from dinner, and so on.
- Around this age, we can also start adding to soups and stews a few grains of peas or beans (previously soaked), but mashed properly.
- Second courses for small children should contain carbohydrates (potatoes, home-made noodles) and goulash – it can be vegetable stew with an addition of a small quantity of meat, finely chopped, or eventually with some meat balls. We add here the same products as to the soups, only in different proportions; in season we try also to add some more green parts of vegetables. And spices are very important too.
- We can make small children some dessert from time to time; for this purpose we use only seasonal and very ripe and sweet fruit; we cook them in a small quantity of water with added spices and honey; then we blend it all together. The child does not have to fill itself up with the dessert, but only try some of it.

- Mother, do not give your child ready-made juices, yogurts, cheeses, fruit and ready-made soups. These kinds of foods have no energy, plus you already know the effect of the sour flavour and how harmful it can be to your child's body. Your milk, properly cooked porridge and soups are all your child needs for proper development.

- Do not give your child sweets. Protect them against the pressure of the family and friends who, in order to please, themselves buy them lots of sweets. When your child is nourished properly, they do not crave sweets. It is we adults who teach them to eat sweets. Children do not even realize that such things exist. Sweets for them are soups and any other meal.

- Do not teach your child to snack between meals. Your little ones, when they are fed properly, do not even think about food. They think about games and toys. There should not be anything colourful and edible around them. It is you who offers them biscuits, salty sticks, crisps, bananas, bread roll or yeast cakes…

- Once they have tried something sweet they will never tell you again that they are hungry, but that they want a sweetie. You have to be strong. Very strong!

- Do not worry about the future. Start from today and think about tomorrow at the most. Do not be afraid of all of this knowledge. It is actually quite simple. It only requires your common sense, discipline and iron will.

Nutrition of the elderly

How old do we have to be to feel old? We all know that it is a subjective matter and mostly depends on our attitude and whether we "allow" ourselves to become old. By "allowing" ourselves to become old, we simply speed up the rate of catabolism – decomposition, instead of anabolism – synthesis. In such a case, destruction of the cells exceeds their regeneration.

But can ageing be controlled only by our inner attitude, cheerfulness and the joy of life that has been experienced? Some people claim that it can. But I think that this is not enough. I think that what we eat is also of great importance, because the food and energy that is delivered to our body can activate or kill our cheerfulness and our will for living. I have already mentioned in the *Philosophy of Health* the meaning of relationships between particular functions of bodily organs and the emotions they ignite.

Let's say, then, that, regardless of our real age, we are not old and we do not "allow" ourselves to become old at all. We live a cheerful and creative life, fully conscious of the fact that each age in life has its own privileges and possibilities.

If we think of old age as a dying or extinguishing of life, then we should do everything we can to not let it happen and protect the fire within us.

So, should we really recommend to the elderly the consumption of large quantities of fruit, juices, fresh salads, low-fat cheeses, skimmed milk, yogurts, porridge, puddings and fruit compotes, being fully conscious of the energetic content of such foods? Do you think, Dear Reader, that this kind of energy would be sufficient for a body which is often overcooled, diseased, with major dysfunctions of each of the bodily organs and a very weak blood circulation? I think that it is high time to end this kind of (perhaps unconscious) destruction of the body and reduction of vitality in the elderly. It is time for normal, warm and varied food.

The elderly should eat everything in order to provide the body with all the necessary building compounds (protein), energetic compounds (carbohydrates and fats) and regulating compounds (mineral salts and vitamins). Unfortunately, there are only trace quantities of all of these compounds in fruit, fresh salads, puddings, juices, white cheese or lemon tea. We already know that one can gain strength only from food of an appropriate energetic content sufficient to stimulate life actions. The key to a "youthful" old age is the proper composition of meals. They should be composed in such a way that allows digestion of all of the food content and, consequently, regeneration and improvement of the body.

But we can be almost sure that it will not be easy to convince our beloved "elderly" to change their dietary habits, as they are "programmed" to eat "healthy" food products.

I remember how difficult it was to convince my own father (he is now 86 years old) that all the fresh fruits from his own garden (raspberries, strawberries, apples, black cherries), all home-made preserves, sour milk, sour soups (tomato soup, cabbage soup) and chicken are not good for him and lead to many diseases. It was because he used to eat large quantities of fruit and home-made preserves (because of the alleged vitamins!) during autumn and winter that he would normally be ill at the beginning of January. The first illness to appear was a long-lasting flu, followed by depression and the feeling of hopelessness; eventually all of this resulted in shingles on his face. After eliminating all sour food, he returned to good health. Many times during the summer he phones me and says: "You were right telling me off for eating all of those fresh fruits." Whenever I phone him, I can almost immediately tell what he has been eating judging by his mood. He knows that he should avoid the sour flavour; he feels very ill after eating sour foods and sometimes it even affects his heartbeat.

When I talk to my father I do realize that it must be hard for him to see all the hard work he invested in his garden, taking care of his fruit trees, is of no use to him. We – his children – do not really want this fruit.

Let's think how many strawberry plants or apple, pear and cherry trees should statistically fall per head? How much fruit should (can!) one eat in season? My father has finally accepted the fact that neither he nor we want his apples any more. He has also realized that he feels much better after eating some young potatoes with butter, vegetable soup or steamed carrots.

In my opinion, we should grow more onion, garlic, carrot, parsley root, fennel, parsnip, pumpkin, courgettes and sweet potatoes.

Some advice for elderly people:

- All meals should be balanced according to the Five Elements and Yin–Yang theories.
- We should use all kinds of spices; if we use them in the recipes proposed in this book, then there is no risk of feeling sick afterwards. More harm can be done by not adding enough spices, as it is almost certain that it will badly affect the process of digestion.
- The portions of food should be small and eaten at 2–3-hour intervals.
- As long as it is possible, all meals should be cooked and served warm; bread should be treated merely as a side dish.
- Older people should only eat stale bread.
- Meat is also very important, but it should be of an appropriate energy; I would mostly suggest veal, young beef, turkey, lamb and giblets.
- Sweet vegetables should become the base of all meals and always be accompanied by onion and garlic as additional flavours and important remedies; cabbages of all kinds should be eaten in moderation.
- As to spring vegetables, I would suggest only chives for the elderly, or, from time to time, some lettuce with garlic dressing as a side dish for meat meals.

- One should definitely include in their diet: eggs, butter, fish-liver oil, legumes and grains.

- I strongly recommend the so-called breakfast soups based on oats, as they contain a special cereal protein which is easy to absorb; the only proviso is that it should be cooked for at least 40 minutes.

- I do not recommend: hams and sausages, chicken, low-fat cheeses, sour foods, fresh fruit and vegetables, cold drinks and black tea, white rice, pastas, creamy cakes with fresh fruit and yeasty cakes.

So, the menu consisting of sandwiches with margarine and lean ham or low-fat cheeses, yogurts, fresh salads, chicken or fish, compotes, and for dessert – coffee with cream and cake, apples, oranges, water, should be replaced by stale bread with butter and herbal pepper, eggs with pepper and horseradish, porridge, meat-veg goulashes with large quantities of onion, garlic and spices, vegetable soups based on calf or turkey bone stock, home-made meat for sandwiches, and well-spiced salads made of cooked vegetables.

There is this common opinion that older people should eat small portions of food, regardless of their body weight. Yes, it is true. But in this case they should eat something at least every 3 hours. This is absolutely vital for the regeneration and renewal of the body. Otherwise they will lose weight, as well-balanced food activates the process of proper metabolism and requires frequent replenishment of the building and regulating compounds. Only then can we be sure that the outer symptoms of ageing (wrinkles, flabby muscles) will not be too severe.

Healthy vs. unhealthy

There is much advice and many dietary suggestions, often coming from medical and scientific groups, telling us about good or bad influences of certain products on our health. They change frequently depending on the economic situation and fashion. They are rarely based on an honest analysis of the influence of the nature (energy) of these products on human physiology and the Yin–Yang balance within the body (homeostasis).

This leads to a few questions:

- Are there any products which are healthy or unhealthy for everyone?
- Are there any products which are always healthy and we can eat them with no limits?

Medicine should find answers to the above questions, as it is usually doctors who give very dangerous dietary advice. An uncritically adopted Western fascination with fruit, fresh salads, yogurts and cold water leads to very serious diseases in children as well as in adults. Just have a look at the general health condition of Western societies.

Most of the food products recommended by doctors and dieticians are treated by our body as mono-flavoured; that is, of an energy merely affecting one of the bodily organs. This leads to blockages of energy and blood circulation and all kinds of disorders.

The moment the food lands in our mouth, and consequently in our stomach, it starts emanating a certain kind of energy, which is then responsible for the process of digestion. Therefore, the advice of some medical professionals claiming that it is not so important what we eat (the content of mineral salts and vitamins in our food) but how we digest, only stresses the importance of having a well-functioning digestive system. We will not secure our body with a sufficient quantity of nutritious compounds by eating only mono-flavoured food (fruit, fresh salads, juices, yogurts, cheeses), as the energy of these particular flavours prohibits the process of proper digestion, absorption and metabolism.

If we still doubt all of this reasoning, then let's have one more look at Nature.

Does the Earth, which gives life and feeds and protects it, selectively favour any of the climatic factors or elements? What use would it have of the sun, if there was no moisture? What use would it have of the air, if there were no seeds and pollen ready to travel with the wind? What use would it have of the rain, if it was always cold?

It is similar with flavours. What use would we have of water, if the kidneys did not have enough Yang energy? What use would we have of fruit, if our body was overcooled, our blood circulation weak and our liver dysfunctional? What use would we have of fresh salads, if we were not able to digest them due to intestinal problems; and what use are yogurts, if we suffer from allergies and our lungs can barely manage?

In order to give life, the Earth needs all the climates as well as the sun – the Yang energy that stimulates life. Can we be stimulated with life only by the sun and its cosmic energy? We have so little sunshine in our climate. Therefore, in order to live, we need the essence which renews the body; we need the energy of all the flavours as well as the Yang energy (fire). This constitutes the energetic composition which we will not find in sour, raw and cold food or food cooked in microwaves or electric cookers.

Below I will try to explain why certain products are healthier than others.

Fats

If there are positive opinions about olive oil, they are due to the fact that it contains unsaturated fatty acids which support the functioning of the liver, heart and blood circulation. On the other hand, the subject of linseed oil and rapeseed oil, which are rich sources of unsaturated fats Omega-3, is only mentioned in the context of margarines. I think that this is one big misunderstanding, as oil is oil and margarine is margarine and the two should not even be compared. The oils produced in our climate are as good as olive oil and we should use them for cooking all the time. I will not even comment on the advice suggesting we eat margarine instead of butter or use margarine for frying instead of oil – it is obvious what one should think of margarine.

The majority of the negative comments we hear are directed at animal fats; and they are all treated as one. This is a big mistake, as every fat acquires the nature (energy) of the meat it comes from. And so, lard has the energy of the salty flavour, butter of the sweet flavour, duck fat of the sour flavour, goose fat of the sweet flavour and fish fat of the salty flavour. If the fat has a destructive effect on the body it is merely due to the fact that it is consumed in excess, with no added spices and in the wrong composition with other food products.

It is certain that the most neutral fat is butter. It can be eaten by everyone, regardless of their age. One should only watch the quantity of butter one eats. Its precious compounds (vitamins A, D and E) make it an irreplaceable nutritious product.

Every fat plays an important role, as it contains certain types of energy and also acts as a carrier of specific mineral salts and vitamins. Fat is especially important during puberty. Fats are indispensable for the proper construction and functioning of the nervous system, in the process of forming and regeneration of the connective tissue, and most of all in maintaining the hormonal balance. The whole group of steroidal hormones, produced by the adrenal cortex (e.g. female sex hormones), are created out of cholesterol. Also, the cell membranes and all internal submicroscopic structures are built of lipids, cholesterol and its esters. Can we live without fat, then? It is not the best of ideas.

If something goes wrong with fat metabolism within the body, then a fat-free diet will not fix it. Only a reduction of certain kinds of fat (but not a total exclusion) can help in such a situation. One should identify the true cause of this dysfunction; perhaps it has nothing to do with eating fatty food but actually, or rather for sure, with eating sour, raw and cold food. Fat is harmful when we:

- eat large quantities of soups based on fatty pork bones, fatty sauces (gravies) based on margarine or lard, fatty chicken broths, fatty pork (mostly shoulder), fatty duck and geese. In all of these cases, we are dealing with fat of the energy of the sour and salty flavours.
- eat any of the aforementioned meats with no added spices.
- eat fatty foods containing sugar – sweets, creamy cakes, particular dinner dishes (rice or pasta with butter and sugar, potato pancakes with sugar, pancakes with sugar).
- eat fatty foods with no carbohydrates or simply pure fat – in both cases, the fat is not digested properly and gets accumulated in the intestines in a form of the so-called soap (see the chapter titled "Physiology").
- eat fatty foods combined with fresh salads, fruit or other sour foods.
- drink water, beer or fruit juice with meaty meals.
- eat apples straight after having creamy cakes.

Why is all this bad for us? It is simple – with no spices and without the appropriate balance, the processes of efficient digestion, absorption, circulation, cleansing and excretion are practically impossible. Our body starts producing pathological mucus; this leads to stalling in the form of, for example, tumours, obesity and all kinds of very dangerous diseases.

Carbohydrates

Carbohydrates are indispensable in our diet, as without them we would not be able to digest proteins and fats. On the other hand, fats are indispensable, too, because a deficiency of fat leads to disorders of the endocrine and nervous systems; and meat is important because it provides exogenous amino acids which are necessary for the construction of enzymes and hormones as well as the blood-forming factor – vitamin B12. We should thus eat everything, including carbohydrates, except sweets.

Foods that are rich in carbohydrates include: flour, bread, grains, pastas, cakes, potatoes. Whenever we can, we should combine them with appropriate spices. But we should not mix them with the sour flavour. Excessive consumption of carbohydrates is not recommended at all, as it can affect the tonus of our muscles (flaccid muscles). But on the other hand, a lack of carbohydrates can lead to stiffness and contraction of muscles.

Millet

Despite the common opinion that millet is universal, I think that it can actually be dangerous (especially if consumed in excess) for people suffering from a deficiency of Yang energy, and most of all for those with a weak stomach and spleen.

Millet is of the sweet flavour and is very useful when it comes to stimulating the production of moisture by the spleen. But one must remember that an excess of such moisture can weaken the liver. Millet can be used as baby food but should always be mixed with oats. The same rule applies for adults.

I would never recommend millet as a regenerating kind of remedy, especially for those who suffer from a deficiency of Yang within the body and poor blood circulation (which affects almost everyone).

Common symptoms after eating a portion of millet are mostly related to the middle heater and can manifest themselves as "fire" in the stomach, heartburn or pressure at the back of the head. This state signifies blockage of energy in the meridians of the spleen and stomach, and we already know that the liver and the gallbladder are responsible for this.

Oats

Out of all the grains and cereals, oats contain a protein which is of the best quality and easiest to digest. The only condition is that it should be cooked for a minimum of 40 minutes. Oats can be harmful when:

- they are eaten raw; they are then difficult to digest, with proteins and carbohydrates being difficult to absorb
- they are served with cold milk – cold milk kills the digestive process in the stomach and destroys the energy of the spleen
- they are served raw with cold yogurt
- they are served raw with fresh fruit
- they are cooked without being balanced by the other flavours, especially the sour flavour (lemon juice), which prevents the “loss” of minerals.

Wheat-flour food products

The notion “floury” applies to food products made of white wheat flour. The flour contains harmful gluten, which contains a toxic compound that causes destruction of intestinal mucosa. Those who mostly live on sour, raw and cold food are especially prone to its effects.

Flour products are harmful when:

- we eat them excessively: pastas, noodles, wheat bread, semolina, cakes and biscuits, sauces thickened with wheat flour
- we do not add any spices to them (turmeric, ginger, cinnamon, cardamom)
- we put them together with other food products: excess of fat, raw fruit, fruit

yogurts, inappropriately prepared tomato sauce, sour meats (chicken, duck), milk and sugar (the latter being the most acidifying combination).

All of the inappropriate food compositions mentioned above lead to one of the most dangerous diseases – coeliac disease.

Sweets

One sweetie will not do any harm, but 100g of sweets will do for sure.

This is concerned, of course, with an excess of the sweet flavour, and especially the sweet flavour represented by sugar, which weakens bodily organs and, most of all, the stomach, spleen, pancreas and liver. If we do not take this into account and continue eating sweets whenever we feel like it, whilst drinking and snacking at the same time on sour, raw and cold food products (apples, water, yogurts, juices, beer, ice cream), we can very quickly end up with hyperacidity, peptic ulcers, allergies, pale and soft and a malnourished body, or with proneness to colds, and so on.

***Mistakes made by adults which are usually copied by children include*:**

- eating sweets before a proper meal
- shopping when hungry
- not taking a lunch box to school or work
- eating breakfasts consisting of chocolate bars and juices or water
- excessive consumption of yeasty cakes, thinking that they are healthier than normal cakes (yeast-cakes, doughnuts)
- eating “overly” sweet sweets, such as chocolates, meringues, chocolate bars
- buying children sweets for every occasion.

Do you know who really teaches children to eat sweets? Our Ego. Why? Because it is we adults who take the biggest pleasure in the fact that we can "spoil" our children with sweets.

Pork

Pork is not harmful, but only under one condition – that we are fully conscious of its salty flavour (energy). We already know about the destructive influence of this particular flavour on the body. Therefore, it is time to think of the mistakes we commit when eating pork.

The common mistakes are:

- eating large quantities of pork meat, hams and sausages
- cooking with no added spices (e.g. turmeric, cumin, ginger)
- combining pork with the sour flavour, mostly with sauerkraut and gherkins
- cooking sour soups based on pork bones
- frying food with lard
- eating bread with plain lard (with no spices)
- eating large quantities of pork (e.g. hams and sausages), followed by sweets, compotes, apples or cold water.

We should avoid pork if we suffer from: rheumatism, rheumatoid arthritis, osteoporosis, diabetes, liver dysfunction (cirrhosis, inflammation), proneness to heart attacks, obesity, allergies, asthma, autism, cerebral palsies, depression and other emotional problems. We should also avoid eating pork if breastfeeding.

Beef

Modern dieticians do not recommend eating red meat. Americans even claim that eating red meat can cause cancer, atherosclerosis, heart attack and many other diseases of affluence. According to them, white meat, such as chicken or fish, is much better. I will briefly explain why this recommendation can be dangerous – when it comes to our health, the colour of meat is not as important as its energy.

Examples of red meats include, among others, beef and pork; and they each have a completely different impact on our body. Beef contains energy of the sweet flavour and pork of the salty flavour.

Beef, as long as it is young and properly matured after slaughter (at least 48 hours), and veal are of great benefit to the spleen as they stimulate it to produce appropriate essence. But we can also come across old beef, which I do not recommend, especially to those who suffer from a dysfunction of the middle heater (mostly spleen) and a deficiency of moisture (essence). The body is then on the precipice between dryness and fire; one should try to restore the moisture over a longer period of time by eating well-balanced and rather delicate food. Eating old beef can over-stimulate the metabolism and make us experience excessive heat.

Only fully healthy people can allow themselves to eat old beef, but under the condition that they balance it out by combining it with large quantities of vegetables and by applying an appropriate cooking process (stewing, boiling) with appropriate spices.

Chicken and fish – recommended as replacements for "unhealthy" beef – will never regenerate bodily organs and restore the inner Yin. They will only contribute to intensification of the diseases we already have, and will cause new even more dangerous ones, such as liver cirrhosis, problems with the brain and the whole nervous system.

Chicken

It is good to be a chicken nowadays – everyone respects you and wants you for your white meat, which is recommended to everyone – old and young – and for any health condition. Among pigs with foot-and-mouth disease and mad cows, chicken looks very innocent.

But the truth is that chicken meat destroys our liver, slowly but efficiently. Unfortunately. Chicken meat is of the sour flavour, which has a contracting, concentrating and blocking effect on the body, and leads to problems with various bodily organs as well as emotional problems.

Chicken meat is a strange food. It can be marinated in kilograms of spices but its sour flavour energy remains and has the usual effect on the liver. It simply turns the liver into a "half-baked cake". If we decide to have chicken for dinner, then at least we should add a lot of spices – at least it will be tastier. Should we have chicken for supper? Absolutely not; chicken for supper is not a good idea at all.

There was this family who worked on a chicken farm. Therefore, their diet was dominated by chicken. The man died at the age of 40 due to liver cirrhosis and the woman suffered from depression and anxiety disorder and eventually hanged herself.

I have recently talked to a woman who told me about the tragic situation within her family. She and her children have been suffering from depression for years. They are constantly on medication. Her husband also has many health problems. It turned out that they have their own chickens and for many years they have been eating mostly chicken meat.

Another example. There was this grandmother who wanted the best for her granddaughter. She fed her with large quantities of fatty chicken broth and eventually the girl was diagnosed with advanced liver cirrhosis at the age of 7.

It is shocking, but true. Why do I write about it? I do it to make everyone aware of the danger.

Chicken is even more harmful when eaten with no added spices or accompanied by fresh salads, pastas, tomatoes, or in sour soups.

Broths

There was a time when I could not understand why older people suffered from diarrhoea after eating chicken broth. But there is nothing strange about it, as chicken broth contains energy of the sour flavour. For those with an overcooled body and destroyed stomach lining and intestinal mucosa, chicken broth is not recommended at all. In the old days, nobody cooked broths based only on chicken meat. They were always cooked with the addition of beef or lamb.

Of particular harm to us are chicken broths and rich stocks based on pork bones (salty flavour), prepared with no added spices (turmeric, thyme, cumin, onion, garlic, ginger). Especially harmful is using these kinds of broths and stocks as the base for sour soups (tomato soup, rye-leaven soup, cabbage soup).

The destructive elements in these kinds of soup are both the energy of the flavour of the meat and the energy of all the added vegetables, as well as the large quantities of calcium typical of meat-bone stocks. All of the aforementioned factors have a concentrating, contractive and blocking of circulation effect. The problem should no longer exist once we add to these kinds of soups large quantities of spices, but not too much of the sour flavour.

Therefore the broths and soups that are best for us are based on veal, beef and turkey, lamb or even goose. They should be appropriately balanced with spices and not too sour in order not to weaken the body with the calcium from the bones but rather to make optimal use of it.

Fresh salads

Whose idea was it that sour, raw and cold food is healthier than a bowl of vegetable soup with garlic, onion and spices? Where can we find the so-called sparkle (same as the sun in Nature) in this kind of food? From where can we obtain Yang energy if we mostly eat raw and cold food? Vegetables derive from the soil and are therefore always Yin.

The effects of eating "healthy" fresh salads can be observed in Western societies and among babies whose mothers ate large quantities of fresh salads during the breastfeeding period, thinking that it was good for them and their babies. We can also observe it among the young, especially young girls, who are in most cases pale, thin and suffer from hormonal problems. And adults who are already very ill intuitively stop eating fresh salads.

When should we eat fresh salads? I do not know. We should definitely not combine them with meat; otherwise we will be digesting it for the next 10 hours. We should not combine fresh salads with pastas or eat them first thing in the morning, as our spleen does not like it; we should not eat them in the evening either as it causes liver problems. I simply do not know when is a good time to eat fresh salads.

A fresh salad balanced out with appropriate spices, with no sugar but with the addition of onion and garlic, will be easier to digest. But cooked vegetables with spices, onion and garlic are easiest to digest.

You may have some doubts as to sauerkraut and gherkins. They used to be popular in the old days, but only due to the fact that they were the only source of sour flavour in winter and spring. And besides, people used not to eat large quantities of fruit, frozen fruit and vegetables, compotes, citruses, juices, ice cream, fruit yogurts, cakes, sweets, fast foods, cold drinks, cheeses, milk, chicken, pork, hams and sausages, tomatoes or cucumbers. And even sauerkraut tended to be cooked rather than served raw. So, what do you think?

I am not saying that we should totally eliminate sauerkraut or gherkins, but we should be able to skilfully combine them with other food products. Gherkins are a great side dish and should be served, for example, with potatoes with onion, spices and eggs, or meaty dishes, but only based on beef, veal or well-spiced pork. Gherkins can be also added to other dishes as the sour flavour. Sauerkraut is only good with stewed button mushrooms and carrots or as a side dish to potato dumplings or meaty dishes (but not chicken or fish!).

Milk

If, during the breastfeeding period, a woman eats something inappropriate (e.g. sweets), then her baby becomes anxious and starts suffering from snuffles and catarrh. A wise mother would change her diet – eliminate sweets and introduce spicy and bitter-spicy-flavoured tea in order to get rid of the mucus accumulated in her baby's lungs and sinuses. The baby should fully recover after a few days of such treatment. The mother's milk is the remedy here. I wrote about this in an earlier chapter.

If this mother–baby interdependence affects humans, I dare say that it also affects cows. Allegedly, the physiology of humans and other mammals is similar. Let's talk about this further. Cow milk is quite controversial as it is believed to be a major cause of allergies. Children have to be forced to drink it; the young do not like it; and for adults, milk is simply harmful.

But is the milk nowadays of the same nature (energy) as that of a hundred years ago, when it came from cows eating what God initially intended a cow to eat? Certainly not. If throughout the whole winter these animals are fed with silage, meat and bone meal, just because the owner cares only about his profits, then it is difficult for milk to acquire the appropriate energy. And we already know the impact of food on the quality of milk in mammals!

Besides, we forget one important thing. In order to grow and develop properly, humans need milk from their own mothers and close contact with them. The same thing should apply to cows; they should be able to feed their young ones with their own milk and be close to them. We say that we feel sorry for animals and stop eating their meat, but the truth is that we are not even able to treat rightly those cows that give us milk. The all-too-early separation of young calves from their mothers causes great stress for both of them. And I am sure that this shock of separation affects the immunity of these animals as well as the quality of their meat and milk.

We separate calves from their mothers in order to increase the production of milk, and start feeding the calves with formulas and other animal fodder of doubtful quality. Babies who are fed formula grow weaker; the same thing happens to calves.

And the surplus of milk is often a problem to dairy producers. Have they forgotten that this milk is for calves? Our greed has overshadowed our reason; therefore Nature is making us pay for the mistakes of the last century.

What should we do, then? Let the cows feed their young ones; and also feed the cows properly. Cows, and other farm animals, should be treated with respect and love.

If we like milk, then we should drink it warm with some butter, honey and garlic, just before bed time (always full-fat milk). If we feel like milk soup, then we should always eat it in the evening, not in the morning. To the hot milk we can always add some cardamom, cinnamon or ginger. We must not copy others who give their children milk straight from the fridge with some cornflakes or muesli. This is a major crime. It is up to them whether they eat this way. We should also not combine milk with fruit, meat and, most of all, with sour food products.

How, then, should we serve milk? We can add small quantities of milk to porridge, or use it for béchamel sauce (always use full-fat milk), or add to potato purée. We can also boil some rice in milk and then bake it in the oven with apples and spices.

Give some milk to your kitten, too; but first of all give it to the calves. This milk belongs to them!

Eggs

Can eggs be harmful to our health? They can be if they are eaten in excess (the same as any other food). But if we eat eggs in reasonable quantities, then they can be of great benefit to our health, as they are an absolute dietary marvel. They contain protein (especially egg white) which is very easy to digest. We can even give them to babies who are just a few months old. They also contain many valuable micro- and macro-elements, such as phosphorus, sulphur, calcium, magnesium, potassium, sodium, manganese, zinc, copper, silica, chlorine, and even iodine, fluorine and iron in a form that is very easy to absorb. Eggs also contain larger amounts of precious vitamins A, D, B and K than other food products.

But the thing that makes them so special is the large amount of choline that they contain. A deficiency of choline can lead to serious a dysfunction of the liver and nervous system, including the brain. It can also affect the function of smooth muscles, which form blood vessels and bodily organs. Choline is transformed within the body into acetylcholine, which is a great carrier of nervous impulses.

Also, the cholesterol found in eggs is of no danger to our health. The increased level of cholesterol within the body is a result of liver malfunction (caused by sour, raw and cold food).

Eggs are like a nutritious concentrate created by Nature, and therefore wonderfully balanced.

Physical exertion can exploit inner Yin (especially in sportsmen, physical labourers and teachers). Therefore, breastfeeding mothers, pregnant women, the young who study intensively, convalescents, and all who feel like it, should eat boiled or poached eggs every day.

Water

It is obvious that cold water is not good for the body. Why? Let's have a look at the elements from the Five Elements Theory. Water is presented as the element which, when applied in excess, can destroy life. It will always flood and weaken our "life fire" (Yang energy) and the bodily organs and their functions belonging to the element of Fire.

Doctors and dieticians claim that we need water to moisten and cleanse our body. But 70% of our body already consists of water! According to the Five Elements Theory, an excess of the element of Water causes cold within the body, stalling and depression. The inner moisture within the body is produced by the element of Earth – the spleen. This particular bodily organ produces the right quality and quantity of essence (blood, inner fluids, mucus, hormones and enzymes), not when we drink large quantities of water, but when the food we eat contains energies of all flavours and Yang (fire) energy. Therefore, drinking a few litres of water every day will not contribute to stimulation of life processes and metabolism.

And now an interesting thing: the media are full of justifications explaining the benefits of drinking large quantities of water. It is apparently necessary as the kidneys need to be "rinsed" with large quantities of blood, and drinking water stimulates its production! This is absolutely horrific! If we suffer from a deficiency of blood and the kidneys stop functioning properly, we should already know what caused this state – sour, raw and cold food destroyed the spleen and affected the whole process of blood formation. It is necessary then to regenerate and renew bodily organs and the process of metabolism by eating warm and well-balanced food, and not by drinking water!

The belief in the cleansing powers of water is an illusion. We should realize that it is our liver that is responsible for the process of cleansing and its strength and power depends not on the quantity of water but on its own "rooting" in the element of Earth and its essence, as well as on the right quantity of blood.

I have a strange feeling that recommendations saying that one should drink two litres of water per day appeared around the time when the water business and firms producing mineral water started. We should not compare the modern fashion for drinking water with drinking spring water for medical reasons, when a special kind of water is ascribed for a particular ailment.

And what about the people who live in areas with a deficit of water? They do not die because of it; they simply cook nutritious soups.

Cheeses

On the subject of calcium, which can be found in excessive quantities in cheeses and which, due to our physiology, is difficult to absorb, I have a definite opinion, supported by years of observation. A large portion of cheese (100g of white cheese or a bit less of hard cheese) can cause very serious reactions within the body, such as "wandering" muscle pains (liver wind), strong emotional tension, muscular contractions (e.g. in the calves), pain and redness around the joint areas, strong headaches, sleepiness, a sore throat and diarrhoea in children.

Calcium is strongly Yin and can cause muscular contractions and stiffness of the body, blocking at the same time the production of essence in the spleen and deactivating the process of thermoregulation within the body.

Cheeses should be absolutely forbidden for those who suffer from osteoporosis, rheumatism, rheumatoid arthritis, cerebral palsy, autism, epilepsy, allergies, asthma, diabetes, heart attacks, circulatory problems, and for babies, small children and the elderly, but also in cases of emotional instabilities, such as depression, hyperactivity, aggression and anxiety disorder.

We should eat cheeses in moderation. I have already mentioned in the *Philosophy of Health* that cheeses are calcium-protein concentrates. Being aware of this fact, we should always serve them with large quantities of spices, such as turmeric, cumin, fenugreek, pepper, onion and garlic. The most important thing is not to eat cheeses for supper or straight after a meal (cheese boards).

We should mostly eat full-fat white cheese with an addition of cream and spices; serve it with toast as a side dish to a breakfast soup. On the other hand, hard cheeses can be used in pizzas but always accompanied by large quantities of spices. And processed cheeses should not even be discussed.

Coffee

When is coffee bad for us? When drunk in excess, with no sugar, or as espresso coffee, although espresso is less harmful than brewed coffee. But the energy of either cannot be compared to the energy of boiled coffee.

It actually happens sometimes that the energy of brewed coffee or espresso blocks the function of the liver (destructive circuit), which then leads to a strong nervous aggravation, as well as flatulence and nausea.

I do not think that I even need to convince anybody of the superiority of boiled coffee with spices over instant or decaf coffee…

I would like to warn everyone against excessive drinking of chicory or natural coffee. Even though prepared in the right way – that is boiled with spices – an excess of coffee, like any other excess of flavours, can lead to all kinds of liver and heart problems. The sign that a coffee is good for our liver is when we find it very tasty. Two to three coffees per day are allowed.

Spices

I can often hear on my phone: "I do not feel very well. Hasn't this been caused by using too many spices?" My reply is: "No!" And further: "Think. Maybe you have made some mistakes – eaten an apple before dinner, drunk cold water or eaten a biscuit?" And I usually hear a very shy reply, such as: "Really??? So, it has got nothing to do with spices?"

An excess of spices will never cause any harm; it actually has the opposite effect – not enough spices in our food can lead to many health problems; as can other dietary mistakes, such as a lack of knowledge on the power of various energies and lack of dietary discipline.

Spices can only cause harm when:

- added in large quantities to vegetarian dishes or dishes with no fat; then their strong energetic content cannot be fully absorbed by the small energetic capacity of vegetarian food

- the body (nourished merely with vegetarian food) has too small an energetic capacity to absorb food of a high level of vibration
- one eats well-balanced and well-spiced food and then drinks cold water or eats ice cream (they are most harmful in such cases).

Salt

Is salt bad for us? How can it be bad if it gives life? It concentrates energy and essence in the kidneys, brings stability, "rooting", will of life. Complete elimination of salt can cause problems with the blood-formation process, and consequently problems with our consciousness (our ancestors were fully aware of this). Salt in the old days was well appreciated and imported even from afar. It is especially appreciated in countries with a hot climate. One example is Africa, where salt is still produced in the old way – by evaporation. It has been used for generations in order to protect the kidneys and prevent loss of moisture (sucking bits of salt, adding it to coffee or tea).

Rock salt contains valuable mineral compounds and should be used in its initial form – unpurified. Especially avoid iodized salt - our problems with the thyroid are not related to a deficiency of iodine but to our dietary mistakes, e.g. eating overcooling food.

Salt is indispensable as it activates the glands in the lining of the stomach in the production of hydrochloric acid. Hydrochloric acid is, in turn, indispensable in the blood-formation process and in the initial phase of digestion (especially digestion of meat).

Salt is necessary for circulation of the energies of particular flavours and for production of essence by the spleen. All those recommendations saying that convalescents or those suffering from high blood pressure should not add salt to their food is a complete misunderstanding. If we eliminate salt from their menus, then we will prevent the creation of the necessary balance for a convalescent and destroy their kidneys, weaken the blood-formation process and cause them emotional problems. We should remember that elimination of salt and simultaneous consumption of any kind of meat will cause problems with digestion and absorption.

Fish

Sea fish has energy of the salty flavour and this fact cannot be changed by scientifically supported fashions for replacing red meat (beef) with fish. The spleen is not able to transform them into renewing essence. Of course, I am talking here about an excess of fish. People who fall for these kinds of recommendations will sooner or later suffer from serious emotional problems and dysfunctions of particular bodily organs, e.g. intestinal problems and circulatory problems.

Fish is of overcooling, concentrating and stalling-causing energy. If in other countries people eat more fish and they seem to be healthy, then it is not because of their fish menu but because their cuisine is more balanced in its traditional form. Another reason is that their cuisine has remained unchanged for generations, and unlike in the Western countries, the people there do not follow all scientific and dietary novelties.

Fish is harmful:

- when eaten in excess (because we think that it is healthy)
- when combined with fresh salads, sauerkraut and gherkins
- when we drink water, juices or other cold drinks with it
- when cooked with no spices (bitter and spicy flavour)
- when combined with the sour flavour (fish in tomato sauce or vinegar, smoked mackerel with white cheese).

Here is an example of the most harmful composition of a meal for children and the young: tomato soup, fish and sauerkraut salad. Dear Reader, try to guess the energy of such a combination for yourself.

Should we or should we not eat sea fish? We should eat it, but wisely – with spices, garlic, stewed sweet vegetables, and, of course, not too often. Our present condition does not allow for an excess of fish; it could lead to an intensification of depressive states, aggression, cardiovascular problems, intestinal problems, kidney disorders, liver disorders, allergies, asthma, rheumatic problems, and accelerated process of ageing.

Freshwater fish is much better for us. It contains energy of the sweet flavour, as well as of the cooling kind. It can contribute to the production of essence but only within a body of an appropriate energetic level – only then does it have a strengthening effect on the Yin kidney (see the *Philosophy of Health*). Those prone to depression should not eat fish at all.

Black and green tea

The energy of these teas is indispensable in Chinese cuisine, as this kind of cuisine is highly warming and well-spiced; plus it does not use such food products as milk and cheeses, yogurts, cakes and sweets, fresh salads and fruit, juices, cold drinks and water. The contracting, drying and concentrating energy of these teas is in balance with this kind of diet.

Black and green teas are harmful:

- when we drink them too strong or too often
- when the food we eat is overcooling
- when we are stressed (tea only intensifies contraction within the body)
- when we combine them with lemon and sugar.

These kinds of tea should not be given to babies, small children and the elderly. We should treat them only as a remedy for problems with blockages in the liver or excess of the sweet flavour (not sugar) – the so-called smelly and excessive diarrhoea.

If we really want to regenerate our body, stimulate circulation, improve the functions of bodily organs, prevent the process of ageing (especially considering our genetic determinants and culinary tastes), then we should stop drinking these kinds of tea altogether and replace them with the neutral-warming kind of tea. If we do drink them from time to time, we can sweeten them with some honey.

Fruit teas

Fruit teas contain a lot of sour additives; therefore, they belong to the group of products of the sour flavour. We often have to sweeten them, which indicates that we are not entirely satisfied with their sour flavour. Unfortunately, by adding some sugar or honey we do not eliminate the energy of the sour flavour. We think that these teas are good for our health, whilst in fact we only generate more of the sour flavour within the body. And the results of the excess of this flavour within the body can be very dangerous.

Alcohol

One shot of cognac, whisky or straight vodka can stimulate circulation, ease the tension caused by stress and cold, help with indigestion or rid one of a headache. But 2–3 shots will only intensify these ailments.

Vodka is harmful:

- when drunk in excess (alcoholism)
- when we drink it with mixes, such as juices, water, fizzy drinks
- when we drink cold water and other cold drinks straight after vodka.

In order to avoid a hangover after a party, we should have a good, warm, meaty meal (without any sour food products, such as sauerkraut, herrings, gherkins, chicken) beforehand, and drink with it only hot black tea with some sugar or honey. The morning after the party, the best hangover remedy is boiled coffee with spices and honey.

One thing is certain: we should not let alcohol "overtake" any good party and be a remedy for shyness. Our inner consciousness must always decide whether alcohol is a necessity or a pleasure for us.

Addictions

Is an addiction a bad thing in itself or is it rather a result of deregulation or deficiencies within the body and simply a way for replenishment of energy? Is alcoholism worse than an addiction to sweets? In my opinion, both of these addictions are very dangerous, but I am also fully aware that they are the results and not the causes of certain problems. I also do not think that advertising alcohol is morally much worse than advertising sweets.

We should realize that advertisements for sweets mainly reach children and cause their addiction. The results of addiction to sweets are very dangerous as they are the base of the future addiction to alcohol, cigarettes, drugs, and can eventually lead to social pathology. An excess of sweets destroys our Centre (stomach, spleen, pancreas) and our consciousness.

Alcoholism is a consequence of eating sweets, sour food (chicken, fresh salads), salty food (hams and sausages, schnitzels, herrings) and drinking cold drinks – all of which lead to emotional problems (sadness, sorrow, anxiety, lack of acceptance, aggression, worrying). In this case, the combination of emotional problems and dietary mistakes is very powerful and lasts for a long time; therefore, it should be treated as a single problem. One should not leave alcoholics to themselves but support them with the appropriate kind of diet that has the power to calm their emotions.

Smoking (energy of fire) is just a poor substitute for inner warming up – especially of the stomach and the lungs. Nicotine causes contraction of the outer coating of the body and stimulates the metabolism within certain bodily organs (pancreas, liver, lungs, heart). Thanks to this process, a smoker is able to get rid of the mucus accumulated in the lungs due to malnutrition. Smoking accompanied by excessive drinking of alcohol gives an illusion of energetic balance. Therefore, it can often be observed that those who start excessive drinking of alcohol (mostly beer and alcohol mixed with juices and other cold drinks) also take up smoking, and vice versa.

Drugs are a form of escapism from lung and kidney depression (sadness, sorrow, anxiety, hopelessness), from the feeling of being at the lowest point. They give an illusion of taking off into space.

We should not fight with these addictions! It is not the way. First, we should try to understand them! We should not stigmatize addicts! It is not the way. Instead, they need our help. We should try to explain to them what is happening and cook them some soup.

When was the last time we consciously refused a child some sweeties? Did we feel as if we were refusing ourselves pleasure? Mums and dads – do not judge your children. Feed them first and then help others.

Mediterranean cuisine

Dieticians suggest that Mediterranean cuisine is much healthier than European cuisine. They say that this is because of the olive oil and large variety of fruit used in Mediterranean cuisine. In my opinion, we will not solve our health problems by consuming larger quantities of citruses or olive oil. I have the impression that dieticians, once more, misunderstand the basic issue here. They do not understand the true cause of our health problems, as well as not understanding the essence of Mediterranean cuisine. Without a proper and honest analysis of this issue, in a few years' time it may turn out that we have reached another dead end. And people are becoming more and more tired and impatient.

These serious suggestions and recommendations require taking into consideration all of the energetic factors which either lead to the weakening of our body or its stimulation. And these factors are: farm produce, genetics, mentality and gustatory habits. Our biggest problem here is not a deficiency of vitamins in European cuisine, but the energy of the food we eat (I have mentioned this in the *Philosophy of Health*). And so, we should remember that dietary recommendations treated out of context (cultural and regional factors) can have a destructive effect on the body. For example, green tea plays a different function in Chinese cuisine than it does in our local cuisine; also, a banana in African cuisine or natural yogurt in Bulgarian or Turkish cuisine play different functions than in our cuisine.

Our local cuisine is the best for us. We should then return to the roots of our cuisine and make sure that we introduce factors which have the power to elevate the energy of our meals, such as varied cooking methods and spices. Simultaneously, we should eliminate all bad habits and this requires a thorough knowledge of the nature (energy) of particular food products and meals. For example, an excessive consumption of sour soups is not recommended as it leads to overcooling of the body. Pork is not harmful as long as we are fully aware that it belongs to the element of Water and has a cooling nature, blocking circulation. Therefore pork should always be well-spiced and appropriately combined with other food products. Whenever possible, we should try to replace pork with veal, young beef, lamb or turkey. We have to simply understand that the whole issue of good nutrition is concerned with a skilful adaptation of the energies of various food products and whole meals, as well with as an awareness of the climate we live in.

The cuisines of long and well-cultivated traditions (such as Mediterranean cuisine) rely on an accumulation of the energy of the food, which is sufficient to maintain health. The culinary culture of Mediterranean countries is based on a respect and celebration of food – pleasing one's own palate. The people there appreciate the importance of food and its impact on the quality of life. They eat in accordance with a moment, their needs, climate, and with a full respect for Nature and its rhythms. They respect the meaning of real fire and the process of cooking in its various forms, such as boiling, stewing or frying, even though they are spoilt by the sun nearly all year round. People do not eat raw food over there, any more than they do in China, India or Brazil. They do not eat much fresh fruit either; more often they eat stewed, baked or boiled fruit with spices.

The food products used in the countries of Mediterranean cuisine are practically the same. This refers to the spices as well as vegetables and meat. The only difference is the way of adding spices or local sentiments towards certain dishes and their flavours. The basic dish in this region is always soup – slow-cooked and very rich, mostly based on meat or fish with a lot of vegetables and spices. They also often add chickpeas, peas or beans, and always garlic and onion. And we already know how nutritious these products are. The soups are usually served with bread.

The second most important dish in Mediterranean cuisine is stewed vegetables. The most commonly used vegetables in this are tomatoes, peppers, aubergines, courgettes, onions and garlic (always), green beans and many other vegetables. Meat is usually slow-cooked, with large quantities of spices and stewed with vegetables. They use natural yogurt in Mediterranean cuisine, but merely as a gustatory addition (sour flavour) in salads and soups, or as a neutralizer of the spicy flavour.

How would we describe Mediterranean cuisine? What kind of nature does it have? This cuisine is definitely varied, well-balanced and very energetic. It treats with respect the so-called heavy-to-digest food products, such as garlic, onion, peas, beans, chickpeas, lamb, beef and spices. It also respects the old tradition of using various cooking methods – frying, baking, stewing, boiling – which is of great benefit to health. It is a warming kind of cuisine, rich in the major building compounds: proteins (meat combined with peas or beans), vitamins – B vitamins (beans, peas, chickpeas, meat), energetic factors – “Yangization” through the process of cooking (boiling, frying, stewing), and catalysing factors – spices, which improve digestion, circulation and excretion.

Picking and choosing elements from this cuisine and applying them in our climate can be very harmful. We are often drawn to this kind of food because of the exotic sound of certain dishes. Is it because of our complexes? The mysterious-sounding “risotto” is nothing other than rice with meat and vegetables; afelia is simply stewed pork with coriander; moussaka – minced meat layered alternately with aubergines and baked with béchamel on top; polenta – cornmeal; ratatouille – vegetable goulash; tortilla – potato bake; minestrone soup is a simple vegetable soup, gazpacho is a tomato, garlic, pepper and cucumber salad.

The conclusion from this is that the reason for our health problems is not a deficiency of southern fruits on our tables or the fact that we do not use olive oil (rapeseed oil is as good), but the way we combine food products, cook and add spices to our food.

Differences between Mediterranean and European cuisines		
Products	**Mediterranean cuisine**	**European cuisine**
Dairy products	Milk and cheeses (mostly of sheep and goat's milk), yogurts with honey and dates, yogurt with garlic (yogurts are usually home-made of goat and sheep milk; they are mostly used as a thickener and the sour flavour in soups, goulashes and marinades)	Milk and cheeses (made of cow milk), mostly low-fat white and hard cheeses, fruit yogurts (sugar + sour fruit)
Fats	Butter and olive oil	Mostly lard, margarine, rapeseed oil and sunflower oil
Legumes	Large quantities of beans, lentils, chickpeas, peas, broad bean	Not much peas, beans and broad beans
Potatoes	Mostly fried potatoes	Mostly boiled potatoes or mash
Sweetener	Honey	Sugar
Meat	Lamb, veal, beef, lesser quantities of pork and chicken, not much ham and sausages; all kinds of meat that are well-spiced	Mostly pork, chicken and ham and sausages
Vegetables	Mostly sweet vegetables: pumpkin, aubergine, courgettes, peppers – stewed, fried, with large quantities of onion, garlic and fennel	Mostly fresh salads, not much onion and garlic
Products	Fresh fruit; tendency for a seasonal approach towards various food products	Frozen fruit and vegetables, canned food, compotes, preserves, raw vegetables
Spices	Variety and large quantity of spices; mostly saffron, coriander, cumin, ginger, hot paprika, turmeric	Mostly black pepper, allspice, bay leaf, small quantities of cumin
Herbs	Thyme, basil, oregano, rosemary, sage, aniseed, marjoram	Mostly marjoram
Methods of preparation of warm meals	Cooking on real fire, slow-cooking, stewing, frying, baking	Very often cooking on an electric cooker, in a microwave; boiling in water; short-duration cooking, quick frying in a very hot fat
Meat preparation	Many spices, frying, stewing with vegetables, boiling in soups; using mostly oil or oil with butter	Mostly with no spices, fried in margarine or lard, served with thick sauces
Soups	Thick vegetable soups based on meat or fish, with many added spices, onion and garlic	Traditional soups: mostly sour soups – tomato soup, borscht, fruit soups, eventually chicken broth
Cakes and desserts	So-called tarts with sweet fruit, e.g. dates, pears; fruit boiled in water, honey, wine and spices; marmalades and jams with spices	Cakes with jelly and raw fruit, with creams and yeasty cakes
Fruits	Mostly sweet fruit – dates, figs, pears, peaches	Mostly sour fruit – lemons, strawberries, apples

Cooking

Such will be our nation as our nutrition

I know that even people who follow the rules of a well-balanced diet make mistakes. One of the biggest mistakes is concerned with adding the sour flavour. Just because one of the pieces of advice is about the elimination of sour dishes, it does not mean that we should eliminate the sour flavour altogether. One should carefully, and with full consciousness, use the knowledge from this book; for example, if we feel that our body is overcooled, then we should eliminate the sour flavour. Excess of the sour flavour happens very often. It leads to a dysfunction of the middle heater and, most of all, such bodily organs as the gallbladder and the stomach, as well as the liver and spleen. The symptoms of this state are flatulence, nausea, headaches and a feeling of heaviness.

The sour food products which can effectively balance our meals are: lemon juice, tomato stewed with some olive oil, mustard, vinegar or sour cream. This is the way our mothers and grandmothers balanced food with the sour flavour; it is done in a similar way in Mediterranean cuisine. In Mediterranean cuisine, natural yogurt is used as the balancing sour flavour and is not combined with fruit. We can, for example, add a spoon of sour cream to a bowl of pumpkin or vegetable soup (having in mind the order of flavours). We can also use sour cream interchangeably with natural yogurt in salads made of boiled vegetables or even in meat-veg stews. The green parts of vegetables – parsley, dill, basil – are not sufficient to balance out a big pot of food, unless we add a significant amount of greens, as in the summer soups when we add celery leaves, parsley, kohlrabi leaves, dill or young beetroot leaves.

Another very common mistake is adding small quantities of spices. The changes happening within our body are then simply too small to notice. Many people are deeply convinced that spices are not good for us. Sometimes, when they experience some health indisposition after the application of a well-balanced cuisine, they ask: "Isn't it caused by an excess of spices?" I then try to explain that it is most likely caused by hidden emotional problems combined with some other dietary mistakes; or that they simply have one foot in the new dietary method and the other foot still in the old one.

For example, drinking cold water or eating an apple just before dinner can cause serious digestive problems.

Another big mistake is overdosing on products of a particular flavour with a simultaneous neglect of the other flavours, such as the excess of the sweet flavour in the following soup:

Bitter: very little thyme and turmeric

Sweet: veal, potatoes, carrots, parsley root, parsnip, pumpkin, cornmeal

Spicy: onion, garlic, ginger (not much)

Salty: salt

Sour: parsley

This kind of soup can cause diarrhoea in children, and stalling and flatulence in adults.

Also inappropriate is the following combination of food products in a cauliflower soup:

Bitter: turmeric, thyme

Sweet: carrots, cumin

Spicy: turkey, ginger, rice, onion, cauliflower

Salty: salt

Sour: parsley, lemon juice.

After this soup we can be left with a taste of metal in the mouth. An excess of products of the spicy flavour, such as kohlrabi, cabbage or celeriac, can lead to flatulence in children, but, most of all, the soup will simply not be very tasty.

A similar thing happens with an excess of the sour flavour by adding too much lemon juice or greens – this kind of soup is also not very tasty. Children are especially sensitive to this kind of excess.

During the preparation of food we must always remember the power and energy of flavours – of their mutual creation and destruction. I have already said before that it is not a big deal to cook a soup, but the hard thing is to balance it with flavours. In the first instance, we should put into a saucepan the basic spices, e.g. ½ or 1 tsp. of thyme, turmeric, cumin, ginger, salt; then we add meat, and at the end, vegetables. By subsequently adding spices and tasting the dish, we can taste the changes in the overall flavour. For example, when we add hot spices (spicy flavour), the saltiness of a dish automatically increases; when we add pepper we should also add salt. If we add very little salt, then the overall flavour is more sour.

By adding the sour flavour, on the other hand, the salty flavour is less noticeable and the bitter flavour becomes more noticeable. If by accident we add too much lemon juice, then we should also add some turmeric and the tip of a teaspoon of butter.

It does not matter which flavour we add as the last one; we can always add some sweet flavour afterwards – butter, honey or a spoon of sweet cream; the sweet flavour is great to balance out a dish. But it is only allowed when there are appropriate quantities of the other flavours, which are necessary for a decent process of digestion and metabolism. Otherwise, the dish finished with the sweet flavour will be bland and will cause flatulence.

I would like to remind you here that once we decide to introduce the rules of a well-balanced diet we should forget about any other dietary theories. If we are not fully aware of the principles and do not do it wholly, then we risk a very serious nervous dysfunction. We must be fully conscious of the fact that the more varied the meal, the more spiced, the better the digestion and absorption of nutrients. When choosing food products for a particular dish, we should pay special attention to the energy of each of the products. In a well-balanced diet, there is no room for theories on, for example, avoiding carbohydrate–meat combinations. I would like to remind you once again that there is no such thing as pure proteins or fats in Nature; therefore the theory that mono-flavoured food is much better for us (e.g. fruit in the morning, fresh salads in the afternoon, grains in the evening) is a complete misunderstanding.

Another problem is concerned with visits to family and friends. Who should we listen to? Simply the voice of our reason; we should politely refuse cakes, fruit or dishes which we know are harmful to our health. We should not be afraid that we may insult the host in some way but be fully conscious of the consequences of such food. Is it better to put one's own health at risk for the sake of etiquette? I know what I would do. But you, Dear Reader, if you still hesitate, then it means that you still need to work on your priorities.

I want to stress one more thing, even though I have already mentioned it in the *Philosophy of Health*. We should start cooking in our own time – not sooner, not later. Therefore, we should not listen to what others say to us. The conclusion is that we cook when we feel like it, and we should not even talk about it to others. We should feed our families and do not listen to their moaning. After some time, everything will change. The same with our friends – we should not try to force them to do anything. We can serve them something – if they like and adopt it then they are the winners too; if not, then we should not moan about it.

I have already said in my previous book – the magic of flavours and energies of food will only work when we fully accept and trust this knowledge. If someone only skips through the recipe chapter, without even trying to understand the Order, it is most likely that they will not avoid making serious mistakes and their consequences. A selective approach to my advice is not the best solution, as it will be of no help, even though the expectations will be high. We can only draw the wrong conclusions in this way and get the wrong picture of the whole matter.

A trivializing and ironic approach towards the Order is also not the best approach. The Order benefits those who respect it. Only then can the Order secretly do its duty – to lead and protect us. We should cook with joy and passion and be aware of the fact that it is a Divine privilege indeed.

RECIPES

Abbreviations used in recipes:

- S – sour flavour
- B – bitter flavour
- SW – sweet flavour
- SP – spicy flavour
- SL – salty flavour

SOUPS

Rice Soup

Prepare some calf bone stock; then add a large portion of greens (see the recipe in *Philosophy of Health*).

Roast 1 glass (200 ml) of rice with some turmeric, butter and ginger. Then put the rice in a larger saucepan, add 2 glasses (400 ml) of the earlier prepared stock (without the greens), 1 tbsp. butter, 1 egg yolk and blend it altogether. Then slowly add the rice mixture to the rest of the stock (make sure the soup is not too thick).

Lentil Soup

Put ½ kg of lentils in a saucepan, pour in the cold water and bring it to the boil. Then drain the lentils, pour in some fresh cold water and boil it for 10 min.

B – to 3 l of boiling water add pinch of thyme, calf or cow bone, 1 tsp. cumin and boil it all together for about 1.5 hours. Then add: 3 large carrots (cut into quarters), 2 large parsley roots/or parsnip (cut into quarters)

SP – 3 large onions (cut in half), 4 garlic cloves, 1 tsp. ginger, 1 tsp. coriander, ⅓ tsp. chilli

SL – then add the lentils together with the water they were boiled in, 1½ tbsp. salt

Boil it all together for 30–45 min. until all vegetables are soft. Remove the vegetables, leaving only 1 carrot, 1 parsley root/or parsnip and 1 onion. Then blend it all together and add: SL – some salt (to taste), S – 1 tsp. lemon juice, some parsley, B – pinch of marjoram, SW – 1 tsp. butter.

Lentil and Chickpea Soup

Soak overnight ½ kg of chickpeas. Dice finely ½ kg of veal or very young beef. You can also use meat on the bone, but you need to cook it first; then dice it finely and put it back into the soup.

B – to 3 l of boiling water add:

B – pinch of thyme

SW – the meat, 1 tsp. ground cumin and cook it for 1 hour (if the meat is on the bone) or 30 min. (if the meat is off the bone)

If the meat is very lean, then add 1 tsp. of butter followed by: 1 tsp. cinnamon, 2 large onions (finely chopped and fried in a pan with 2 tbsp. of oil).

SP – add 1 tsp. ground coriander, 1 tsp. ginger, pinch of cayenne pepper

SL – soaked chickpeas and 1 glass (200 ml) of lentils, 1–2 tsp. salt (to taste)

Cook it all together for 1.5 hours. Then add:

S – bunch of chopped parsley, 4 very ripe tomatoes, chopped (seeds removed) and stewed in a pan with 1 tbsp. of oil

B – ½ tsp. turmeric

Cook some fine pasta and add to the soup. Season it with some pepper and salt to taste.

Note: You can also use chickpeas from cans.

Mediterranean Bean Soup

Soak overnight ½ kg of white beans. The next day, drain the beans, pour in some fresh cold water and some salt and cook the beans until soft.
Prepare earlier some beef stock:

B – to 2–3 l of boiling water add:
B – 1 tsp. thyme
SW – ½ kg beef, ½ tsp. ground cumin
SP – 1 tsp. ginger
SL – 1½ tsp. salt
S – 1 tsp. basil
B – ½ tsp. turmeric

Cover it with a lid and simmer all together for at least 2 hours. You can use the meat in pancakes or stuffing for dumplings, in sandwiches or simply chop it finely and put it back into the soup.

Now get the vegetables ready: slice 3 large carrots, finely chop 3 large onions, dice 1 fennel, peel 6 garlic cloves, chop 3 celery sticks, slice 2 small courgettes, peel and stew in a pan with 1 tbsp. of oil and 4 very ripe tomatoes.

In a deep saucepan, heat up 6 tbsp. of olive oil; then keep adding and stirring in the following vegetables and spices:

SW – carrots and courgettes
SP – onion, garlic, fennel, celery, 1 tsp. ginger, ⅓ tsp. chilli, black pepper
SL – add the beans together with the water they were cooked in, stir it all together, season it with some salt (1 tsp.) and then add:
S – stewed tomatoes
B – some stock (depending on the consistency you want to achieve)
SW – 1 tsp. ground cumin
SP – black pepper (to taste)
SL – salt

Serve as a main course together with some bread. You can also sprinkle it with some grated cheese.

Lemon Soup

Bring to the boil 3 l of broth. Whisk 5 eggs in a large saucepan. Stir them with a wooden spoon and keep slowly adding the boiling-hot broth, but make sure the eggs do not set. Add some black pepper (SP), salt to taste (SL), juice of 1–1½ lemons and pinch of turmeric (B).

Add some cooked fine pasta and simmer it all together for a few minutes (but do not bring to the boil).

The Autumn Blues Broth

B – to 2½–3 l of boiling water add:

B – ½ tsp. thyme, ½ tsp. marjoram and ½ tsp. rosemary

SW – 1 tsp. cumin seeds, 600 g beef on the bone (rump steak or ribs), 1 calf bone with bone marrow

SP – two turkey wings, 2 whole onions, 6 large garlic cloves (finely chopped), 1 tsp. ground coriander, 1 heaped tsp. ginger, ½ tsp. cayenne pepper, 1 tsp. cardamom, 1 large bay leaf, 6 grains allspice

SL – 1½ tsp. salt

S – bunch of parsley (tied with a string), ½ tsp. basil

B – 1 tsp. turmeric

Cover with a lid and simmer for about 3 hours; then add 2 medium carrots and 1 parsley root/or parsnip. Cook it all together for another 30 min. until the vegetables are soft. Serve with fine egg noodles. If you want to keep it for another day, make sure to pour it through a sieve first.

One portion of this broth will bring you back to life. You can cook and eat it as often as you want. You can use the leftover meat in stuffing for dumplings or simply serve it with stewed carrots and some horseradish.

Good-For-All-Carrots

Fry 1 kg of carrots (diced) in a pan with a few tbsp. of oil for about 2–3 min; drain the carrots and put them in a saucepan. To ½ l of boiling water add ⅓ tsp. ginger and ½ tsp. ground cardamom; stir it, add some salt (1 tsp.), 1 tbsp. of lemon juice; stir it again, then add 1 tsp. turmeric, 1 tsp. butter and 1 tsp. honey. Stew it all together for about 30 min. until the carrots are soft. Then thicken it with some potato starch mixed with water (if needed).

Clear Tomato Soup

Prepare earlier some beef, veal or lamb broth but use a larger than normal quantity of onion, garlic and spices. Remember to add "salty" as the last flavour. Then take all the vegetables and meat out of the saucepan. Add to the broth some home-made tomato purée (make sure that the soup is not too sour).

Serve it with pasta (or egg noodles) like any other broth. This soup is truly exquisite.

Mushroom Soup II

B – to 3–4 l of boiling water add:
B – ½ tsp. thyme
SW – calf shank, 1 tsp. ground cumin; cook it for about 2.5 hours, then add: 6 medium carrots, 1 large parsley root, 1 parsnip
SP – 4 large onions (chopped), 1 tsp. ginger, ⅓ tsp. chilli
SL – 3 tsp. salt; cook it all together until the vegetables are soft; then take the meat and vegetables out of the saucepan (you can use them in pancake stuffing) and add:
S – ½ tsp. basil
B – add some more boiling water (if necessary), ⅓ tsp. turmeric
SW – 650 g button mushrooms (sliced and stewed with some butter)

SP – cayenne pepper; blend it all together
SL – add some salt (if necessary)
S – 1 tsp. lemon juice
B – pinch of turmeric
SW – ½ kg potatoes (diced)

Cook it all together until potatoes are soft. This soup is delicious!

Pumpkin Soup

Cut 1 kg of pumpkin into big chunks; fry it in a pan with a few tbsp. of oil.

S – put ½ a chicken (washed and cut into small pieces) or 600 g of chicken wings in a large saucepan, then add:

B – 3 l of boiling water, 1 tsp. thyme

SW – 1 tsp. cumin, 3 carrots (cut in half lengthways), 2 parsley roots (cut in half lengthways)

SP – 1 tsp. ginger, ¼ tsp. chilli, 4 whole leeks (white parts), 6 large garlic cloves (pressed)

SL – 1½ tsp. salt (to taste); cook it all together for about 1 hour until all the vegetables are soft; then take the chicken, carrots and parsley root out of the saucepan and add:

S – 1 tsp. lemon juice

B – 1 tsp. turmeric

SW – 1 kg of pumpkin (cut into big chunks); cook it for about 30 min.

SP – add some black pepper

SL – blend it all together with the leeks; then add some salt and cook for another 10 min.

You can also base this soup on cow bone stock. Only remember to serve it with some sour cream. This soup is very healthy. You can use the vegetables in salads and chicken meat in fried cutlets in butter. The beef, on the other hand, you can use in sandwiches or pancake stuffing.

Garlic Soup - Great in Autumn and Winter

2 l of beef broth, 4 eggs (1 per person), 8–10 large garlic cloves.

SW – bring the broth to the boil; then add 1 tsp. ground cumin, 1 tsp. sweet paprika

SP – whole garlic cloves, fried on a pan with 3 tbsp. of oil (be careful not to burn the oil) and then pressed through a sieve

SP – black pepper (to taste)

SL – salt (to taste)

S – 1 tsp. lemon juice

B – pinch of turmeric and thyme

SW – beat the eggs into a separate bowl; then pour them one by one in the simmering broth; cook it all together for another 3 min.

Pour the soup carefully into bowls, making sure the eggs do not fall apart. Serve it with croutons, fried with the same oil you used for frying the garlic.

Sorrel Soup

To start with, follow the recipe for the mushroom soup (see *Philosophy of Health*). Then take the vegetables out of the stock (you can use them in a salad). Then add a large quantity of spices, onion and garlic.

Wash and put in a saucepan ½ kg of sorrel; pour in ½ l of boiling water and stew for about 30 min. Then blend it and add it to the vegetable stock (make sure the soup is not too sour, though). Then add:

B – ½ tsp. turmeric

SW – 1 tsp. ground cumin, 1 tsp. butter, and if you like, some sweet cream

Serve it with boiled eggs or boiled potatoes. I would not recommend serving it with rice. Remember, though – sorrel soup can be served only once a year.

SECOND COURSES

Traditional Meat Marinade

(for about 400 g of meat)

Mix together: 1 heaped tsp. of potato starch + 1 tsp. ginger + 1 tsp. salt.

If you use this marinade for frying or roasting meat, then you should add more spices and make sure it contains all five flavours.

Beef Goulash for Russian Dumplings

Cut 1 kg of beef (good for roasting or goulashes) into thick slices (about 2 cm); tenderize the meat with a mallet, then cut it into smaller pieces (1 × 3 cm). Season it with ⅓ tsp. black pepper (SP), ½ tsp. ginger (SP), mix it all up; then add 1½ tsp. salt (SL) and mix it all again.

Leave it to rest for half an hour, whilst you can start on the vegetables: finely chop 4 medium onions, grate 1 large carrot and peel 3 large garlic cloves.

Heat up in a large saucepan:

SW – 6 tbsp. of oil; then add the onion and fry it gently; then add the carrots and fry it all together for a bit longer

SP – then add the garlic (pressed), 1 bay leaf, 1 tsp. ground coriander, ⅓ tsp. cayenne pepper; keep stirring it

SL – add the meat; keep stirring it; season it with some salt (to taste)

S – add 1 tbsp. lemon juice and stir it again

B – then add 1 glass (200 ml) of dry red wine and 3 glasses (600 ml) of boiling water, ½ tsp. thyme and ½ tsp. rosemary.

Stir it all together thoroughly; cover it with a lid and stew until the meat and vegetables are soft (for about 2–3 hours)

SW – then add ½ tsp. honey, 1 tsp. ground cumin

SP – some black pepper (to taste)

SL – some salt

S – thicken it with 1 tsp. of wheat flour mixed with ¼ glass of cold water; keep stewing it for a bit longer

B – in case there is not enough sauce, add ½ glass (100 ml) of wine or boiling water (the sauce must not be too thick).

This sauce is very energizing. It goes well with Russian dumplings and is great in winter. You can also serve it together with steamed dumplings, rice or new potatoes.

Russian Dumplings

Dough:

1 kg of wheat flour (S), mixed with 1 tsp. turmeric (B), knead the dough, slowly adding ½ l of boiling water (B); once that is done, add 2 small eggs (SW), 1 tsp. ginger (SP), some cold water(SL), and keep kneading until the dough is well worked and soft.

Roll out the dough on a pastry board to ½ cm thick and, using a round cookie cutter or a glass, cut the dough into circles. Then fill each one of the circles with 1 tsp. of stuffing.

Stuffing:

SW – mince 1 kg of boiled potatoes; mix them with 1 large onion (finely chopped and fried in a pan with 1 tbsp. of butter and 2 tbsp. of oil); then add:

SW – 1 heaped tsp. ground cumin

SP – 1 tsp. ginger, 1 tsp. ground coriander, ⅓ tsp. cayenne pepper, ½ tsp. black pepper; mix it all together

SL – add some salt to taste (1–2 tsp.); mix it again

S – add 250 g white cheese (or more if you like), pinch of basil; mix it again

B – add 1 tsp. turmeric

Put the dumplings in the boiling and salty water and simmer for about 2–3 min (do not overcook them, though, otherwise they will be flat and watery). Serve them with melted butter or pancetta fried with some ginger or with the beef goulash.

If you are left with some dough, simply roll it out and dry it slightly; then cut into small noodles. Once they are completely dry, put them into a glass jar and leave for another occasion. If you are left with some stuffing, you can shape it into small croquettes, which you then roll in breadcrumbs and fry in a pan with some butter and oil.

Sweet White Runner Beans with Beef

Soak overnight in, firstly boiled and then cooled, water ½ kg of sweet white runner beans. The next day, drain the beans and pour in some fresh cold water (so the beans are covered) and cook until the beans are soft.

Cut ½ kg of young beef into slices and mix it with marinade (1 tsp. potato starch + ½ tsp. chilli + ½ tsp. salt + ¼ glass (50 ml) water). Then leave it to rest for half an hour.

Slice 5 medium carrots and 1 large parsley root and leave it on a side. Chop 7 medium onions and 1 leek; press 4 garlic cloves; peel and cut into pieces 4–5 medium tomatoes.

B – bring to the boil in a medium saucepan (about 3.5 l) 1 l of water; then add:

B – ½ tsp. thyme

SW – fry the meat in a pan with 4 tbsp. of oil, then put it in the water; add ½ tsp. cumin, stir it and bring to the boil

SP – fry the onions, leek and garlic in a pan with 1 tbsp. of oil and add it to the meat

SP – add 1 tsp. whole black pepper, 1 tsp. five-spice powder, 1–2 tsp. chilli; stir it all together, then cover with a lid and stew until the meat and vegetables are soft

SL – add some salt (to taste) and stir it again

S – fry the tomatoes in a pan with 1 tbsp. of oil; then add to the stew together with ½ tsp. of basil; stir it

B – add 1 tsp. turmeric; stir it again

SW – fry the carrots and parsley root in a pan with 1 tbsp. of oil; then add to the stew and stir it

SW – add ½ tsp. cumin

SP – and some more hot spices (the meat should be quite spicy)

SL – then add the beans together with the water they were cooked in; add some more salt, cover with a lid and cook for another 30 min. until the carrots are soft (stir it from time to time and do not let it burn). Serve it with boiled, unpeeled potatoes fried with onion.

Veal Cutlets with Fried Eggs

Mince 1 kg of veal (shoulder). Soak in water 2 bread rolls and mince them too. Add to the meat 1 egg and 1 heaped tsp. of potato starch; mix it all together thoroughly and then add:

SP – ½ tsp. chilli, ½ tsp. black pepper, ½ tsp. ginger; mix it all again

SL – add 1½ tsp. salt

S – minced bread rolls and pinch of basil

Mix it again. Then form small, flat cutlets (1 cm); dip them in a whisked egg and roll in breadcrumbs. Fry them on a medium heat for about 10 min. Put them on a plate and sprinkle with ground pepper.

At the same time, heat up, in another frying pan, 1 tsp. of butter and fry the eggs (1 egg per cutlet). Season them well and cover with a lid; let them set but make sure the egg yolks stay runny.

Put 1 egg on top of each cutlet. Serve it with all kinds of vegetables: Brussels sprouts, beetroot, red cabbage or simply lettuce with garlic-vinaigrette dressing.

Beef Cutlets with Garlic

You need for this 1 kg of beef shank (remove the bone and use it in stock or a broth). Cut the meat into thin slices (1 cm); if they are too big then cut them in half and gently tenderize with a mallet.

Marinade: 1 heaped tsp. potato starch (SW) + 1 tsp. ginger (SP) + 3–4 large garlic cloves, pressed (SP) + 1 tsp. salt (SL) + ½ a glass (100 ml) cold water; stir it all together properly.

Cover the meat in the marinade and leave it to rest for about 1 hour.

In the meantime, grate 1 large carrot and cut into slices 2 large onions. In a saucepan, bring to the boil 1 l of water; then add ½ tsp. of thyme (B). Heat up 6 tbsp. of oil in a frying pan; fry the meat slices briefly on each side (SW) and put them in the boiling water (B). Then, using the same oil, fry the onion.

SW – add the grated carrot to the meat; stir it

SP – add the onion, ⅓ tsp. chilli, 1 big bay leaf, 1 tsp. ground coriander

SL – add some salt (to taste)

S – 1 heaped tsp. of mustard

B – ½ tsp. turmeric; stir it, cover with a lid and stew for about 1 hour until the meat and vegetables are soft.

Serve it with boiled potatoes and boiled seasonal vegetables or some salad.

Beef Cutlets with Greens

Slice 1 kg of beef (beef shank or other kind of beef) into thin (1 cm) and not very big slices; tenderize them gently with a mallet and dip in a marinade (1 tsp. olive oil + 1 tsp. ginger + ½ tsp. cayenne pepper + 2 tsp. salt + ¼ glass (50 ml) cold water + ½ tsp. lemon juice + ½ tsp. turmeric). Mix it all together and leave it to rest for about 1 hour.

In the meantime, slice 300 g of button mushrooms and 1 parsley root, chop 3 medium onions, peel 3–4 garlic cloves, chop a big bunch of greens (dill + parsley + young kohlrabi leaves).

Heat up some oil in a frying pan. Fry the cutlets briefly on each side and then put them in a saucepan; then fry the mushrooms and the onion and add them to the meat. Add 1 tsp. ground cumin; stir it. Then add 1 tsp. ground coriander, ½ tsp. cayenne pepper, ½ tsp. ginger, pressed garlic and stir it all properly. Add some salt to taste; then add the greens and 1 small tsp. of mustard or lemon juice. Add some more boiling water, so the meat is covered. Then add ½ tsp. thyme or rosemary; cover it with a lid and stew for about 1 hour until the meat and vegetables are soft. Then thicken it with some potato starch and add some butter and ginger.

Serve it with new potatoes and boiled vegetables (cauliflower, cabbage or asparagus).

Beef Stew with White Wine

Cut 1 kg of young beef into thick slices (3 cm); then cut them into 5 cm square shapes. Season them with black pepper and salt.

Soak a handful of dried porcini mushrooms. Heat up some oil in a frying pan. Fry the pieces of meat briefly on each side, then put them in a saucepan and add:

SW – 1 tsp. cinnamon,
SP – 2 medium onions (sliced and fried)
SP – 6 garlic cloves (pressed), 1 bay leaf, some black pepper
SL – 100 g of diced pancetta, chopped porcini mushrooms
S – 1 glass (200 ml) of dry white wine
B – ½ tsp. thyme and ½ tsp. rosemary

Cover it with a lid, put it in the oven and stew on a medium heat for about 3 hours. The stew goes nicely with thick pasta (or egg noodles) sprinkled with some grated cheese and broccoli salad on a side.

Beef Tenderloin in a Hot Tomato Sauce

Dice ½ kg of beef tenderloin and put it into marinade (1 tsp. potato starch + 1 tsp. cayenne pepper + 1½ tsp. salt). Leave it to rest for half an hour.

Sauce: peel and chop 6 medium very ripe tomatoes (seeds removed)

SW – heat up 3 tbsp. of olive oil in a frying pan (optionally rapeseed oil) and add 1 tsp. ground cumin

SP – 3 large garlic cloves (pressed)

SP – 1 hot chilli pepper or ½ tsp. chilli flakes

SL – ½ tsp. salt

S – add the tomatoes

B – ¼ tsp. turmeric and ½ tsp. thyme

Stew it all together for about an hour on a low heat.

SW – heat up in a frying pan 4 tbsp. of oil and fry the meat briefly; then put it in the saucepan together with the tomatoes. Using the same oil, fry 200 g of spinach and add it to the sauce; stir it all together and then add:

SP – chilli (this dish should be rather hot), 2 bay leaves and stew it for another 10 min.

SL – add some salt to taste

Serve it with rice (golden style) or pasta (egg noodles).

Beef Schnitzels

Mince 1 kg of young beef; then add:

SW – 2 medium onions (finely chopped and briefly fried with 1 tbsp. of butter); stir it and add:

SP – 1 small tsp. black pepper, ½ tsp. cayenne pepper

SL – 1 tsp. salt

S – 2 soaked bread rolls

B – pinch of thyme

Mix it all together thoroughly. Then mince it again and form small schnitzels.

Heat up some oil in a frying pan and fry the schnitzels. Serve them with boiled potatoes, steamed carrots and roasted apples with cardamom.

Beef Rolls

Slice 1 kg of beef; tenderize the meat with a mallet (make sure the meat is quite thin). Then put all the slices on a pastry board, fill them with stuffing, roll into little roulades and tie with string. Heat up in a frying pan some oil and butter and fry the rolls briefly on each side. Then put them in a saucepan.

Stuffing:

SW – 2 large onions (chopped); heat up 2 tbsp. of butter and fry the onions briefly, then remove them from the heat and add 3 egg yolks; keep stirring it and adding:

SP – ⅓ tsp. black pepper, some cayenne pepper

SL – ½ glass (100 ml) of water, 1 tsp. salt

S – 2 tbsp. breadcrumbs, pinch of basil (½ tsp.)

B – pinch of thyme, pinch of turmeric; stir it all together thoroughly

Sauce:

Heat up in a pan 2–3 tbsp. of oil and ½ tbsp. of butter. Add 2 tbsp. of wheat flour and stir it until you get a nice roux. Let it cool. Then add ½ l cold water. Heat it up slowly, stirring all the time, and eventually bring it to the boil (if the sauce is too thick, add some more water); then add:

SL – 1 tsp. salt

S – pinch of basil, handful of chopped parsley

B – ½ tsp. thyme or rosemary

Bring it all to the boil and pour over the roulades. Cover it with a lid and stew in the oven for about 2 hours. Serve it with pearl barley or buckwheat with some beetroot salad or boiled French beans on a side.

Beef Rolls II

Slice ½ kg of beef and tenderize it with a mallet (there should be about 5 slices; cut the same number of slices of smoked bacon).

Season each slice of meat (SW) with some black pepper (SP) and salt (SL) and cover with a slice of bacon. Then put 1 tbsp. of stuffing on each of the slices, roll them into little roulades and tie with a string.

Stuffing:

SW – mix 200 g of grated cheese with ½ tsp. of ground cumin and 2 chopped boiled eggs

SP – add 3 garlic cloves (pressed), ½ tsp. black pepper

SL – some salt to taste

S – 2 bunches of finely chopped parsley

B – pinch of turmeric, pinch of thyme; mix it all together

Fry the rolls on each side and put them in a saucepan.

SP – fry 1 chopped onion and add it to the roulades

Season it with some black pepper (½ tsp.), add 1 bay leaf

SL – 1 tsp. salt and a glass (about 150 ml) of cold water

S – 1 tsp. lemon juice

B – 1 glass (about 150 ml) of dry red wine

Cover it with a lid and put in the oven for about 1 hour. Then thicken the sauce with some potato starch, season it with pepper and salt (to taste). Serve it with steamed dumplings or boiled potatoes and

Veal Goulash with Button Mushrooms

Chop 1 kg of veal into rough chunks, then mix it with the traditional marinade and leave it to rest for half an hour.

Prepare vegetables: wash and slice 300 g button mushrooms, chop 2 carrots and 1 large parsley root, slice 2 large onions, peel 5 large garlic cloves, peel and stew in a frying pan 1 large and very ripe tomato.

SW – heat up some oil in a frying pan, fry the meat and put it in a saucepan; then (one by one) fry the vegetables: carrots, parsley root, mushrooms and add them to the meat

SP – fry the onion together with the garlic (pressed) and add 1 tsp. ginger, ½ tsp. cayenne pepper, some black pepper

SL – add some salt (to taste); stir it

S – add the tomato

B – in the frying pan you used for frying all the other ingredients, bring to the boil 1 l of water, then add it to the goulash together with ½ tsp. turmeric, ½ tsp. thyme

SW – ½ tsp. cumin; cover it with a lid and stew until the meat is soft

SP – then season it with some more hot spices (the goulash should be really hot)

S – add some more salt

S – and thicken it with 1 heaped tsp. of wheat flour mixed with some cold water

B – add some more thyme and turmeric

Serve it with rice.

Veal and Pork Goulash with White Wine

Chop 400 g of veal into rough chunks; mix it with the traditional marinade and leave it to rest for half an hour. Do exactly the same with 400 g of pork (loin).

Cut 4 large leeks (white parts) into thin slices.

SW – fry the veal in a pan with some oil and put it in a saucepan

SP – then fry the leeks and add them to the meat together with ½ tsp. chilli, 1 tsp. cayenne pepper and 1 tbsp. green pepper (optional); stir it

SL – fry the pork and add it to the veal and leeks; season with salt and add:

S – ½ tsp. basil, 1½ glass (300 ml) of dry white wine; cover it with a lid and stew in the oven (medium temperature) for 1.5 hours until the meat is soft

Serve it with boiled potatoes or pasta and boiled vegetables on a side.

Cabbage Parcels

Peel the rotten leaves off 2 large cabbages, then remove the hard centres. Boil some water in a large saucepan; put the cabbages (one by one) into the water and after a few moments peel the outer leaves off and put them on a separate plate; keep repeating the same thing all over again until you have peeled all the leaves off.

In another large saucepan, bring to the boil 4 l of water. Rinse ½ kg of rice and ½ kg of buckwheat. Put it into the boiling water and cook for about 10 min. (stir it from time to time). Drain the rice-buckwheat mix and put it in a large bowl.

Mince ½ kg of pork (or lamb) and ½ kg of beef (rump steak). Chop finely 5 large onions and fry them in a pan with ¼ glass of oil (50 ml).

Add to the rice-buckwheat mix: minced meat, fried onion, 2 tsp. ground cumin, 2 tbsp. melted butter and mix it all together thoroughly. Then add 2 tsp. ginger, 1 tsp. cayenne pepper, 1 tsp. ground coriander; mix it all again. Then try it for spices (if necessary, add some more black pepper). Then season it with salt (3–4 tsp.). Add 1 tsp. basil, 1 tbsp. lemon juice; mix it all again. Then add 1 tsp. turmeric. Taste it again – remember that the stuffing should not be bland; it needs to be well seasoned and quite spicy.

Then put some stuffing on each of the cabbage leaves; roll them and secure the edges, so they look like small parcels.

At the bottom of a large saucepan put some smaller leftover leaves. Then on top of it put the cabbage parcels (put them quite tightly one next to the other and if necessary one layer on top of the other). Season it with some salt and cover with the rest of the leftover leaves. Pour in at least ½ l of boiling water (make sure the parcels are covered with water), cover it with a lid and put in the oven (180°C) for about 1.5–2 hours.

It is a big portion of cabbage parcels, but you can divide it into smaller portions and keep them in the freezer for later. Each time, heat them up in a saucepan with some butter and water. You can serve them with a garlic-tomato sauce (see recipe). But personally I only make the sauce in spring; in autumn and winter the parcels taste better with just some melted butter.

Roast Pork with Garlic

Cut 1½ kg of fatty pork ham (SL) in such a way that you end up with one thick and flat piece; tenderize the meat with a mallet. Season it with 1 tsp. of salt (SL), sprinkle with 1 tsp. lemon juice (S), ½ tsp. turmeric (B), 1 tsp. ground cumin (SW). Rub the meat with all these spices plus 5 large garlic cloves (SP) (pressed), ⅓ tsp. black pepper and ⅓ tsp. chilli (SP) and leave it in a cool place for a few hours.

Then heat up some oil in a frying pan. Fry the meat briefly on each side and put it in a saucepan; sprinkle it with cumin seeds. Then cover the saucepan with a lid and put it in the oven (medium temperature) for at least 2 hours.

This kind of pork goes well in sandwiches but you can also serve it as a separate dinner dish.

Pork Goulash

Cut ½ kg of pork (ham) into thin strips and marinade in the traditional marinade (1 tsp. potato starch + 1 tsp. ginger + ½ tsp. salt + ¼ glass (50 ml) water); mix it all together and leave it to rest for about half an hour.

SW – heat up 2–3 tbsp. of oil and 1 tbsp. of butter in a frying pan; fry two large chopped onions

SP – add 1 tsp. green pepper, ¼ tsp. cayenne pepper, 1 tsp. coriander

SL – add the meat and fry in all together on a high heat for about 15 min.; add some salt (to taste); stir it

S – add 2 handfuls of chopped greens (dill, parsley, kohlrabi leaves); stir it again

B – add ½ tsp. turmeric, 1 tbsp. fresh marjoram (or 1 tbsp. dry marjoram), a few sprigs of rosemary (or 1 tbsp. of dry rosemary), 1 glass (200 ml) of boiling water

SW – 1 tsp. ground cumin

Stew it all together for about an hour until the meat is soft. You can thicken it with potato starch and add some more hot spices and salt. Serve it with potatoes, buckwheat or pearl barley and some boiled vegetables.

Meat à la Paul

Cut 200 g of pork tenderloin into thin strips, marinade it in the traditional marinade (½ tsp. potato starch + ½ tsp. ginger + ½ tsp. salt + ¼ glass (50 ml) water) and leave it to rest for half an hour.

Cut 150–200 g of raw pancetta into thin strips and 4 large onions into thin slices; sprinkle it with ½ tsp. ginger, ½ tsp. black pepper, ½ tsp. chilli, ½ tsp. salt, pinch of basil, pinch of marjoram and pinch of cumin; mix it all together and leave it to rest for half an hour.

SW – heat up 2 tbsp. of oil in a frying pan

SP – add ½ tsp. ginger, the pancetta and fry it all together for about 15 min; then add the meat, keep frying and stirring it

S – add some more basil

B – ¼ tsp. turmeric and pinch of marjoram

SW – ½ tsp. cumin

SP – then add the onion; keep stirring it

Then add some more pepper and fry it for another 10 min.

Serve it with bread rolls and olives.

Spicy Pork Chops

Cut ½ kg of young pork tenderloin into thin slices; tenderize each slice with a mallet, then marinade the meat (1 heaped tsp. potato starch + 1 tsp. ginger + ⅓ tsp. cayenne pepper + 2 tsp. salt).

Crack 2 eggs into a plate; add ½ tsp. of cayenne pepper. On another plate, mix 1 glass (200 ml) of flour with 1 tsp. of turmeric. Dip each slice of meat first in the flour, then in the egg, and again in the flour. Heat up some oil in a frying pan (medium temperature). Fry the pork chops for a maximum of 10 min (until they are a golden colour, no longer; otherwise, they will be too hard).

Sweet Ribs with Turmeric and Wine

1½ kg of ribs, cut into small pieces, sprinkle with 1 tsp. of lemon juice, ½ tsp. turmeric, 3 tbsp. of runny honey, 3 tsp. ground coriander, 1 tsp. ginger, ½ tsp. cayenne pepper, 1 tsp. salt; mix it all together and leave it to rest for a few hours.

Heat up 2 tbsp. of oil in a frying pan. Roll each slice of the ribs in wheat flour. Fry the ribs and put them in a saucepan. Then add 1½ glasses (300 ml) of dry red wine.

Wash the frying pan and heat up 3 tbsp. of fresh oil. Fry 3 large onions (cut into slices). Add the onion to the ribs together with 1 tsp. of ground coriander, some black pepper and salt; stir it thoroughly. Then cover it with a lid, put it in the oven and stew it for about 2 hours (medium temperature).

The ribs go well with some plum sauce, fresh bread rolls or steamed dumplings. You can make it with some pork ham instead of the ribs.

Lamb Goulash

Clean 1 kg of young lamb (you can use lamb shank) of the fat and veins; cut it into rough chunks and marinade it (2 heaped tsp. potato starch + 3 large garlic cloves (pressed) + 1 tsp. ginger + 2 tsp. salt + ½ a glass (100 ml) water). Then leave the meat to rest in the fridge for 24 hours.

Chop 3 carrots and 2 parsley roots, slice 3 large onions and 300 g white button mushrooms, peel 5 garlic cloves. Heat up ½ a glass (100 ml) of oil in a frying pan. Then fry the vegetables one after another and put them in a saucepan.

B – add the meat

SW – carrots, parsley roots, mushrooms, onion; stir it all

SP – add garlic (pressed), 1 bay leaf, ⅓ tsp. black pepper, 1 tsp. coriander, 3 hot chillies (chopped) or ½ tsp. cayenne pepper; stir it all together and then add:

SL – salt to taste

S – 1 tsp. basil, 1 tsp. lemon juice

B – 1 glass (200 ml) of dry red wine, ½ tsp. turmeric, ½ tsp. thyme and some boiling water (so the meat is covered). Cover it with a lid and stew it for about 2–3 hours (the meat should be really tender).

Thicken the sauce with some potato starch. Serve it with rice or pasta (egg noodles). If you need to strengthen your body, then serve it with potatoes.

Chicken in a Vegetable Sauce

Cut 1 chicken into pieces; rub it with 1 tsp. turmeric (B), 1 tsp. cumin (SW), 1 tsp. ginger (SP), ⅓ tsp. chilli (SP), 2 tsp. salt (SL). Leave it to rest for about half an hour. Chop 4 medium carrots and slice 4 medium onions.

Heat up 2–3 tbsp. of oil in a frying pan. Fry the pieces of chicken on each side, then put them in a saucepan.

B – add ½ tsp. thyme, ½ tsp. rosemary, 1 glass (200 ml) of boiling water

SW – then fry the carrots and onions and add them to the chicken

SP – add some black pepper and 1 tsp. of coriander

Cover it with a lid and stew it on the hob or in the oven for about 1 hour. Then take the chicken out of the saucepan; to the sauce add some salt, small cup of yogurt and, if necessary, some boiling water. You can thicken the sauce with some potato starch.

Serve the chicken with potatoes, rice with turmeric, butter and ginger and boiled vegetables (French beans, cauliflower) or some salad (in summer time).

Chicken with Garlic and Lemon

Cut in half 8 chicken legs. Use the drumsticks to make some well-spiced broth. You will need 2.5 glasses (½ l) of this broth for this recipe.

Rub the rest of the chicken legs with turmeric (B), ground cumin (SW), ginger (SP), salt (SL) and leave them to rest for an hour.

Peel 20 large garlic cloves and 1 lemon. Cut the lemon into thin strips. Pour 2½ glasses of the chicken broth into a saucepan; add the garlic and boil it for about 40 min. Heat up 2 tbsp. of butter and 2 tbsp. of olive oil in a frying pan. Fry the chicken legs on each side, then put them in a saucepan, cover them with the garlic and slices of lemon. With the rest of the fat in the frying pan make some roux (add 2 tbsp. of wheat flour (S) and stir it; do not let it burn); let it cool for a bit; then add the broth in which you boiled the garlic, 1 glass (150 ml) of dry white wine (S) and bring it to the boil, stirring from time to time.

Add to the sauce ½ tsp. thyme (B), ½ tsp. ground cumin (SW), some black pepper (SP), 1 tsp. salt.

Pour the sauce over the chicken legs. Put it in the oven (but do not cover) for about an hour (180°C).

Serve it with rice or boiled potatoes and some boiled vegetables.

Chicken Livers

Wash and cut into small pieces 300–400 g of chicken livers.

SW – heat up 100 g of butter in a frying pan

SP – fry 2 sliced onions, 2 garlic cloves (pressed), ½ tsp. ginger, ½ tsp. black pepper

SL – add some salt; stir it, then add:

S – chicken livers

B – 1 tsp. sage; fry it for another 10 min. stirring regularly

SW – add 1 tsp. ground cumin

Serve it with potatoes as a main course or blend it, season it with some more pepper and salt and let it set. Serve it as a paté with some bread or toast.

Turkey Livers

Wash some turkey livers; roll them in some flour mixed with turmeric and cumin; fry them on each side and season with some black pepper and salt. You can add 2 fried onions and make some paté like in the previous recipe.

Turkey Stomachs

Wash and clean ½ kg of turkey stomachs.

B – to 2 l of boiling water add ½ tsp. thyme

SW – 1 tsp. ground cumin

SP – pinch of black pepper, ½ tsp. ginger, 1 large onion (chopped), 1 bay leaf, 4 grains of allspice and the stomachs. Cook it all together for about 1 hour; then add:

SL – 1½ tsp. salt

S – ½ tsp. basil, a handful of chopped parsley

B – ½ tsp. turmeric, ½ tsp. marjoram

SW – 1 medium carrot (chopped), 1 medium parsley root (chopped).

Cook it all together for about half an hour until the stomachs are soft. Take the stomachs out of the saucepan, cut them into strips and put them back into the sauce. Thicken the sauce with some potato starch, add 1 tsp. of butter and some black pepper (to taste). Serve it with fresh, warm bread rolls.

Turkey with Vegetables

Rub 1 large turkey breast (1 kg) with black pepper (SP) and 1 tsp. of salt (SL). Leave it to rest and in the meantime prepare the vegetables. After half an hour, fry the turkey breast on each side; then put it in a saucepan.

S – cover the breast with a handful of chopped greens (dill, kohlrabi leaves, parsley)

B – 1 tbsp. of fresh marjoram (chopped) or pinch of dried marjoram instead

SW – 1 large carrot (sliced)

SP – ½ fennel (sliced), 1 onion (sliced) and 1 leek (chopped); some black pepper

SL – season it gently with salt

S – sprinkle it with some lemon juice

B – some thyme

SW – and 1–4 tbsp. of melted butter

Cover it with a lid, put in the oven and stew for about an hour (low temperature). Take the meat out of the saucepan and cut it into slices. Blend the sauce together with the vegetables. Sauce should be very strong in flavour. Serve 1 tbsp. of sauce on top of each slice of meat.

Serve it with new potatoes, asparagus or other boiled or stewed vegetables.

Turkey Legs with Vegetables

Dry 2 turkey legs with a paper towel. Tenderize them gently with a mallet, stretch the skin and rub the legs with black pepper and salt. Leave them to rest for 30 min.

Cut 8 medium carrots and 3 parsley roots into big sticks. Heat up some oil in a frying pan. Fry the meat until it is a slightly golden colour (especially the skin). Then put the meat in a saucepan and cover it with the vegetables, sprinkle ⅓ tsp. cayenne pepper, 1 tbsp. whole green pepper, some salt, lemon juice, some turmeric and pinch of tarragon. Then on top of each of the turkey legs pour some melted butter (70 g). Cover it with a lid and put in the oven (medium temperature). Roast it for about 1.5 hours.

Serve it with boiled potatoes and stewed vegetables. You can also serve it with some marinated garlic, gherkins or beetroot salad on a side.

Turkey Goulash

Cut 1 kg of turkey breast into rough chunks and marinade it in the traditional marinade. Now prepare the vegetables: cut 3 peppers (different colours) into strips (1 cm), slice 3 onions, peel 5 garlic cloves. Heat up 1 tbsp. of oil in a frying pan. Then peel and fry 2 very ripe tomatoes.

SW – put the peppers in a saucepan

SP – add the onion and the garlic (pressed)

SP – add the meat, 1 tsp. ginger, 1 tsp. coriander, ½ tsp. cayenne pepper

SL – some salt

S – and the tomatoes with ½ tsp. of basil

B – bring to the boil in the frying pan 1 l of water and add to the meat; also add ½ tsp. turmeric and stew it all together for 10 min.

SW – then add 1 can of sweet peas (together with the brine) and 1 tsp. of ground cumin

Thicken it with some potato starch and season with some more black pepper (it needs to be spicy). Serve it with thick pasta (egg noodles).

Spicy Duck with Oranges

Wash the duck and dry it with a paper towel. Then cut it into small pieces (4cm × 4cm). Cut the skin gently and rub the meat with five-spice powder, cayenne pepper and salt. Leave it to rest for 1 hour.

Cut 1 kg of sweet oranges into halves and squeeze out the juice. Heat up 1 tbsp. of oil in a frying pan. Fry the pieces of duck on each side (pour the melted fat into a separate saucepan, so the meat does not burn). Put the meat in the saucepan, add some turmeric, the orange juice, cover it with a lid and put it in the oven. Stew it until the meat is tender, stirring occasionally. The duck should be quite spicy. If necessary, you can add some honey, some more hot spices and salt. It goes best with fresh bread rolls.

Different Style Risotto

Heat up 70 g of butter and 3 tbsp. of oil (SW) in a saucepan (with a thick bottom).

SP – add 3 medium onions (finely chopped), 3 large garlic cloves (pressed); stir it, then add:

SP – 1 tsp. ground coriander, 1 tsp. ginger; stir it continuously and add 1.5 glass (300 ml) of rice

Keep cooking it and add:

SP – black pepper

SL – 2 tsp. salt

S – slowly start pouring in ½ glass (100 ml) of white wine

S – then add pieces of previously fried chicken meat

B – 1 tsp. turmeric, ½ l of boiling water; keep stirring it

SW – add 1 tsp. ground cumin and 1 can of sweet pea together with the brine

Bring it to the boil; keep stirring it and add 100 g of grated cheese (SW). Then cover it with a lid and put in the oven for about 30 min. (low temperature).

You can serve it as a separate dish or as a main course after having some thick vegetable soup.

Pasta with Meat

Mince some meat and vegetables you previously used in a broth.

SW – heat up 4 tbsp. of oil and 1 tbsp. of butter in a frying pan; fry 2 large onions (finely chopped); then add the minced meat and fry it all together

SW – add 1 tsp. ground cumin

SP – ½ tsp. chilli, ½ tsp. ginger, 1 tsp. ground coriander, black pepper (to taste); the meat should be quite spicy

SL – 1 tsp. salt (make sure the meat is also quite salty)

S – 1 tsp. basil, ½ tsp. lemon juice

B – ½ tsp. turmeric, pinch of thyme, pinch of marjoram

Fry it all together for 15–20 min. until all moisture has evaporated. Cook some pasta. Mix the pasta with the meat; top it with some melted butter and serve it with boiled or stewed vegetables.

Noodles with Sauerkraut

To ½ kg of flour (S) add ½ tsp. of turmeric (B), 2 eggs (SW), pinch of ginger (SP); knead the dough, adding from time to time some cold water; make sure the dough is well worked and quite soft. Roll the dough out on a pastry board (quite thinly – 2mm). Cut it into small rectangles (1cm). Bring to the boil some salty water with 1 tbsp. of oil. Cook the noodles in the water (make sure they do not stick together). Traditional noodles are usually fried together with some sauerkraut in a frying pan, but you can also serve them with some grated and fried vegetables.

S – put 1 kg of sauerkraut (drained) in a saucepan

B – pour in ½ l of boiling water; add 1 tsp. thyme

SW – 4 grated carrots, 1 tsp. cumin seeds and 4 juniper berries

Cook it all together for about 1 hour (with the lid slightly off the saucepan); make sure that the water does not evaporate completely. Then mince the sauerkraut and fry it.

SW – heat up 2 tbsp. of butter and 4 tbsp. of oil in a frying pan; fry some finely chopped onion and the sauerkraut; keep stirring it, then add:

SW – 1 heaped tsp. ground cumin

SP – 1 tsp. ground coriander, 1 tsp. ginger, black pepper and other hot spices (the sauerkraut needs to be quite spicy).

Fry it all together until all the juice and water has evaporated. Season it with some salt. Then mix the sauerkraut with the egg noodles (you do not need to use all of the sauerkraut at once).

Dumplings

Mince 1 kg of boiled potatoes. Put on a pastry board and add:

SW – 1 heaped tbsp. cornflour, 1 tbsp. potato starch, 1 small egg

SP – ½ tsp. ginger

SL – pinch of salt

S – 2 tbsp. wheat flour

Knead the dough. Then form the dough into long thin rolls (2–3cm diameter) and chop them into small dumplings. Cook them in some salty water for about 2–3 min.

Serve them with breadcrumbs fried with some butter. They go really nicely with stewed cabbage and carrot.

Potato Casserole (Tortilla)

Cut 1 kg of peeled potatoes into thick slices (1cm); finely slice 2 large onions.

SW – whisk 6 eggs in a bowl; add 1 tsp. ground cumin

SP – ½ tsp. ginger, ½ tsp. ground coriander, ½ tsp. cayenne pepper, some black pepper and nutmeg

SL – ½ tsp. salt

Heat up 1½ glass of olive oil or other kind of oil in a large frying pan. Fry the potatoes together with onion; season it with some black pepper and salt; stir it. Then cover it with a lid and fry it on a very high heat for about 10 min. (stir it once or twice).

Then dip the potatoes (they should still be quite hard) in the eggs; mix it all together. Leave only 2 tbsp. of oil in the frying pan (the rest of it store in a jar for some other time). Fry the potatoes and the eggs; reduce the heat and keep frying until the bottom is a slightly golden colour. Then put a big plate on top of the frying pan and turn it upside down. Put the potatoes back in the pan and fry them on the other side for another 2–3 min.

Serve it with some cheese sauce.

Cheese Sauce

Mix together: 100 g of full fat white cheese, 2 small natural yogurts or thick cream, ½ tsp. turmeric, 1 tsp. ground cumin, ½ tsp. cayenne pepper, black pepper, salt (to taste).

Potato Cutlets

SW – mince 1 kg of boiled potatoes

SW – add 2 medium onions (finely chopped and fried with 1 tbsp. of butter)

SW – 1 tsp. ground cumin

SP – ½ tsp. coriander

SP – ⅓ tsp. ginger, ⅓ tsp. white pepper, black pepper (to taste)

SL – 1 small tsp. salt

S – handful of finely chopped parsley

B – ½ tsp. turmeric or marjoram or thyme

Form small, flat cutlets. Dip them in a whisked egg, then roll them in breadcrumbs. Fry them on a medium heat in a frying pan with some oil. Serve them with some garlic-yogurt dressing.

Potato with Eggs

Make some béchamel sauce based on sour cream (see *Philosophy of Health*).

Chop 6 boiled eggs and mix them with the béchamel sauce.

To prepare the potatoes, you can use the previous recipe, but instead of making small cutlets, spread the potato mix on a big round tray. Then put the béchamel-eggs mix in the middle of this tray. Pour on top some breadcrumbs fried with butter. Sprinkle it with grated cheese and bake it in the oven. Serve it with a green salad with vinaigrette dressing.

Potato Blinis

SW – mince 1 kg of boiled potatoes (still hot); then add: 100 g butter, 8 egg yolks, 1 tsp. ground cumin; mix it all up thoroughly

SP – add 1 tsp. ginger, ½ tsp. black pepper, ½ tsp. nutmeg

SL – 2 tsp. salt

S – 200 g wheat flour

B – 1 tsp. turmeric

SW – whipped egg whites (8 egg whites); stir it in gently

Heat up some oil in a frying pan. Fry small blinis until a golden colour.

Serve them with yogurt-garlic sauce.

Raw Potato Dumplings

Preparation:

SW – grate 1 kg of peeled potatoes (use a fine grater); squeeze the juice out and pour it into a bowl. At the bottom of the bowl you will find set potato starch; put the starch back to the grated potatoes. Now mince ½ kg of boiled potatoes and mix them with the raw potatoes; add 1 egg and mix it all up thoroughly

SP – add 1 small tsp. ginger

SL – some salt (to taste)

S – 1 heaped tbsp. of flour; mix it all up again (make sure the dough is quite thick)

Then, using a tablespoon, throw small dumplings on to the salty, boiling water. Cook them for about 3 min. Serve the dumplings with sauerkraut stewed with carrots or some melted butter or pancetta fried with onion.

Country Delight

Use 1 onion and 100 g of pancetta per person.

Chop 300–400 g of raw pancetta and fry it until the fat has melted. Then put it together with the fat in a separate bowl. Fry 4 finely chopped onions in a frying pan with 4–5 tbsp. of oil; add 1 tsp. cumin, 1 tsp. ginger and 1 tsp. ground coriander; stir it all together; then add the fried pancetta, 1 tsp. salt, 1 tsp. basil, 1 tsp. thyme, ½ tsp. turmeric and a bit more oil. Taste it and if necessary add some more spices (make sure it is quite spicy). Serve it with some pasta and white cheese sprinkled on top. This dish is truly delicious.

Pilaf

Preparation:

Roast, in a frying pan, ½ glass (100 ml) of peanuts or ½ glass of chopped walnuts. Also, fry ½ finely chopped aubergine. Prepare a handful of finely chopped parsley, ⅓ glass (70 ml) of raisins, 1 large finely chopped onion and 4 garlic cloves.

SW – heat up in a saucepan 4 tbsp. of oil

SP – add the onion, garlic (pressed), ½ tsp. ginger; stir it

SP – 1 glass (200 ml) of rice; fry in all together for some time

SL – add 1½ (300 ml) of cold water and/or the peanuts; add some more salt to taste; cook it for 5 min.

S – then add the chopped parsley, raisins; stir it

B – 1 small tsp. turmeric and/or walnuts

SW – add the aubergine; cook it all together for another 10 min.

Serve it with meat or yogurt-garlic sauce.

Couscous with Vegetables

Couscous:

B – to ½ l of boiling water add (continuously stirring):

SW – 1 tbsp. oil

SP – 1 tsp. ginger

SL – 1 small tsp. salt

S – 2 glasses (400 ml) couscous

B – pinch of turmeric

SW – 1 tbsp. butter; stir it all together thoroughly; then remove from the hob cover with a lid and leave it to rest

Vegetables:

Slice 2 medium carrots, divide 1 cauliflower into smaller chunks, cut 250 g of courgettes into thick slices, chop 1 red pepper and 1 large onion, peel 3 large garlic cloves, peel and stew in a frying pan 4 large tomatoes; you also need 1 can of chickpeas (can be cooked chickpeas instead).

Heat up in a saucepan 5 tbsp. of olive oil and start adding and stirring in the following vegetables and spices:

SW – carrots, peppers, courgettes, 1 tsp. ground cumin

SP – onion, garlic, cauliflower, 1 tsp. ground coriander, 1 tsp. ginger, ½ tsp. chilli

SL – chickpeas; add some salt

S – then add the tomatoes, ½ tsp. basil

B – ½ tsp. turmeric, 2 glasses (400 ml) of boiling water; stir it, cover with a lid and stew it all together for about 15 min.; then add:

SW – some more cumin

SP – cayenne and black pepper (it should be quite spicy)

SL – salt

Put the vegetables on top of the couscous.

French Dumplings

Knead the dough by hand (do not use a food processor).

SW – whisk 8 eggs (portion for 4); add 100 g melted butter

SP – 1 tsp. ginger

SL – pinch of salt

S – and as much flour as required (the dough should be quite thick); mix the dough using a wooden spoon

B – add 1 tsp. turmeric; then, using a tablespoon, throw one small dumpling on to the salty, boiling water – the dumpling should come out quite soft and delicate; if it is not, then add to the dough 2–3 tbsp. of oil (SW).

Throw the dumplings on to the boiling water and cook them under a lid for 3–4 min.

Meat, Gherkin and Tomato Sauce

This is a special sauce that goes nicely with the French dumplings.

Cut 1 kg of veal or beef into small chunks and marinade in the traditional marinade. Leave it to rest for half an hour.

SW – heat up some oil in a frying pan; fry the meat and put it in a saucepan

SP – fry 4 finely chopped onions together with 4 large garlic cloves (pressed); add it to the meat together with some black pepper, 1 tsp. ginger, ½ tsp. cayenne pepper; stir it, then add:

SL – 1½ tsp. salt; stir it

S – add ½ tsp. basil, 4 ripe tomatoes (peeled and stewed in a frying pan), 2 medium gherkins (grated); stir it

B – add some more boiling water (about 1½ l), 1 tsp. turmeric, ½ tsp. thyme and ½ tsp. rosemary; stew it all together until all soft (if necessary, add some more boiling water)

SW – then add 1 tsp. ground cumin; thicken the sauce with some potato starch mixed with cold water; add ½ tsp. of butter

SP – season it with some more black pepper

Serve it with French dumplings.

CAKES AND DESSERTS

Cherry (or Apricot) Cake

Dough (bottom):

S – to 400 g of wheat flour add:

B – ½ tsp. turmeric

SW – 150 g icing sugar, 200 g butter (straight from the fridge); cut the butter into small chunks, add the sugar, 6 egg yolks and mix it all together with your hand

SP – add ½ tsp. ground cardamom, 1 tsp. ginger

SL – pinch of salt

Knead the dough and leave it in the fridge to cool.

Dough (top):

S – to ½ glass (100 ml) of wheat flour add:

B – pinch of turmeric

SW – 1 glass (200 ml) of sugar, ½ glass (100 ml) of potato starch, 100 g butter, 2 small eggs; cut the butter into small chunks and mix it all together with the rest of the ingredients with your hand

SP – add ½ tsp. ginger

SL – pinch of salt

Wash and pit some cherries, put them in a sieve and drain the juice (you can use some very ripe apricots instead, just pit them and cut in half).

Whip up 6 egg whites.

Take the dough out of the fridge; roll it out on a pastry board, then put it in a baking tray. Then spread the whipped egg whites on top of the dough. The next layer is the fruit (put them quite tightly next to each other). Then roll out the other piece of dough (½ cm) and put it on top of the fruit (make sure there are no holes in the dough).

Put the tray in the oven (200°C); after half an hour reduce the temperature and bake it for another half hour.

French Pastries

Prepare the leaven: 100 g yeast + 1 tsp. sugar + 2 tbsp. wheat flour + 50 ml warm water; mix it all together in a small saucepan.
Dough:

S – 700 g wheat flour mix with:

B – 1 tsp. turmeric

SW – 200 g butter (chopped), 2 tbsp. sugar, 2 eggs

SP – 1 tsp. ginger, 1 tsp. ground cardamom

SL – pinch of salt

K – the yeast mixture; now mix it all together and knead it thoroughly with your hands.

Roll out the dough on a pastry board and cut it into small rectangles (or squares). Then put some marmalade in the middle of each rectangle; fold it in half and, using a fork, stick the edges.

You can brush the pastries with a whisked egg. Bake them at 200°C until they are a golden colour. You can brush them at the end with some icing.

Poached Pears in White Wine

S – pour 2 glasses (400 ml) of dry white wine into a saucepan

B – add pinch of turmeric

SW – ½ glass (100 ml) of honey, 50 g sugar; bring it to the boil

Then dip in the wine ½ kg of peeled and seedless pears (cut in half).

SP – add 6–8 cloves, 1 cinnamon stick, ⅓ tsp. ground cardamom

SL – pinch of salt

Boil it all together for 10–15 min.

Fruit Tart

S – 300 g of wheat flour mix with:

B – ½ tsp. turmeric

SW – 100 g butter (chopped), 2 tbsp. icing sugar, 1 egg; mix it all together with your hand

SP – add 1 tsp. ginger, ½ tsp. ground cardamom

SL – pinch of salt

Knead the dough; then roll it out on a pastry board (medium thick) and put it in a baking tray.

Filling:

SW – 100 g of butter (chopped) mix with 100 g of sugar and 2 medium eggs (optionally, you can also add 100 g of ground almonds)

SP – add ½ tsp. ginger, ½ tsp. ground cardamom, 1 shot of cognac

SL – pinch of salt

S – 1 tsp. of lemon juice, 2 tbsp. wheat flour

B – ½ tsp. turmeric

Mix it all together thoroughly. Then spread it on top of the dough. Then you can decorate it with all sorts of fruit (plums, dates, pears, apricots, peaches – cut in half or even smaller pieces). Bake it in the oven – initially at a very high temperature (220°C); then reduce the temperature to 180°C. This tart is truly delicious!

Cupcakes

S – to 1 kg of wheat flour add:

B – 1 heaped tsp. turmeric; mix it all together

SW – add 500 g of cold butter (chopped), 5 tbsp. icing sugar; mix it with your hand

SW – add 10 egg yolks

SP – 2 tsp. ginger, 1 tsp. ground cardamom

SL – a big pinch of salt

Knead the dough thoroughly. Then divide it into 6 pieces. Roll out each piece of the dough on a pastry board (½ cm). Cut it, with a round cookie cutter or a glass, into circles. Then put each piece of dough into a round cupcake mould (7 cm diameter). Make sure there are no holes in the dough. Then bake the cupcakes at high temperature (200°C) until a golden colour. Make sure they are well baked because some of them may bake quicker than the others.

Remove the baked cupcakes and keep repeating the whole thing until you have baked all the cupcakes.

This is a portion for about 120 cupcakes, which will keep the whole family happy for about a week.

I only make them once a year for Paul's name day (of course) and fill them with some cherry jelly made of a home-made cherry juice.

Fill the cupcakes straight before serving with a spoon of half-set jelly and some whipped cream on top. Truly delicious!!!

Poppy Seed Cake I

SW – mix 100 g of butter with 250 g of icing sugar, 6 egg yolks and some vanilla essence

SP – add 1 tsp. ginger

SL – pinch of salt

S – 2 glasses (400 ml) of wheat flour mixed with 2 tsp. of baking powder

B – ½ tsp. turmeric

SW – 8 tbsp. milk; mix it all together thoroughly; then whip up 6 egg whites and stir them gently in with the dough

Heat up the oven to 180°C. Put half of the dough in a baking tray, then spread the poppy seed mix and top it with the other half of the dough.

Poppy seed mix:

SW – wash and then drain ½ kg of poppy seeds and mix them with 1 l of boiling milk; bring it to the boil and simmer for about 30 min; then drain the poppy seeds, mince them and put in a bowl

SW – whip up 4 eggs with 1½ glass (300 ml) of sugar; add it to the poppy seeds

SP – add 1 shot of cognac or rum, 1 tsp. ginger

SL – pinch of salt

S – 1 tsp. lemon juice

B – 100 g of chopped walnuts; mix it all together thoroughly and spread on the dough

Bake the cake for about 1 hour (do not let it burn). Then pour some chocolate glaze on top of the cake.

Chocolate glaze:

Melt 100 g of butter; add 3 tbsp. of sugar and stir it in. Then add 2 tbsp. of cocoa and bring it to the boil (stirring all the time). Whip up 1 egg; add it to the glaze together with ½ tsp. ginger. Simmer it all together for a minute (but do not boil!).

Cool the glaze and pour it on top of the cake.

Poppy Seed Cake II

Pour 1 l of boiling milk over 200 g of poppy seeds; boil it for about an hour, then drain and mince the poppy seeds.

Dough:

SW – whip up 6 egg yolks with 100 g of sugar (they must be very fluffy); add the minced poppy seeds, stir it and add:

SP – ½ tsp. ginger, ½ tsp. ground cardamom, few drops of almond essence

SL – pinch of salt

S – 2 heaped tbsp. of breadcrumbs

B – pinch of coffee; mix it all together thoroughly but gently, then add:

SW – whipped egg whites

Put it in a round baking tray and bake at medium temperature (170–180°C).

Leave the cake to cool down. Then cut it into three equal rings.

Walnut Cream:

Grind 1 glass (200 ml) of walnuts, then add ½ glass of boiling milk and leave it to cool.

SW – mix 300 g of butter with 1 egg yolk and 100 g of sugar

SP – add ½ tsp. ginger, 1 shot of cognac

SL – pinch of salt

S – 1 tsp. lemon juice

B – the walnuts; mix it all together

Spread the cream on top of each of the cake rings. Then put the rings one on top of the other. Decorate the cake according to your own preferences and imagination (I, personally, pour some chocolate glaze on top of the cake and sprinkle it with walnuts and poppy seeds).

Cold Cheesecake

Mince ½ kg of reduced fat white cheese. Mix 3 egg yolks (SW) with 150 g sugar (SW) and 100 g butter (SW), then add ½ tsp. ginger (SP), ½ tsp. ground cardamom (SP), few drops of rum essence (SP) or a shot of rum (SP). Mix it all together thoroughly; then add pinch of salt (SL), minced cheese (S) and ½ tsp. turmeric (B). Mix 3 tsp. of gelatine with 3 tbsp. of cold water and leave it to soak for half an hour. Bring to the boil, in a separate saucepan, 1 glass (200 ml) of milk, add and stir in the gelatine and, when slightly cooler, mix it with the cheese mixture. Then pour the mixture into a round, plastic tray and put it in the fridge to set.

Now poach some pears (peeled, seedless and cut in half) in the following mixture:

SL – to 1 l of cold water add pinch of salt

S – 1 tsp. lemon juice or ½ glass of white wine

B – pinch of turmeric

SW – 1–2 tbsp. honey

SP – 1 cinnamon stick (or 1 tsp. ground cinnamon), 3–4 cloves, ½ tsp. ground cardamom

Bring it to the boil and cook all together for about 15 min. Leave the pears in the mixture to cool down. Then put the pears on top of the cheesecake. Now, prepare some lemon jelly (or other jelly of yellow colour) mixed with the mixture used for poaching the pears. Then let it cool for a while and, when half-set, pour the jelly on top of the cheesecake. Put the cheesecake in the fridge again. Serve it with whipped cream. Instead of pears, you can also use peaches or apricots.

Croissants

To make the dough, use the same recipe as for the strawberry cake (see recipe in *Philosophy of Health*). Fill them in with some home-made cherry jam or date marmalade. Then brush them with a whisked egg and bake in the oven. If they don't taste sweet enough, you can brush them with some icing.

Angel Wings

S – mix 700 g of wheat flour with 6 big tbsp. of sour cream (or even more)

B – add pinch of turmeric

SW – 7 egg yolks

SP – 3 tbsp. of rectified spirit

SW – pinch of salt

Knead the dough thoroughly and for a long time. Then beat it with a rolling pin until very well worked and elastic. Roll out the dough very thinly (1 mm) and cut it into long thin ribbons (15×2.5 cm). Make a small cut in the middle of each ribbon and twist it inside out. And remember – the thinner the dough, the crisper the pastries.

Now melt 2 kg of lard in a saucepan (not too high, otherwise the pastries will not be as crisp as they should). Make sure the fat is really hot; you can check if it is the right temperature by frying one angel wing – if it comes to the surface straight away and turns a golden colour within a few seconds, it means that the fat is hot enough. Fry the angel wings portion by portion, but make sure not to put too many of them in the pan at once – there should be enough room to comfortably turn them around. It is good to have someone to help you with frying these pastries, as they should be fried straight after being cut out (otherwise they will get too dry).

Put fried angel wings on a paper towel and leave them to cool. Then sprinkle them with some icing sugar mixed with vanilla sugar.

Mountain Cake

Dough:

B – bring to the boil 1 glass (200 ml) of water, then add:

SW – 100 g butter

SP – ½ tsp. ginger

SL – pinch of salt

S – 1 glass (200 ml) wheat flour; stir it all together (but do not mix it in a food processor!)

B – add ½ tsp. turmeric; stir it again and let it cool

SW – then add 4 eggs and mix it all together thoroughly

Put half of the dough in a large, round baking tray (buttered and sprinkled with breadcrumbs). Bake it at 170–180°C for about 40 min. Bake the other half of the dough in exactly the same way in another baking tray. Make some cream following the recipe for the coconut cake (see *Philosophy of Health*) but with only 200 g of butter. Spread the cream in between the two layers of pastry and sprinkle some icing sugar on top. Truly delicious!

Sour Cream Cupcakes

S – mix in a bowl ½ l of sour cream with 200 g of wheat flour and add:

B – ⅓ tsp. turmeric; stir it all together

SW – add 4 egg yolks, 100 g melted butter, 3 tbsp. icing sugar (to taste) and mix it thoroughly; then stir in 4 whipped egg whites and add:

SP – 1 tsp. ground cardamom or ½ tsp. ginger

First melt then bring to the boil some butter. Put 1 tsp. of melted butter into each cupcake mould; then fill them with the dough and bake at 180–200°C.

Cocoa Cake

SW – ½ kg of soft butter mix with 500 g of icing sugar, 18 egg yolks and 300 g of ground almonds

SP – add 2 tsp. ginger, 1 tsp. ground cardamom (optionally, you can add 50 g of rectified spirit)

SL – pinch of salt; keep mixing it

S – add 1 tsp. lemon juice

B – 100 g dark cocoa; keep mixing

SW – add 300 g potato starch; then gently stir in 18 whipped egg whites

Divide the dough into two equal portions. Bake each portion separately at 160–180°C in a big, round baking tray. Spread some fruit marmalade or minced cherry jam in between the two layers of cake. Spread the marmalade on the top and on the side of the cake. Then decorate it with some chopped almonds and chocolate glaze.

Chocolate glaze:

Mix in a saucepan 2 heaped tbsp. of cocoa and 100 g of melted butter; add 4 tbsp. sugar, ½ tsp. ginger and 2–3 tbsp. water; stir it thoroughly. Bring it to the boil and simmer for a brief moment. Cool it down stirring.

Orange Cake

Dough:

S – mix 400 g of wheat flour with:

B – ½ tsp. turmeric

SW – 100 g icing sugar, 100 g butter, 3 egg yolks

SP – 1 tsp. ginger

SL – pinch of salt

Knead the dough; roll it out on a pastry board, then put in a baking tray and bake it in the oven.

Orange filling:

Mince 400 g of sweet oranges and 100 g of lemons (all fruits washed and pitted). Peel and grate 150 g of sour-sweet apples. Put all the fruits (S) in a saucepan, add a drop of cold water (SL). Cover it with a lid and stew it for about 15 min. Then fry it, adding:

B – pinch of turmeric

SW – 300 g sugar

SP – 2 tsp. ginger, 1 tsp. ground cardamom

SL – pinch of salt

Fry the mixture until it is quite thick. Then spread it on top of the cake and sprinkle with grated almonds.

Redcurrant Cake

S – mix 400 g of wheat flour with:

B – ½ tsp. turmeric

SW – 150 g icing sugar, 250 g butter (chopped), 6 egg yolks

SP – 1 tsp. ginger, ½ tsp. ground cardamom

SL – pinch of salt

Knead the dough, then roll it out on a pastry board, put it in a baking tray and bake at 180–200°C until a golden colour.

Wash 3 glasses of redcurrants. Whip up the egg whites with 150 g of sugar and mix it with the redcurrants. Spread it on the cake and bake it at 180°C for another 30 min. Be careful not to burn the pastry.

Cheesecake I

S – mix 1½ glass (300 ml) of wheat flour with:

B – ½ tsp. turmeric

SW – add 125 g of butter, 1 glass (200 ml) of sugar, ½ glass (100 ml) of potato starch; mix it all together thoroughly, then add 2 small eggs

SP – 1 tsp. ginger

SL – pinch of salt, 1 tsp. baking powder

Knead the dough, roll it out on the pastry board (1cm) and put it in a baking tray.

Cheese mixture:

Mince 1 kg of reduced fat white cheese, then add:

SW – 50 g butter, 300 g sugar, 10 egg yolks

SP – 1 tsp. ginger, 1 tsp. ground cardamom, few drops of rum essence and a shot of rum or cognac

SL – pinch of salt, 1 small tsp. baking powder; mix it all together

S – add the cheese

B – pinch of crushed saffron

SW – 1 glass of sweet cream (18%), 1 bag of custard powder; mix it all again then stir gently in 10 whipped egg whites; spread the mixture on top of the dough

Dough for the top:

Make the "top" dough the same way as in the recipe for the cherry cake. Cover the cheesecake with torn pieces of the "top" dough. Then bake it at 180°C for about 1.5 hours.

Cheesecake II

Dough:

S – mix 400 g of wheat flour with:

B – 1½ tbsp. dark cocoa

SW – ¼ glass (50 ml) sugar, 200 g butter (chopped), 6 egg yolks

SP – 1 tsp. ginger, ½ tsp. ground cardamom

SL – pinch of salt

Knead the dough, divide it into two portions and leave it in the fridge overnight.

Cheese mixture:

Mince 1 kg of full fat white cheese. Keep stirring with a wooden spoon (clockwise) and slowly adding:

SW – 150 g butter, 300 g icing sugar, 6 egg yolks

SP – 1 tsp. ginger, few drops of rum essence and/or 50 ml of cognac or rum

SL – pinch of salt

S – minced cheese

B – pinch of crushed saffron; mix it all together thoroughly

SW – then add 1 bag of custard powder and stir in gently 6 whipped egg whites

Then grate one part of the dough and spread it evenly on the bottom of a baking tray. On top of it spread the cheese mixture. Then grate the other part of the dough and sprinkle it on top of the cheese. Bake the cheesecake for 1.5 hours (180°C for the first half-hour and 160°C for the rest of the time).

Poppy Seed Roulade

S – 400 g of wheat flour mix with:

B – 1 tsp. turmeric

SW – 150 g butter (chopped), 2 heaped tbsp. sugar, 2 eggs; mix it all together thoroughly, then add:

SP – 1 small tsp. ginger, ½ tsp. ground cardamom

SL – pinch of salt

S – 50 g of yeast mixed with 1 tbsp. of water

Knead the dough, divide it into two portions (it is a portion for two roulades). Then roll out the dough on a pastry board (length and width of the baking tray you are planning to use later). Spread the dough with the poppy seed mixture (half of the portion) and roll it into a roulade. Do the same with the other portion of the dough. Put the roulades in a baking tray and leave them to rise.

Poppy seed mixture:

Soak 400 g of poppy seeds in 1 l of milk, bring it to the boil and simmer for 30 min. Then drain and mince the poppy seeds.

Melt, in a saucepan with a thick bottom, 150 g of butter, then add:

SW – ¼ glass (50 ml) honey, 150 g raisins, minced poppy seeds

SP – 1 tsp. ginger, 1 tsp. turmeric, 1 shot of cognac

SL – pinch of salt

S – 1 tbsp. lemon juice

B – 100–250 g chopped walnuts; fry it all together for a moment; then cool it down

SW – whip up 3 egg yolks with ¼ glass (50 ml) of sugar and add it to the poppy seed mixture.

Then whip up the rest of the egg whites and also gently stir them in.

Once the roulades have risen a little, brush them with a whisked egg. Bake them at 170°C until very dark colour.

Yeast Cake

SW – whip up 10 egg yolks with ¼ glass (50 ml) of sugar and 1 bag of vanilla sugar until it is very fluffy, then add:

SP – grated lemon peel of half a lemon, 1 tsp. ginger

SL – pinch of salt; mix it all together

S – add 500 g of wheat flour and yeast leaven (mix 100 g of yeast with 1 tsp. of sugar, ½ glass (100 ml) of warm milk and 1 tsp. flour – leave it in a warm place until it starts rising)

Knead the dough with your hands, adding:

B – pinch of crushed saffron mixed with 1 tbsp. of hot milk

SW – ½ glass (100 ml) of warm milk and ¼ glass (50 ml) of melted butter

Knead it all together until the dough is well worked. Then sprinkle the dough with some flour, cover it with a clean kitchen towel and leave it in a warm place to rise. Once the dough has doubled its size, put it in two deep and long baking trays (buttered and sprinkled with breadcrumbs). Baking trays should be only half full. Then leave the dough to rise again and bake at 160–170°C for about 1 hour.

Turn off the oven and leave the cakes inside to cool. Remove from the baking trays when the cakes are still warm. Once cold, brush them with some icing or simply sprinkle with icing sugar.

BREAKFAST AND SUPPER DISHES

Breakfast Cottage Cheese

S – mush 200 g of white cheese in a bowl

B – add ½ tsp. turmeric

SW – 200 ml of sweet cream (30%), 1 tsp. ground cumin

SP – black pepper, chilli, cayenne pepper (to taste)

SL – some salt and mix it all together

Put it into a glass jar and store in the fridge for up to a week. Use it in sandwiches. Eat only for breakfast.

Vegetable Jelly

To 1 glass (200 ml) of boiling, home-made tomato juice (S) add:

B – ⅓ tsp. turmeric, ½ tsp. thyme

SW – 1 glass (200 ml) of beef broth, 1 tsp. ground cumin, 3 tbsp. of soaked gelatine

SP – black pepper and chilli (to taste)

Bring it to the boil, then cool it down.

Vegetables:

Wash 3 red and 3 yellow peppers, remove the seeds and cut them into quarters; put them in a baking tray (skins up) and roast in the oven at 250°C until the skins are slightly brown; then put them in a bowl, cover with a kitchen towel and leave them to cool down. Then peel the skins off.

Cut 1 aubergine and 1 courgette into thick slices (1 cm); then put them on an oiled baking tray and roast in the oven until the vegetables are a nice golden colour. Then leave them to cool.

Fry 1 large onion (cut into slices) together with: ⅓ tsp. black pepper, ⅓ tsp. chilli, ⅓ tsp. ginger, salt to taste. Add a handful of raisins and 1 glass (200 ml) of tomato juice; then cover with a lid and stew until it acquires a thick consistency.

Arrange layers of vegetables in a deep bowl: red pepper, yellow pepper, onion, aubergine, courgette, red pepper, yellow pepper and so on. Top each layer with the gelatine sauce. Put the bowl in the fridge. Serve it cold and cut into slices together with cold meat dishes.

Meat Jelly

For the meat jelly you need 1 ham hock, 1 pig trotter and ½ a beef shank. Instead of ham hock you can also use 1 turkey leg. This is a large portion and will feed a family of 4 for a good few days.

SL – put the ham hock and the pig trotter to 3½ l of cold water; season it with 2 tsp. of salt and put it on a hob; then add:

S – 1 tsp. basil

B – 1 tsp. thyme, ½ tsp. turmeric

SW – 1 tsp. ground cumin, put the beef shank in, add 5 juniper berries

SP – 1 heaped tsp. ginger, 6 grains allspice, 1 big bay leaf, ½ tsp. cayenne pepper

Cover the saucepan with a lid and cook it for about 3 hours until the skin on the ham hock is soft and the meat comes off the bone easily. Cut the meat on the bone – this way the meat will get cooked right through. Cook it for another 15 min. Then add:

SP – 1 large onion, 5 garlic cloves (cut in half), ¼ of celeriac

SL – salt, to taste

S – 1 tbsp. of white wine vinegar or ½ glass of dry white wine

B – ½ tsp. marjoram

SW – 2 large carrots (cut in half) and 2 parsley roots

Cook it all together until the vegetables are soft (about 45 min.; slightly shorter in the summer). Then take the vegetables out of the saucepan. Check if the meat is really soft (it should come off the bone really easily).

If you think there is too much broth, then bring it to the boil and reduce it to the required amount.

Take the meat out of the broth (there should be about 2 l left). Soak 1 bag of gelatine in a few tablespoons of cold water; leave it for half an hour. Then add it to the broth, bring it to the boil and add some black pepper (to taste). In the meantime, remove the meat from the bones, let it cool for some time; then chop it finely together with the skin. Do the same with the vegetables. Mix the meat together with the chopped vegetables and put it in a large bowl. Pour the broth over the meat-vegetable mix and leave it to cool down. Then put it in the fridge to set. The next day remove a layer of fat from the top of the jelly.

This dish is great for cold autumn and winter evenings. Take it out of the fridge some time before serving, so it acquires room temperature. Then cut it into thick slices and use in sandwiches with a bit of mayonnaise.

Polenta Casserole

Prepare polenta according to the recipe.

SW – cut ½ kg of ripe and peeled tomatoes into chunks

SW – fry 2 large, finely chopped onions

SP – add 3 garlic cloves (pressed), ⅓ tsp. chilli, 1 tsp. ground coriander

SL – 1 tsp. salt

S – chopped tomatoes, pinch of basil

B – ½ tsp. turmeric, pinch of thyme

SW – 1 tsp. honey

SP – black pepper

SL – salt, to taste

Stew it for 1 hour on a low heat.

Cut polenta into chunks. Arrange a layer of polenta over the base of a buttered casserole. Top it with the sauce and sprinkle with some grated cheese (100 g). Bake it until it is a nice golden colour.

Lentils with Rice

Soak overnight 2 glasses (400 ml) of lentils (in boiled and then cooled water). Drain it the next day. Pour in some fresh, cold water, so that it covers the lentils and cook for 1 hour. Then drain it again.

SW – heat up 2 tbsp. of oil in a saucepan; fry 1 finely chopped onion; add 2 heaped tsp. of ground cumin, ½ tsp. cinnamon

SP – ½ tsp. ginger, ⅓ tsp. black pepper and 1 glass (200 ml) of rinsed rice

SL – add the lentils, 1 glass of water, salt (to taste); stir it, bring it to the boil, then cover it with a lid and put it in the oven for about 30 min. Serve it with onion fried with some butter.

Fried Sausages

Cut 400 g of smoked sausages into thick slices. Fry them in a frying pan with some oil. Then remove the excess fat, leaving only 3–4 tbsp.

SW – fry 2 large onions (cut into slices)

SW – add 1 tsp. ground cumin

SP – ½ tsp. ginger, black pepper, 1 tsp. coriander, chilli

Then add the fried sausages, mix it all together and stew for a moment. Serve it with some salad and fresh bread rolls.

Hummus

Soak ½ kg of chickpeas overnight. Drain the next day; pour in fresh, cold water and bring it to the boil. Cook it for about 1 hour until soft; then drain.

SL – to the cooked chickpeas add:

S – juice of 1 lemon

B – ½ tsp. turmeric

SW – 1 glass (200 ml) of tahini, 6 tbsp. olive oil

SP – 4 large garlic cloves (pressed)

Mix it all together and add (to taste):

SP – ½ tsp. cayenne pepper, black pepper

SL – salt

Mix it all together thoroughly and put into glass jars. It goes nicely in sandwiches and with boiled vegetables. You can also make the hummus with canned chickpeas instead of the dried one.

Croutons

Bake them only in the oven. Only then they will acquire the energy of fire.

SALADS

Kidney Bean Salad

Drain 2 cans of red beans and put them in a bowl. Chop 4 boiled eggs, 2 medium onions, 4 medium gherkins and peel 4 garlic cloves.

SL – mix the beans with:

S – chopped gherkins, 1 tsp. lemon juice, pinch of basil; mix it all together

B – add 2 pinches of thyme, ¼ tsp. turmeric; mix it again

SW – 2 tbsp. of mayonnaise chopped eggs, 1 tsp. ground cumin; mix it again

SP – add chopped onion, pressed garlic, ⅓tsp. chilli and black pepper (to taste)

SL – salt (to taste)

Serve it with buttered bread or as a side dish.

French Bean and Sweet Corn Salad

Drain 1 can of French beans and 1 can of sweet corn. Finely chop 1 onion and peel 2 garlic cloves.

SW – put the sweet corn in a bowl, add 1 tsp. mayonnaise, ⅓ tsp. ground cumin; mix it all together

SP – add chopped onion, ½ tsp. ground coriander, pepper and salt (to taste); mix it all again

SL – add the beans and more salt

S – 2 tsp. lemon juice, pinch of basil; mix it

B – pinch of thyme; mix it again

Apple and Onion Salad

S – peel and cut 3 medium apples first into slices (½ cm) and then into thin strips; put them in a bowl and sprinkle with 1 tbsp. of lemon juice

B – add pinch of turmeric; mix it all together

SW – add 2 boiled and chopped eggs, 2 tbsp. mayonnaise, 1 tsp. ground cumin

SP – 3 medium onions (cut into small slices), black pepper (to taste), ½ tsp. ground coriander; mix it all again

SL – add some salt (to taste).

Tuna Salad

SW – chop 4 boiled eggs and put them in a bowl

SP – add 2 large garlic cloves (pressed), ⅓ tsp. black pepper

SL – 1 can of French beans, 1 can of tuna chunks (drained), 1 can of anchovies (chopped); mix it all together

S – add 4 ripe tomatoes (chopped), 1 chopped gherkin

B – pinch of thyme, pinch of turmeric, chopped leaves of 1 chicory

SW – 1–2 tbsp. mayonnaise or just some olive oil; mix it all again

SP – add a handful of chopped radish, some black pepper; mix it again

SL – add ½ glass of black olives (chopped)

Broccoli Salad

Divide 1 large broccoli into smaller pieces (3–4 cm). Peel the hard centre off the skin and slice it too. Then put it all in a saucepan with salty, boiling water and cook for 5–10 min. Drain it.

SW – mix 1 can of drained sweet corn with ½ tsp. ground cumin and 1 tbsp. mayonnaise

SP – add 2 garlic cloves (pressed), white and black pepper (to taste)

SL – some salt (to taste)

S – cooled broccoli, 3 tbp. of natural yogurt; mix it all together

B – add pinch or two of thyme

Mix it all up gently and taste for the spices.

Spinach

Spinach belongs to the sour flavour.

S – wash and drain ½ kg of spinach; chop it finely and put in a saucepan

B – add ½ l of boiling water, pinch of thyme

SW – 1 tsp. butter

SP – 3 garlic cloves (pressed), ⅓ tsp. ginger, black pepper (to taste)

SL – ½ tsp. salt

Cover the saucepan with a lid and stew the spinach for about half an hour; then add:

S – 1 tsp. lemon juice

B – pinch of turmeric

SW – if necessary, thicken it with 1 tsp. of potato starch mixed with some cold water.

Sauerkraut with Carrot

S – drain 1 kg of sauerkraut and put it in a saucepan

B – add ½ l of boiling water, 1 tsp. thyme, 1 tsp. turmeric

SW – heat up 2 tbsp. of butter and 3 tbsp. of oil in a frying pan; then fry 4 medium and finely chopped onions; add them to the sauerkraut

SW – add 1 tsp. ground cumin, 5 large carrots (grated), 5 juniper berries; stir it and start stewing

SP – add 1 tsp. ginger, 1 bay leaf, 5 grains allspice, ⅓ tsp. chilli, black pepper (to taste); stir it again

SW – salt (to taste)

Cover the saucepan with a lid and stew it for about an hour. Serve it with dumplings or roast meat.

Cucumbers in Sour Cream

Slice 2 peeled cucumbers into thin slices, mix them with 1 tsp. of salt and leave them to rest for 1 hour. Then drain them, put in a bowl, add 0.2 l sour cream and mix it all together. Add ⅓ tsp. turmeric, mix it; add ½ tsp. ground cumin, mix it; add 1 large onion (cut into small slices), black and cayenne pepper (to taste) and mix it again.

Cucumbers in Natural Yogurt

Peel 1 cucumber; grate it, add some salt (SL) and leave for half an hour. Then rinse it in a sieve, drain it, put in a bowl, add handful of chopped dill (S), 1 glass (200 ml) of natural yogurt (S), pinch of turmeric (B), pinch of ground cumin (SW), 3 garlic cloves, pressed (SP) and some black pepper (SP).

Canned Sweet Corn

Heat up 1 tsp. of butter in a frying pan. Add 1 can of sweet corn (with the brine). Keep frying it until the brine has evaporated. You can add 1 tsp. of butter and some cayenne pepper. Great as a side dish for supper.

SIDE DISHES

Young Fried Potatoes

Wash new potatoes and boil them in salty water for about 10 min. Drain the potatoes, rinse with cold water and leave them to cool. If they are baby potatoes and have very soft skins, you can leave them unpeeled. Otherwise peel the potatoes (bigger potatoes cut in half) and fry them in deep oil. Then put them on a paper towel to drain. Serve them with garlic sauce mixed with chopped greens or saffron (see recipe).

Fried Potatoes

Boil ½ kg of unpeeled potatoes. Heat up 1 tbsp. of oil and 1 tbsp. of butter in a frying pan. Fry 2 medium, finely chopped onions (until a golden colour). Add ½ tsp. ground cumin (or cumin seeds), the potatoes, season them with white pepper and salt. Keep stirring. Add ½ tsp. basil and pinch of turmeric. Fry it for a moment, continuously stirring. Serve the potatoes with Ukrainian borscht or fried eggs with vegetables.

Baby Potatoes

Boil 1½ kg of unpeeled baby potatoes, rinse with cold water and leave them to cool. Then peel the potatoes and chop them into big chunks. Heat up a few tbsp. of oil in a frying pan. Fry the potatoes (SW) together with 1 tsp. ground cumin (SW), 1 tsp. ground coriander (SP) and some salt. You can add a bit less of ground cumin and coriander and add some chopped greens instead: parsley, dill (S) or fresh marjoram (B).

You can also fry them together with some previously fried, chopped onion (SW), ¼ tsp. ginger (SP) and ½ tsp. ground coriander (SP).

Or you can simply fry them with some pressed garlic (SP) and season them with some pepper (SP) and salt (SL).

This is how you should serve potatoes over the whole summer. This way they retain all their goodness. You can cook them the same way in autumn and winter but make sure the potatoes are healthy.

Potatoes à la Figaro

Boil 1 kg of unpeeled potatoes (so they are half-soft); then peel them and cut into rings. Chop 200 g of ham or bacon.

S – to ½ l of sour cream add:

B – 1 tsp. turmeric

SW – 1 tsp. ground cumin, 4 egg yolks, 100 g grated cheese; mix it all together

SP – add 1 tsp. ground coriander, ½ tsp. ginger, ⅓ tsp. cayenne pepper

SL – 1 tsp. salt (to taste)

Arrange a layer of potatoes over the base of a buttered baking tray or casserole; sprinkle it with the ham or bacon; then continue with another layer of potatoes and top it with the sour cream sauce. Bake it in the oven for about 45 min. You can also add some garlic.

Potato Croquettes

Boil 1 kg of peeled potatoes (during summer or early autumn you can boil them with the skin on). Mash the potatoes and add:

S – 250 g mashed feta cheese

B – ½ tsp. turmeric; stir it

SW – 2 whipped eggs, 1 tsp. ground cumin; stir it again

SP – add 1 finely chopped onion, white and black pepper (to taste)

SL – salt (to taste)

Mix it all together thoroughly; then form small balls, roll them in breadcrumbs and fry in a frying pan with some oil. Serve it together with beef or pork goulash.

Rice for the Turkey Stew

Crush 1 bag of saffron and mix it with 1 tbsp. of boiling water. Heat up in a thick bottomed saucepan:

SW – 3 tbsp. butter

SP – add 2 large onions (chopped and fried)

SP – ½ tsp. ginger, ⅓ tsp. black pepper, 3 garlic cloves (pressed), ½ l of rice; fry it all together until the rice gets slightly glazed; then add:

SW – ½ l of broth or water, 1 tsp. salt (to taste)

S – ½ glass (100 ml) of dry white wine

B – saffron or 1 tsp. turmeric; stir it and bring it to the boil

SW – you can also add 100 g of grated parmesan

Put it in the oven for about 30 min. Serve it with stews or sauces.

Rice with Turmeric

Rinse ½ l of rice; drain it. Bring to the boil 1 l of water (B) and add:

B – ½ tsp. turmeric

SW – 1 tbsp. butter

SP – ½ tsp. ginger, rice

SL – 2 small tsp. salt (to taste)

Stir it and boil for a moment. Then put it in the oven at minimum temperature for about an hour.

Buckwheat

Buckwheat is best with just butter and salt.

B – rinse 1 glass (200 ml) of buckwheat

B – add 1½ glass (300 ml) of boiling water

SW – 1 tsp. butter

SP – pinch of ginger

SL – 1 tsp. salt (to taste)

Bring it to the boil, cover with a lid and put it in the oven at minimum temperature.

Buckwheat with Rice

Follow the previous recipe but using ½ glass of buckwheat and ½ glass of rice (remember to add the rice as the spicy flavour).

Rice

B – to 1 l of boiling water add:

B – ½ tsp. turmeric

SW – 1 tbsp. butter

SP – 1 tsp. ginger, 2 glasses (400 ml) of rice

SL – salt (to taste)

Bring it to the boil and put in the oven at minimum temperature.

Pearl Barley

Follow the previous recipe; only remember to add pearl barley as the spicy flavour. You can sprinkle it with ginger and add some more salt (to taste). If the pearl barley is quite thick then add twice as much water and keep it longer in the oven.

Polenta

To 2 glass of boiling water (B) add:

SW – 1 glass (400 ml) of cornmeal

SW – 1 tsp. sweet paprika

SP – ½ tsp. nutmeg or ¼ tsp. ginger

SL – salt (to taste)

Boil it all together for 5 min., constantly stirring. Then put it in a baking tray and leave it to set.

Cut it into slices and serve with all kinds of warm sauces. You can also fry it in a frying pan with some butter.

Steamed Dumplings

Dough:

To 100 g of yeast add: 2 tbsp. flour, 1 tbsp. honey, ¼ glass (50 ml) water; stir it and leave in a warm place to rise.

S – mix 1 kg of wheat flour with:

B – 2 heaped tsp. turmeric; mix it all together

SW – add 3 eggs, 2 egg yolks, 100 g melted butter

SP – 1 heaped tsp. ginger

SL – salt

S – add the yeast leaven and knead the dough

The dough should not be too thick and sticky but rather smooth and elastic. Cover it with a kitchen towel and leave it in a warm place to rise (it should double its size).

Then roll out the dough on a pastry board; make sure it is quite thick – about 3 cm. Cut out, with a small round pastry cutter or a small glass, round dumplings.

Leave them on the pastry board for a while to rise a little.

Bring to the boil some water in a large saucepan. Put a flat sieve on top of the saucepan. Arrange the dumplings on the sieve and steam them for about 7 min.

The dumplings go well with all kinds of fatty and meaty dishes and some beetroot salad or red cabbage on a side.

SAUCES

Garlic Yogurt

To 2 pressed garlic cloves (SP) add:

SL – pinch of salt

K – ⅔ glass (140 ml) of thick natural yogurt or sour cream

B – large pinch of turmeric

SW – large pinch of ground cumin

Serve it with potato pancakes, fried potatoes or potato casserole.

Yogurt Sauce (for beef tenderloin)

S – to 1 glass (200 ml) of natural yogurt add:

B – ¼ tsp. turmeric

SW – ½ tsp. ground cumin

SP – 1 large onion (grated), 1 tsp. ground coriander

SL – some salt

Mix it all together.

Garlic Sauce with Greens

S – to 1 tsp. of mustard add:

S – 2 tsp. white wine vinegar

B – pinch of turmeric

SW – 2 egg yolks

Then keep whisking it and slowly adding:

SW – 1 glass (200 ml) of olive oil

SP – 5 garlic cloves (pressed), 2 tbsp. chopped chives, 2 tbsp. cress, cayenne and black pepper (to taste)

SL – salt, to taste

S – 2 tbsp. of chopped parsley

Mix it all together thoroughly. Serve with boiled eggs and boiled vegetables (carrots, asparagus, French beans, potatoes).

Garlic Sauce with Saffron

S – keep whisking 1½ tsp. of mustard and adding:

SW – 2 egg yolks, 1¼ glass (250 ml) of olive oil

SP – 1–2 garlic cloves (pressed)

SL – salt, to taste

S – 1–2 tsp. lemon juice

B – 1 bag of crushed saffron mixed with 2 tsp. of hot water

Serve it with fried new potatoes or boiled vegetables.

Plum Sauce

SL – warm up ½ l of home-made plum marmalade (see *Philosophy of Health*) and add:

S – 10 tbsp. white wine vinegar

B – 1 tsp. turmeric

SW – 1 sp of cinammon

SP –1 tsp. ginger, 1 tsp. ground cloves, 1 tsp. chilli, 1 large garlic clove (pressed); keep stirring and frying it for a while.

SL – add pinch of salt (to taste)

Serve it with ribs, cold meats and pancakes with meat stuffing. You can put it in a glass jar and store in the fridge for up to a few months.

Typical Tomato Sauce

Peel and finely chop 1 kg of ripe tomatoes (remove the seeds).

SW – heat up 6 tbsp. of olive oil in a frying pan, add 1 heaped tsp. of ground cumin; then add:

SP – 3 large, finely chopped onions, 4 garlic cloves (pressed), 1 tsp. ginger, 1 tsp. cayenne pepper

SL – 1 tsp. salt

S – chopped tomatoes

B – 1 tsp. thyme, 1 tsp. turmeric

Stew it all together (with no lid on) for about 1.5 hours. You should end up with a thick sauce.

Serve it with sausages roasted with bacon and cheese in the oven, roast beef tenderloin, cold meats, or simply as the sour flavour together with all kinds of dinner dishes. You can also dilute it with water and serve it as a pasta sauce.

Horseradish Sauce

Prepare a standard béchamel sauce (see *Philosophy of Health*). Add, when it is time for the spicy flavour, some horseradish. Serve it with all kinds of meats or boiled eggs.

Vinaigrette Sauce

Mix 2 tsp. of honey with 2 large garlic cloves (pressed), pinch of white and black pepper, salt, at least 1 tbsp. of lemon juice, pinch of turmeric or thyme. Keep whisking it and slowly adding ⅓ glass (70 ml) of oil.

Instead of lemon juice, you can add 1 tsp. of mustard.

Use it as a dressing for green salads or new potato salad.

SPECIAL RECIPES

Refinement of Ham and Sausages

To 3 l of boiling water (the amount of water depends on the amount of meat; there should be more water than meat) add ½ tsp. thyme, ½ tsp. rosemary, ½ tsp. turmeric, ½ tsp. marjoram, 1 tsp. cumin, 1 tsp. ginger, 1 tsp. chilli and the meat (1 kg of raw/smoked ham or raw/smoked pancetta). Cook it at low heat for about 1.5 hours. Then take the meat out of the water, drain it, cool it, put it in a container and store in the fridge. This way the ham will stay fresh for up to 2 weeks.

You can do the same with other kinds of meat (e.g. sausages). Only remember to shorten its cooking time.

Herbal Mix by Paprzecki

This is a great herbal remedy, which can significantly improve the condition of the blood. It is especially recommended for those suffering from cancer and undergoing chemotherapy.

Ingredients: 50 g dried nettles, 50 g wood betony, 50 g agrimony, 50 g fenugreek; grind it all together. Eat ½ a teaspoon 2 times a day (be careful not to choke) followed by drinking some thyme-liquorice-ginger tea.

Meat Essence for Convalescents

Chop ½ kg of young beef, put it in a glass jar and cover with a lid. Then put the jar in a saucepan of boiling water. Simmer it for 1 hour. Then pour the beef essence out of the jar and give it to the ill. This kind of beef essence is especially good for strengthening the Centre (stomach, spleen and pancreas) and the whole body. In case of wasting diseases, give 1 shot of essence twice a day (half a portion for children).

Buckwheat Remedy

Mash 1 glass (200 ml) of fine buckwheat (B); mix it with 1 egg yolk (SW).

Add this mixture to ½ l of boiling broth (SW); then add ½ tsp. of butter (SW) and boil it for 20 min.

Then add 1 glass (200 ml) of beef broth, 1 tsp. butter and whisk it.

This mixture is highly warming, energizing and stimulating for the spleen.

MEALS FOR SPECIAL OCCASIONS

Christmas Sauerkraut

S – put 1 kg of sauerkraut (drained) in a saucepan

B – add ½ l of boiling water, 1 tsp. thyme, 1 tsp. turmeric

SW – 1 large onion (chopped and fried), 4 large carrots (grated), 3 juniper berries, 1 tsp. ground cumin, 2 heaped tbsp. of gently fried and minced button mushrooms; mix it all together

SP – 1 tsp. ginger, 4 grains allspice, 1 bay leaf, black pepper (to taste)

SL – 1 tbsp. of cooked and minced porcini mushrooms, salt (to taste)

Stew it all together for about 1.5 hours, stirring from time to time.

Split Pea (to mix with the Christmas sauerkraut)

Soak overnight ½ kg of split pea; drain it the next day.

B – bring to the boil 1 l of water, add ½ tsp. thyme, 1 tsp. turmeric

SW – 1 tbsp. butter, split pea, 1 tsp. ground cumin

SP – 1 tsp. ginger, 1 tsp. ground coriander, ½ tsp. cayenne pepper

SL – 1 tsp. salt (to taste)

Cook it until soft.

Christmas Tortellini

Dough:

½ kg of wheat flour, pinch of turmeric, 3 eggs, pinch of ginger, ¼ glass (50 ml) of water.

Knead the dough. Then roll it out on a pastry board (very thinly) and cut out small circles. Put ⅓ tsp. of stuffing on each of the circles. Fold them in half and stick the edges. They should look like half-moon shaped dumplings. Then join together the two ends of the dumplings.

Stuffing:

Gently fry and mince 1–1½ kg of button mushrooms. Cook and also mince 200 g of dried porcini mushrooms.

SW – heat up 5 tbsp. of oil in a frying pan; then fry 1 finely chopped onion; add minced button mushrooms, 1 tsp. ground cumin; stir it

SP – add 1 tsp. ginger, ⅓ tsp. black pepper, some cayenne pepper (the stuffing should be rather spicy)

SL – add minced porcini mushrooms, salt (to taste); stir it again and fry until all the moisture has evaporated

S – add 1 tbsp. of breadcrumbs

B – pinch of turmeric

Portion of 150 tortellini. Serve them together with clear borscht.

Carp in Jelly

Cut one carp into smaller pieces. Remove the skin.

Vegetable stock:

B – to 2 l of boiling water add:

B – ½ tsp. thyme, pinch of turmeric

SW – 2 medium carrots (cut in half), 1 large parsley root, 1 small tsp. cumin seeds

SP – 1 tsp. ginger, 1 tsp. cayenne pepper, 1 large onion (cut in half)

SL – salt (to taste)

Cook it all together until soft (for about 40 min.). Then take the vegetables out onto a plate. Season the vegetable stock and add 8 pieces of carp. Cook it on a low heat for about 20 min. Then take the carp out of the stock and arrange it nicely on a big plate.

Dice the carrots and parsley root and put it in a separate bowl.

S – to the stock add:

S – ⅓ glass (60 ml) of dry white wine

B – add boiling water (so there is about 1½ l of liquid)

Cool the stock down. Add 6 tsp. of gelatine soaked in water. Then add 1 whipped egg white. Bring it to the boil and simmer very gently on a very low heat for about 15 min. Then leave it to cool down. Sieve the stock through a linen cloth. Put some chopped carrots and parsley root in between the pieces of carp and top it with half set vegetable stock jelly. Serve it with tartar sauce.

BABY FOOD

Grind all kinds of grains (buckwheat, pearl barley, millet, oats), except for cornmeal, and store them in separate glass jars.

Carrot Soup

B – to ½ l of boiling water add:

B – pinch of turmeric

SW – ½ kg of nice, fresh carrots (diced)

SP – 1 garlic clove, pinch of ginger

Cook it all together for 1 hour; then blend it.

Great for all sorts of gastric problems: constipation, diarrhoea, colic, flatulence, but also for any symptoms of a cold. You can dilute the soup and bottle feed your baby. But I would recommend feeding your baby with a small spoon during breastfeeding.

Carrot soup can be mixed with oat soup – this combination is good for babies and young children.

Porridge for breastfed babies

B – to ½ l of boiling water add:

B – pinch of turmeric

SW – 1 tbsp. of cornmeal

SP – 2 tbsp. of oats, pinch of ginger, pinch of cardamom

SL – pinch of salt; cook it for about 40 min; then blend it and add:

S – few drops of lemon

B – boiling water (if the porridge is too thick) or pinch of turmeric

SW – some honey (to taste), 3 drops of olive oil or a tiny bit of butter

The porridge usually comes out very thick, but you can always dilute it in boiling water (not the other way round!).

If the baby is fed with formula then do not dilute the porridge in boiling water but rather add some full fat cow or goat milk (⅓ of the porridge's volume).

You can mix the porridge with some carrot or vegetable soup and serve it as a separate meal.

Every few days add to the porridge 1–2 tsp. of egg yolk (do not boil it afterwards). You can prepare the porridge with all the other grains too (even buckwheat – not smoked though!) but the combination of millet, cornmeal and oats is the most nutritious.

This portion should last for up to 3–4 meals (2 days) for a 6–7-month-old baby.

Soup I

B – to ½ l of boiling water add:

SW – 3 carrots, 1 large potato, pinch of ground cumin, 2 tsp. of cornmeal (after a week of feeding your baby with this soup you can start adding ⅓ parsley root)

SP – 1 leek (white part), 1 garlic clove, pinch of ginger, 1 tbsp. oats

SL – pinch of salt

Cook it all together until all vegetables are soft (shorter in summer and longer in winter); then blend it.

S – add few drops of lemon juice

B – pinch of turmeric

SW – a tiny bit of butter

SP – pinch of ginger (the soup must be well spiced)

Thicken the soup with either some grains or potatoes, and after a month of feeding your baby with this soup, you can start adding some egg yolks (start with 1 tsp.).

Soup II

SL – to ½ l of cold water add 1 sprig of parsley; bring it to the boil and add:

B – small pinch of turmeric

SW – 3 carrots, 1 medium potato, ⅓ parsnip or parsley root, 1 tbsp. millet

SP – 1 slice of young kohlrabi, 1 small onion, 1 garlic clove, pinch of ginger, 2 tsp. ground oats

SL – salt

Cook it all together until all soft; then blend it and add:

S – few drops of lemon juice

SW – a tiny bit of butter

Soup III

B – to ½ l of boiling water add:

B – pinch of turmeric

SW – small piece of veal on the bone (70 g), pinch of ground cumin

Cook it all together for about 1.5 hours; then add:

SW – 3 medium carrots, ½ medium parsley root, 1 large potato, 1 heaped tbsp. cornmeal

SP – 1leek (white part), small piece of celeriac, small piece of kohlrabi, 2 garlic cloves, pinch of ginger

SL – salt (to taste); cook it all together until all vegetables are soft, blend it and add:

S – few drops of lemon juice

B – pinch of turmeric

SW – a tiny bit of butter

SP – pinch of ginger

After two or three weeks of feeding your baby with this soup, you can blend it together with the meat. Try to use veal interchangeably with turkey wings. Every few days instead of meat add 1–2 tsp. of egg yolks.

You can use many other vegetables and food products. You must only remember the order of the flavours: sweet – carrots, parsley root, parsnip, pumpkin, potatoes, sweet potatoes, courgettes, pattypan squash, beetroots (not too much), butter, egg yolks, veal, young beef tenderloin, multi-floral honey; spicy – onion, garlic, leeks, dill, fennel, Savoy cabbage or Napa cabbage (one leaf is enough), cauliflower or broccoli (one small piece is enough); sour – greens (parsley, kohlrabi leaves, celery leaves, beetroot leaves), 1 tsp. of tomato (peeled and stewed in a frying pan with some olive oil), few drops of lemon juice; bitter – fresh marjoram.

Very important: there is no need to cook grains straight away in a soup; you can cook them separately and then add to the soup in different proportions 1:1 or 2:1 (2 portions of grains, 1 portion of soup). It is more convenient to do it this way as you can then have many different combinations: pure porridge, porridge with a smaller portion of soup, half porridge and half soup, pure soup.

Especially babies who are not breastfed should eat this kind of warm meal – thin porridge with some spices, to which you add some milk or honey. Initially, you should use only millet and cornmeal together with oats.

Soup IV (for 7–8-month-old babies)

Base this soup either on turkey wing, pigeon, veal or very young beef. Initially, the portion of meat should be relatively small (50–70 g). After two or three weeks of feeding your baby with this soup, you can start blending the meat together with the soup.

B – to ½ l of boiling water add:

B – pinch of turmeric

SW – small piece of veal, pinch of ground cumin; cook it all together for about 1–1.5 hours; then add:

SW – 3 carrots, small piece of parsley root, 2 medium potatoes, 1 small beetroot

SP – 1 medium onion, 2 garlic cloves, ½ a leaf of Savoy cabbage, pinch of ginger

SL – salt (to taste); blend it, then add:

S – 1 tsp. of wheat flour mixed with some cold water

B – pinch of turmeric

SW – a tiny bit of butter

If the soup is too thin, you can thicken it by adding one mashed potato.

Soup V

B – to ¼ l of boiling water add:

B – pinch of thyme

SW – pinch of ground cumin

SP – pinch of ginger, ¼ of turkey wing

SL – salt (to taste)

S – 1 sprig of parsley, 1 young kohlrabi leaf

B – pinch of turmeric

Cook it all together for about 1.5 hours; then add:

SW – 1 heaped tbsp. of millet, 3 medium carrots, small piece of courgette or pattypan squash, 10 grains of sweet pea, 1 medium potato

SP – 1 small piece of cauliflower, 1 medium onion; cook it all together for about 30 min.

SL – blend it and add some more salt

S – few drops of lemon juice

B – pinch of turmeric

SW – a tiny bit of butter

If the soup is based on veal and potatoes, then you can also thicken it by adding some rice. For a child over one year old you can add some egg noodles (1 egg yolk + 1 tsp. flour) instead of millet.

Feeding plan for a 7–9-month-old baby who is still breastfed

Breastfeed the baby first thing in the morning after waking up, last thing in the evening before going to sleep and during night and day as much as the baby requires it.

8 am – breakfast: porridge

12 pm – lunch: thick soup

4 pm – dinner: initially the same soup as for lunch; after 2–3 months though you can introduce some solid food

7 pm – supper: porridge

All of the meals should be nutritious and rather thick. Between feeding times you can only give your baby a small amount of herbal tea or a piece of bread.

Baby Goulash (for at least 1-year-old baby)

You can give this to your baby only when he or she is able to bite and chew.

B – to 1 glass (200 ml) of boiling water add:

B – pinch of thyme

SW – small slice of beef tenderloin (1 cm), ½ grated carrot, pinch of ground cumin

SP – 1 small onion (chopped), 1 garlic clove (pressed), pinch of ground coriander, pinch of ginger

SL – salt (to taste)

S – 1 tbsp. of chopped greens (parsley, dill, beetroot leaves, kohlrabi leaves), pinch of basil

B – pinch of turmeric

Cover it with a lid and cook for about an hour.

You can mash the vegetables with a fork; chop the meat very finely. Then thicken the goulash with some potato starch. It should be very tasty. Serve it with mashed potatoes, fine egg noodles or grains. Additionally, you can serve it with some other boiled vegetables on the side (small piece of cauliflower or broccoli or asparagus).

You can also base this goulash on turkey meat or veal tenderloin and add such vegetables as courgette, pattypan squash, kohlrabi, Savoy cabbage. From time to time, you can also make it with some pork tenderloin.

TEAS

Tea for indigestion, colic and high temperature

B – to ½ l of boiling water add:

B – pinch of thyme

SW – small pinch of liquorice, large pinch of dill seeds

SP – pinch of cardamom, ¼ tsp. ginger

Bring it to the boil and simmer for 2–3 min.

Give it to your baby using a special pipette or a spoon (3–4 tsp.). Babies do not like it but it does them good.

Refreshing Tea

B – to ½ l of boiling water add:

B – pinch of thyme

SW – pinch of liquorice

SP – pinch of ginger

Give this tea only to babies who are not breastfed (you can add some honey too). Breastfed babies (up to 4 months old) do not need any additional drinks.

Harmful Excesses

Sour	Chicken	White cheeses	Natural and fruit yoghurts	Fruits	Juices	Sauerkraut, gherkins	Products marinated in vinegar, e.g. herrings, gherkins	Fresh salads
Bitter	Beer	Natural coffee, instant coffee, filter coffee	Black tea	Green tea	Buckwheat	Dark rye bread	Marjoram	Thyme
Sweet	Sweets, chocolate	Cakes biscuits	Sugar	Honey	Sweet cream and milk	Processed cheese	Carrot juice and fresh carrot salad	Cucumbers
Spicy	Onion	Garlic	Leeks	All kinds of cabbage	Radishes	Pepper mint	Hot spices, e.g. pepper, ginger, chilli	Vodka
Salty	Pork	Hams and sausages	All kinds of sea fish and seafood	Soya	Tofu, miso	Beans	Lentils	Salt
Cold	Exposure to cold	Ice cream	Cold water	Cold drinks	Beer	Drinks on ice	Cold food	

Lemon tea	Sour fruit teas	Sour soups, e.g. tomato soup, sour rye soup	Wheat bread, yeast, pastas	Allergies, asthma, coughs, tonsillitis, catarrhs, colds, low body temperature, celiac disease, diarrhoea, constipation, poor blood circulation, osteoporosis, acidification of the body, peptic ulcers, diabetes, high level of cholesterol, high blood pressure, tumours, headaches, heartburn, cerebral palsies, epilepsy, autism and other mental diseases, emotional oversensitivity, hyperthyroidism, hormonal imbalance, anaemia, arthritis, rheumatism, cellulite, rectal bleeding, teeth problems, periodontitis, eye problems, lung diseases, alcoholism, craving for sweet flavour, acne, flatulence, indigestion, dermatitis, psoriasis and other skin problems, cancers, heart attacks, strokes, blood clots, gallbladder stones, liver cirrhosis, kidney stones, spinal diseases, cystic fibrosis, bad mental and physical development in children, Alzheimer disease
Turmeric	Rosemary			Dry skin, deficiency of moisture, stiffness of the body, insomnia, mental diseases, phobias, emotional excitability, heart diseases, liver diseases, joint problems
Potatoes	Butter and fatty food	Boiled vegetables, e.g. carrots, parsley root, pumpkin	Ice cream	Diabetes, high level of cholesterol, blood circulation problems, lung diseases, asthma, anaemia, allergies, acne, obesity, jaundice, heart attacks, headaches, painful legs, varicose veins, lack of intestinal peristalsis, limp and out of shape body, mental apathy, diarrhoea, high blood pressure, Alzheimer disease, rheumatism
				Alcoholism – destruction of the whole body and mental instability; pepper mint – eye problems, muscles problems; cabbage – thyroid problems
Vegeta	Crisps			Blood circulation problems, low body temperature, heart attacks, cancers, diabetes, allergies, asthma, rheumatism, rheumatic fever, arthritis, diarrhoea, constipation, obesity, headaches, colds, kidney diseases, spinal diseases, kidney stones, liver diseases, liver cirrhosis, heart problems, atherosclerosis
				Cardiovascular problems, deficiency of the energy Yang, low body temperature, heart attacks, cancers, diabetes, allergies, asthma, constipation, diabetes, headaches, colds, metabolism disorders, kidney diseases, intestinal problems, false fire, lung diseases, emotional problems, depression

SOMETHING TO THINK ABOUT

- Do not cook in anger – you may poison your family.
- It does not matter what you do – it is all about your intentions.
- If you are about to start changing your life – do not be afraid! You will get what you need.
- If you cannot have what you want so badly, then perhaps you do not need it as much, or at least not at this moment in time. Occupy yourself with something else.
- Stand up straight, look confidently forward – you are about to enter a new phase of life!
- When you function under the influence of anger, aggression, hatred, frustration (Ego), you burn your internal fluids (Yin).
- There is no "good" and "evil" in Nature – in Nature one thing leads to another; there is no competition as such; all of these notions are mere creations of the intellect.
- Do not be afraid of anything except of your own fear.
- Fear knocks you down, whilst trust gives you wings.
- You can see the world through the eyes of a victim or of an adventurer going for the treasure.
- Nothing is too small or trivial in the surrounding world to teach us a lesson.
- Every single day we can be better than the previous day.
- Health does not leave us, rather we drive it away.
- Each one of us has their own "defects" within the body; therefore the same causes may lead to different health problems in different people.

- Every person treats their body in their own way and wears it out in their own way.
- Powerful and long-lasting stress can completely block our consciousness.
- You can always choose what you want – and it is truly wonderful. But are your choices good for you? Well, this is a completely different matter.
- Suffering depends on our point of view, or as we call it – our consciousness.
- The joy of life means the joy of the body, and therefore it is visible.
- Blues, bad mood, pain – these are all signals of our body asking us to stop and listen to ourselves.
- By worrying too much you do not gain anything. You only lose your health and the joy of life.
- Free your children from yourself; they are here to learn life their own way. Also, free yourself from your grown-up children – you still have plenty to do with your own life.
- To be responsible for one's own life means to follow the path of virtue, to be open, and to know one's own destiny, or, as Paulo Coelho said: "to follow the path of one's own Legend".
- To be a person of pure heart means to be free of superstitions, stereotypes, obsessions, fears; such heart forms the Centre of the Universe.
- When the heart is pure and free, then there are no limits to what one can achieve.
- Our mind becomes calm (empty) only through contact with our Overmind and intuition. This happens when our liver (subconscious), which supports the mind, is calm and strong and resistant to all kinds of fears, stresses and obsessions.

- The spleen "creates" our thoughts; when it is strong, then our thoughts do not run towards the past or future – we become focused on the present instead.
- Consciousness is a derivative of our emotions, or, in other words – the balance of our bodily organs.
- Soul consists of our body and subconscious.
- Looking into somebody's eyes we can see their soul and their true intentions.
- Our attitudes, reactions, intentions depend on our subconscious (liver).
- Our thoughts are followed by energy.
- We need feelings to lift the energy up.
- Emotions stimulate the motion of bodily organs; they have the power of the elements.
- Long-lasting emotions can destroy the Centre of regulation of our life processes – they destroy our consciousness (spleen).
- The hidden "intention" of the kidneys is the will to live.
- Our life (Tree) has its roots in the kidneys and their maximally concentrated "intention".
- Without strong kidneys (roots), our life turns into chaos.
- The essence, blood and body – they are all manifestations of our Spirit; good quality of essence attracts the Spirit. When the quality of essence is bad, then our Spirit cannot articulate itself.
- When the heart is not sufficiently nourished by the essence (blood), then our Spirit is not present and our consciousness becomes disturbed.

- The ultimate ideal of human life is to connect with the Spirit.
- Insecurity and fear signify weak roots – weak kidneys.
- Fear separates fluids from energy – fluids go downwards (urine, swollen legs, feeling of heaviness), whilst the energy goes upwards (heat flashes, heart palpitations). We lose our consciousness.
- By dwelling on sorrow and resentment about our past, we block our imagination and creativity.
- If we get stuck in our past, our creativity becomes burdened by sadness, anguish and suffering.
- By trying to understand the past and put it in order, we enter the present, and thus give ourselves the right to joyful creativity.
- When we create too much – we destroy the balance; when we contemplate and think too much – we destroy our willpower, eagerness/momentum to work and courage; instead, we instigate fear and anxiety, which kill the joy of life.
- Doubt can destroy the subtle power of a newborn thought.
- The biggest trap is your own impatience!
- By working on yourself you always make a change to the World.
- Pick the products you eat regularly and see what kind of problems they may cause in the future.